AQA GCSE Design and Technology

textiles technology

Orders: please contact Bookpoint Ltd, 130 Milton Park, Abingdon, Oxon OX14 4SB. Telephone: +44 (0)1235 827720. Fax: +44 (0)1235 400454. Lines are open from 9.00 to 5.00, Monday to Saturday, with a 24-hour message-answering service. You can also order through our website www.hoddereducation.co.uk

If you have any comments to make about this, or any of our other titles, please send them to educationenquiries@hodder.co.uk

British Library Cataloguing in Publication Data
A catalogue record for this title is available from the British Library

ISBN: 978 1 444 123 722

First Edition Published 2011
This Edition Published 2011
Impression number 10 9 8 7 6 5 4 3 2
Year 2016, 2015, 2014, 2013, 2012

Cover photo from © Dean Turner/iStockphoto.com

Typeset by DC Graphic Design Limited, Swanley Village, Kent

Printed in Dubai for Hodder Education, an Hachette UK Company, 338 Euston Road, London NW1 3BH

AQA GCSE Design and Technology

GET BETTER RESULTS FOR AQA

textiles technology

series editor: Bryan Williams

Rose Sinclair
Hermione Lewis

Contents

Acknowledgements

Rose Sinclair would like to thank her husband Audley Sinclair for all his support and continued encouragement. Thanks are also due to the following schools for allowing their students' coursework to feature in the book: Langley School for Girls, Bromley, Kent; Feversham College, Bradford; and St. Paul's School for Girls, Birmingham. Rose would also like to thank the following teachers for their insight, help and support: Helen Jedlinska, Tracey Goodyear, Lesley Pollacko and Katie Miles. Also thanks to the editors at Hodder, Stephen Halder and Gemma Parsons, who helped it all happen.

Hermione Lewis would like to thank Sabira Alim, Caitlin Comins, Vinothni Cumarasamy, Chloe Ogbonna-Marks, Georgia Haigh, Mohini Patel and Ella Thorold for use of student work; and Graham Stapleton, Principal of Graveney School for his support during a challenging period.

The authors and publishers would like to thank the following for use of photographs in this volume:

Figure 1.17 CandyBoxPhoto – Fotolia; Figure 1.25 anne kyyrö quinn; Figure 2.2 © Anthony Hatley/Alamy; Figure 3.1 Lidove noviny/Tomas Hajek/isifa/Getty Images; Figure 3.2 © Rob Crandall/The Image Works/www.topfoto.co.uk; Figure 3.3 Paul Chesley/Stone/Getty Images; Figure 3.4 Galina Barskaya – Fotolia; Figure 3.5 Public Record Office/HIP/www.topfoto.co.uk; Figure 4.12 The Woolmark logo is a registered trade mark of The Woolmark Company, which is owned by Australian Wool Innovation and indicates high quality of wool products. The Woolmark is an assurance by the manufacturer that a product is made of pure new wool. End products carrying these symbols have been tested by The Woolmark Company for compliance with its fibre content and performance specifications (Woolmark indicates 100%). The Woolmark is one of the most recognised symbols globally and represents the world's largest fibre quality assurance scheme; Figure 4.13 NILIT Fibers; Figure 4.14 weberfoto – Fotolia; Figure 4.19 © V&A Images; Figure 4.24 © RubberBall Selects/Alamy; Figure 4.31 © Alan Gallery/Alamy; Figure 4.43 © ra-photos/iStockphoto.com; Figure 5.1 Society of Dyers and Colourists; Figure 5.5 © Peter Alvey/Alamy; Figure 5.7 ITAR TASS/Bandphoto/UPPA/Photoshot; Figure 5.9 Fuse/Getty Images; Figure 5.12 reproduced with kind permission from Jayne March and Sarah Fox; Figure 5.13 Greentree – Fotolia; Figure 5.14 © Edwin Remsberg/Alamy; Figure 5.18 Andrzej Fryda – Fotolia; Figure 5.19 © Micha Adamczyk/iStockphoto.com; Figure 6.2 Photos reproduced with kind permission from Jayne March and Sarah Fox; Figure 6.3 Photos reproduced with kind permission from Jayne March and Sarah Fox; Figure 6.4 Photos reproduced with kind permission from Jayne March and Sarah Fox; Figure 6.5 Photos reproduced with kind permission from Jayne March and Sarah Fox; Figure 6.7a © Petre Milevski/iStockphoto.com; Figure 6.7b © Sean Locke/iStockphoto.com; Figure 6.8 YURY MARYUNIN – Fotolia; Figure 6.9 Simplicity; Figure 7.2 Donna Wilson; Figure 7.4 Cool Hunting Figure 7.5 © Diana Hirsch/iStockphoto.com; Figure 8.1 NASA; Figure 8.2 Crispian Woodgate/Daily Mail/Rex Features; Figure 8.3 Tony Kyriacou/Rex Features; Figure 8.5 EU Ecolabel; Figure 8.6 Fairtrade Foundation; Figure 8.7 © Colin Underhill/Alamy; Figure 8.9 Ray Tang/Rex Features; Figure 8.10 Trading Standards; Figure 8.14 Intertek; Figure 8.15 © thumb/iStockphoto.com; Figure 8.17 Contains public sector information published by the Health and Safety Executive and licensed under the Open Government Licence v1.0; Figure 9.8 Photos reproduced with kind permission from Jayne March and Sarah Fox; Figure 9.9 Photos reproduced with kind permission from Jayne March and Sarah Fox; Figure 9.10 'Birds & Flowers' artwork by Helen Amy Murray. Digitally printed and hand sculpted silk. Photographed by Michael Duerinck for Vogue Magazine, 2005; Figure 9.11 Photos reproduced with kind permission from Jayne March and Sarah Fox; Figure 9.12 Photos reproduced with kind permission from Jayne March and Sarah Fox; Figure 9.13 BERNINA of America, Inc.; Figure 9.14 BERNINA of America, Inc.; Figure 9.15 Silver Viscount; Figure 9.16 Jose Manuel Gelpi – Fotolia; Figure 9.17 Dorling Kindersley/Getty Images; Figure 9.18 Photos reproduced with kind permission from Jayne March and Sarah Fox; Figure 9.19 Photos reproduced with kind permission from Jayne March and Sarah Fox; Figure 9.20 Photos reproduced with kind permission from Jayne March and Sarah Fox; Figure 9.21 Photos reproduced with kind permission from Jayne March and Sarah Fox; Figure 9.22 ABACA/Press Association Images; Figure 10.2 © Victoria Chukalina/iStockphoto.com; Figure 10.3 © Haze McElhenny/iStockphoto.com; Figure 10.5 Gareth Davies/Getty Images; Figure 11.2 Cotton Incorporated; Figure 11.3 Pantone® and other Pantone trademarks are the property of, and are used with permission of, Pantone LLC © Pantone LLC 2011. All rights reserved; Figure 11.5 Survey Monkey; Figure 11.8 Webspiration; Figure 11.11 Alan Ward – Fotolia; Figure 11.12 Bernina My Label images © Bernina International AG, www.bernina.co.uk; Figure 11.13 PHILIPPE PLAILLY/SCIENCE PHOTO LIBRARY; Figure 11.15 ITAR TASS/Bandphoto/UPPA/Photoshot; Figure 11.18 © Youssouf Cader/iStockphoto.com.

Chapter 1 Designing skills

1.1 Investigating the design opportunity/context

Learning objectives

By the end of this section, you should have a key understanding of:

- how to investigate the design opportunity and/or context
- the place of research in the design process
- how to use mood boards as part of your design thinking skills
- how to define your specification and criteria.

Key points

- Analytical skills
- Communication skills
- Creative skills
- Values

Introduction

The focus of Criterion one – investigating the design context – is on your design, research and analysis skills; that is the ability to sort through a wide range of written and visual information. Your relevant findings will be summarised and will assist you to make key decisions on how to develop your design ideas in Criterion two. It is essential at each stage of your research to clearly communicate what you did, how you did it and why you did it, to help you write your design specification at the end of this section.

For Criterion one you will be awarded a maximum of eight marks. This section of your design folder should be a total of five pages and should be carried out in four hours.

Project planning skills

The time allocated to complete your project is 45 hours. Therefore, it is essential that you plan your project to know how long each section will take. In the fashion and textiles industry, designers use specialist product data management (PDM; see page 266), which allows them to plan all aspects of a design project. For your own work, you may use either mind-mapping software or spreadsheet software, such as Microsoft® Excel® to produce a Gantt chart, or a simple flow chart. You can refer back to the time plan when you complete each task to remind yourself that you should spend the majority of your time working on the areas worth the most marks. Planning your time will help you to properly evaluate the overall project in stages.

Knowledge link

For more information on product planning, see Chapter 10.

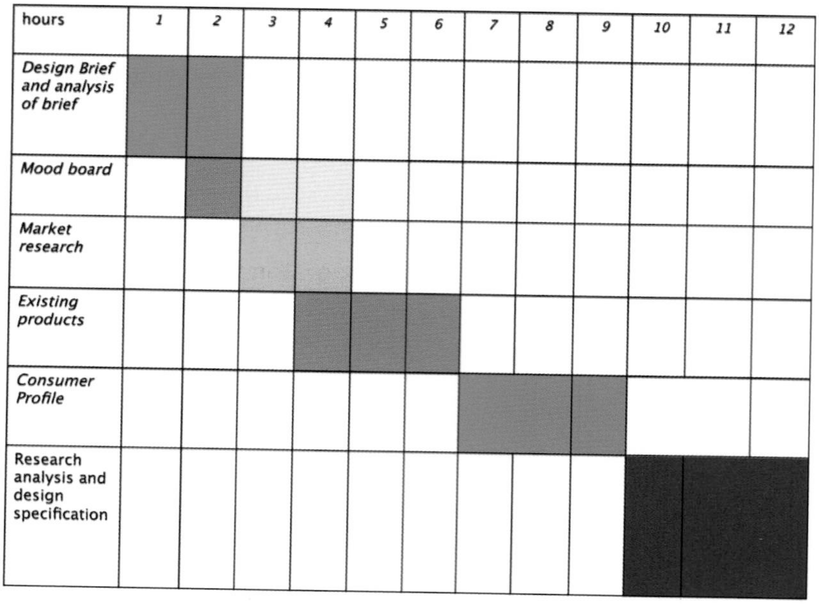

hours	1	2	3	4	5	6	7	8	9	10	11	12
Design Brief and analysis of brief												
Mood board												
Market research												
Existing products												
Consumer Profile												
Research analysis and design specification												

△ **Figure 1.1** A student's example of a simple planning chart, illustrating how they planned their project

The design task (brief)

The design brief outlines the requirements specified by the client. In the controlled assessment task, you are given an open brief(s) by the examination board that can be adapted to fit the context.

CONTEXT

Designers have a responsibility to design products that address environmental issues. Be inspired by the following word bank - Designing for sustainability, the use recycled second hand textile products, re used fabrics and components, vintage fabrics, organic cotton, fabrics from other industrial sources e.g. tarpaulin from lorries, hessian from rice sacks, biodegradable fibres/fabrics, ethical trading - Fair Trade.

Design Briefs

- 'The People Tree' is a company which supplies textile products to people wishing to support Fair Trade and look after the environment. You have been asked to design a range of bags using India as an inspirational theme. Make up at least one item from your range. You are to design for manufacturing in quantity.
- Vintage Designs are a company who produce textile products using recycled textile products, materials and components. Design and make an outfit for the teenage market that could be sold by this company on their web site.

△ **Figure 1.2** An example of an AQA controlled assessment context and design task

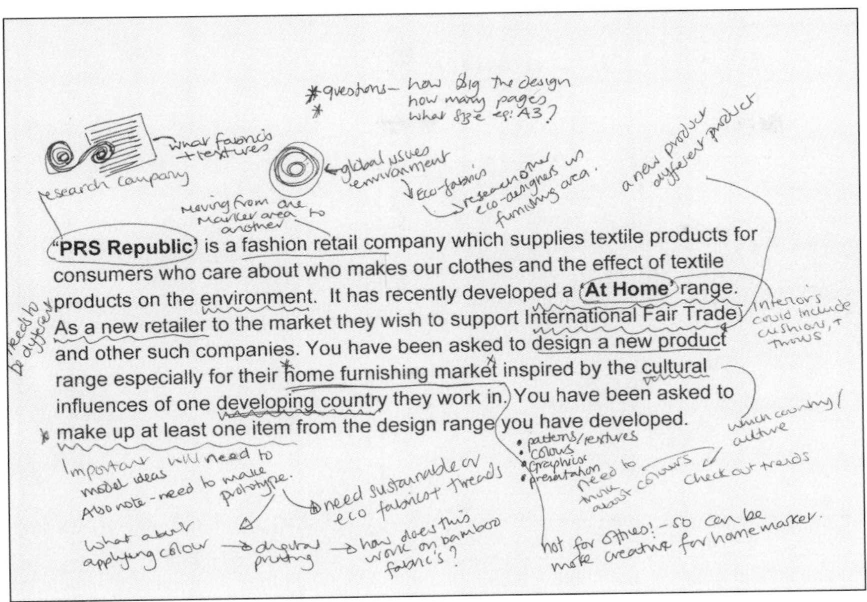

"PRS Republic" is a fashion retail company which supplies textile products for consumers who care about who makes our clothes and the effect of textile products on the environment. It has recently developed a 'At Home' range. As a new retailer to the market they wish to support International Fair Trade and other such companies. You have been asked to design a new product range especially for their home furnishing market inspired by the cultural influences of one developing country they work in. You have been asked to make up at least one item from the design range you have developed.

△ **Figure 1.3** Student's adapted design brief

Why use a design brief?

Designers use the design brief to give them a clear understanding of their client's requirements. The design brief allows you to focus your research skills on particular areas within the design process.

The value of design journals (paper-based sketchbooks, new media – electronic ebooks, e.g. Flickr, Vimeo)

Research can be collected in many different forms (digitally or from magazines, for example). The sketchbook is important because it means you can have all the visual and written information you have collected at your fingertips. It is a fantastic reference tool to bring your idea to life.

Analysing a design task (brief)

The key ways to analyse a brief are:

- to highlight key words, terms and phrases and make sure you understand them
- to identify clearly all the design needs required.

Methods to use to analyse your task are:

- mind-mapping.
- a spider diagram
- a list of bullet points
- a short piece of written work.

Make sure you have a clear understanding of the task before you go any further.

Key terms

Analysis – a method of studying the nature of something or of determining its essential features and their relations.

Design – the process of creatively developing a concept or idea.

Design task (brief) – a short statement explaining what is going to be designed and made.

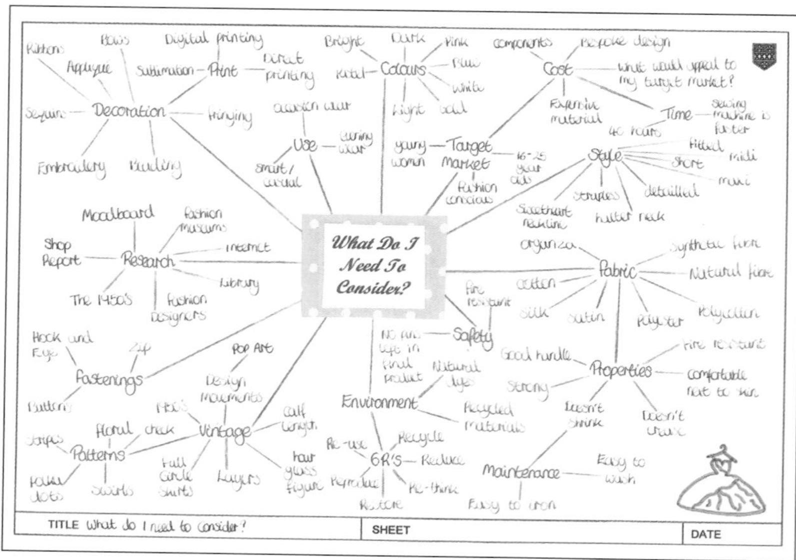

Figure 1.4 Mind-mapping a design task

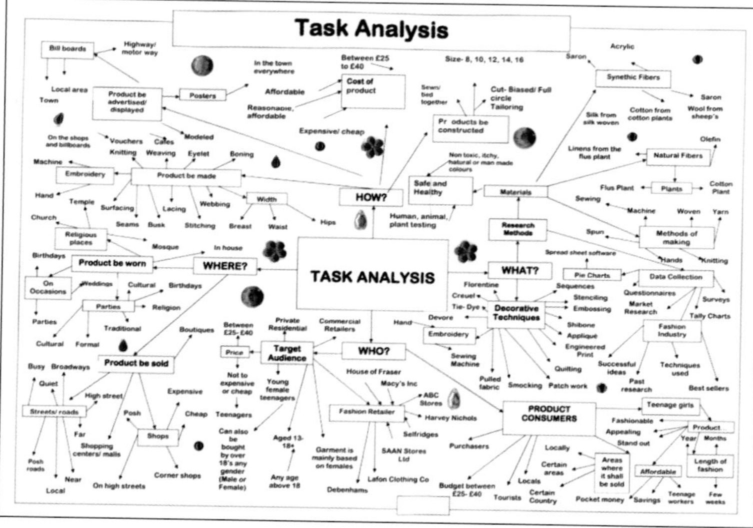

Figure 1.5 A student's design task analysis

What is research?

Research is searching, investigating and learning about the past, present and new information that surrounds us in society. You can accumulate this information by carrying out the following activities:

- reading a range of relevant books, visiting and viewing journals, galleries, museums and historical private collections, art, fashion or textiles exhibitions.
- finding and gathering information that can help you to design your product
- analysing and reporting the information
- extracting key points to enable you to start your own designs.

Excessive amounts of time should not be spent on conducting your research. You need to make sure your research is relevant and identifies the areas highlighted in your task analysis. This information needs to be accurate so you can refer to it throughout the task.

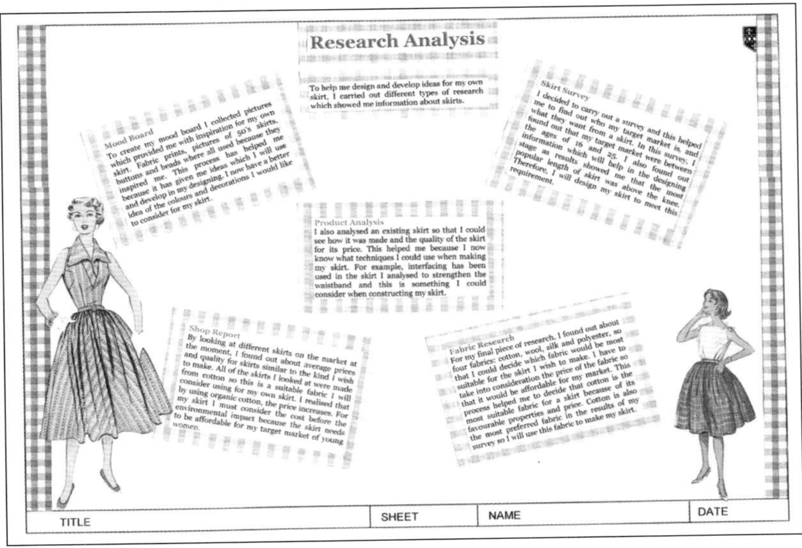

△ **Figure 1.6** A student's research analysis

Knowledge link

For more information on research, see Chapter 7, pages 164–168.

There are two types of research: **primary research** and **secondary research**. Primary research material is information gathered from first-hand sources, which might include exhibitions, shop visits, questionnaires, surveys, photographs and analysing existing products (product analysis/disassembly).

Secondary research is where information about a particular topic has already been collected by other individuals. Sources include books, magazines, databases, the internet, market reports and CD-ROMs.

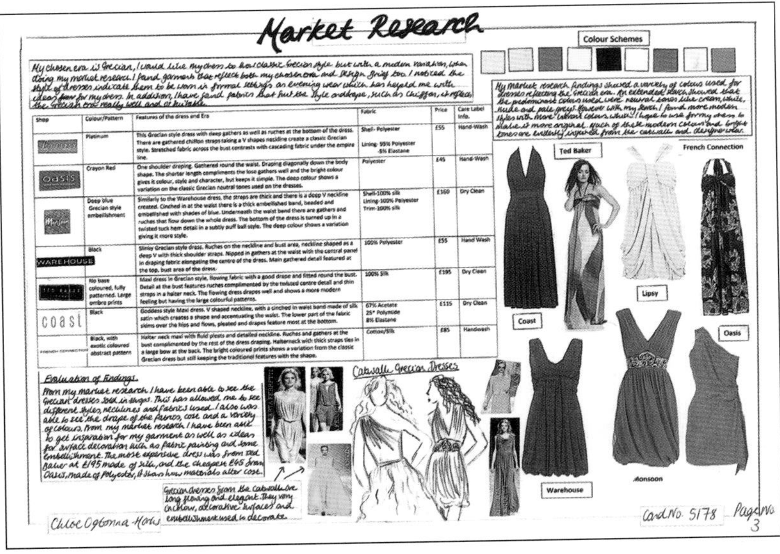

△ **Figure 1.7** A student's market research highlighting existing products on the market

△ **Figure 1.8** A student's comparative product analysis

> **Key terms**
>
> **Primary research** – original research that has not been done before and all resources, such as images and text created by you.
>
> **Research** – finding out information using a series of activities.
>
> **Secondary research** – often referred to as desk research, this is research that has already been done by somone else or information that is in the public domain.

Various areas of research

The controlled assessment criteria highlight different research areas used in commercial design. Not all of the areas listed in this section may be appropriate to your design task, so make sure your research is relevant.

Historical analysis

Historical influences can be found in any design area from any culture. They may be as diverse as Russian war uniforms and the Japanese kimono dress. It is essential to have an understanding of what took place in the past so you can see how ideas and technologies have moved forward. Historical analysis is an important part of being a designer and, for many, it provides a wealth of information on various topics, such as fabric, embellishments and shapes and well-tailored products.

Cultural analysis

Cultural influences range from an appreciation of literature, art and music from your own country to admiring other cultures – for example, Japanese street style. Researching a culture can provide a variety of inspirational ideas that may translate into colour, fabric, print, and garment and interior shapes.

Some cultural aspects can affect consumer demand for new products.

> **Knowledge link**
>
> For more information on cultural analysis, see Chapter 8, pages 179–182.

Designer analysis

Designers are a good research source for understanding how the design process works in industry. The designer requires a starting point, concept or theme (the design task) to design a product or a full collection. As well as gathering written research, the designer will need to collate a range of visual resources such as mood boards or trend boards. This is known as design inspiration. This will help in the design and development stages of your coursework.

Design inspiration can be gathered from a range of sources, such as the natural world, architecture, fabric samples, travel, street and youth culture, art influences (film, theatre and music), trend forecast websites and new technologies.

Knowledge link

For more information on designer analysis, see Chapter 7, pages 155–156.

Mood boards/trend boards

Designers need to ensure that the products they are designing will sell when they have been manufactured. Knowing what consumers will want to buy in the future is important. To achieve this, designers collect information about future concepts and influences that may affect consumers' preferences by visiting colour and trend forecast shows to keep up to date with future fashion trends. Designers in the fashion and textiles industry display this information in sketchbooks or on layout boards to help focus their ideas on the links and themes to identify the target market preferences. Mood boards assist you to collate a comprehensive story of ideas for your chosen design task. It is important to ensure that you annotate or provide accompanying commentary explaining the purpose and use of your mood board as part of the design process. Mood boards included with no visible purpose take up valuable space.

Knowledge link

For more information on mood boards, see Chapter 7, page 169.

△ **Figure 1.9** A student's cultural mood board. Students will have to include a colour palette and key words to identify researched groups.

Key terms

Colour – a visual sensation that is created when light is transmitted through or reflected from an object.

Mood board – a display consisting of fabric samples, alongside images and objects relating to the subject matter of research. Designers and others use mood boards to develop their design ideas and concepts and to communicate with other members of the design team.

Trend board – a display of text and images to assist the designer to predict the future. This may include garments, shapes, components, fabrics and colour samples.

Mood boards clearly summarise the theme with a selection of inspirational pictures/samples and informative items to capture the chosen design task. This information should be displayed on a single sheet to highlight the essential aspects of the chosen themes.

Consumer profiles/target market

Understanding who your consumer is is an important part of your design folder to assist the direction of your product. You need to know your consumer's profile and find their preferences and dislikes to help define your target market's focus. Changes in society can influence the development of fashion and textile products and can reflect the interests and values of consumers.

The main research methods to gather information on your consumers and market are:

- talking directly to and questioning consumers
- talking to manufacturers about their market costing and to gain an understanding of their price ranges
- analysing a shop's environmental spaces
- analysing the market's statistics on your chosen product.

△ **Figure 1.10** A culturally influenced mood board with visual images and fabric samples

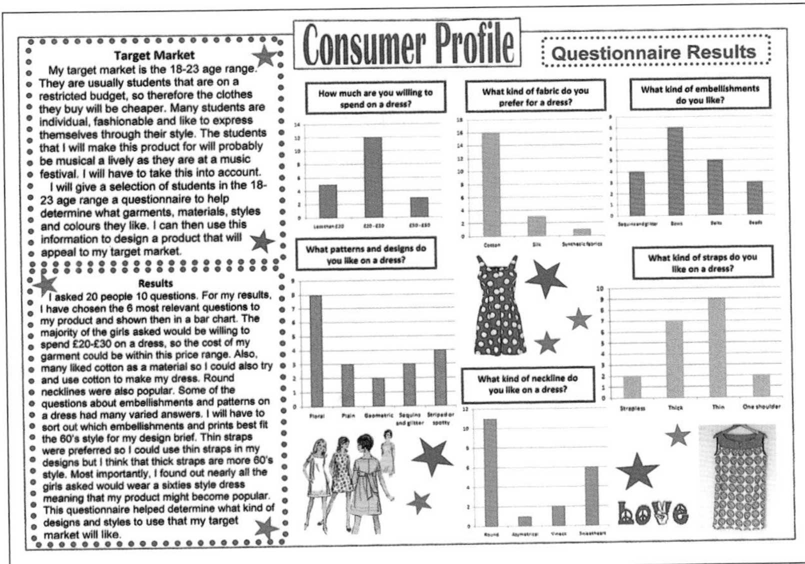

◁ **Figure 1.11** A student's consumer profile and questionnaire page

Knowledge link

For more information on research methods, see Chapter 7, pages 163–167.

Key terms

Consumer – a person who buys, rents or hires products or services; he/she is the end user of a product.

Market – how products are sold and promoted to a particular client.

Social values/sustainable issues

Social values in textile product design could include research into:

- how fibres are made into fabrics
- the effect of colour dyestuffs on the environment
- how the economy could change demand.

Social values in fashion design are related to:

- changes in society
- how we dress and the type of products we wear (including issues concerned with gender, culture and religion).

Designers and manufacturers must consider the environment when producing textiles products, but must also make their product appealing to the customers.

Remember that social values and sustainable issues such as save our greenland, save energy, carbon footprint and the 6Rs should reflect the interests and values of the targeted consumers.

Knowledge link

For more information on sustainable issues, see Chapter 8, pages 183–199.

You must always remember the following:

- As a designer you have to consider the impact of your designed product on society.
- You must identify technological developments, social and cultural factors, fashion trends and economic factors that influence consumer choice and the product's design.
- Consumer choice – consumers can choose products based on not only design but also on sustainable and ethical issues.
- The issues associated with textile and fashion production such as the disposal of colour dyes, cheap labour, etc.

- How the 6Rs (recycle, reuse, reduce, refuse, rethink and repair), waste reduction, organic and fair trade assist the sustainability of the environment.

There are laws and regulations that manufacturers have to follow. The manufacturer has to dispose of their waste property, always remembering safety to the environment.

Product analysis

Product analysis is part of the primary research you should carry out in order to design and make a quality product for your design task.

Analysing existing products can help you understand the following:

- how the product works or how it is used
- the techniques used to construct the product (take the product apart – disassemble)
- what fibres and fabrics are used and how to care for them (see the care label)
- what types of components are needed to make the product
- how well the product meets the end user's needs
- whether the product is good value for money
- what you need to include in your design specification.

Analysis of research

Once your research is completed and clearly presented, you must analyse and conclude your findings (explain what you have found). Your research should have increased your understanding of your design task and given you some ideas for your design specification.

It is important to include the following key information in your coursework:

- what research you have carried out
- why you carried it out
- what you wanted to find out
- what you did find out
- how you will use it to help your design work.

You could use Table 1.1 to help with your analysis.

Knowledge link

For more information on analysing your research and to help you get started, see Chapter 7, pages 173–178.

Research activity	What did you hope to find out?	What key things did you discover?	How and where will you use this in your designing?
List all the research activities you carried out	Why did you do it? Find out what existing products are already in the shops. Is there a gap in the market for your product?	Do not repeat what you wrote in the previous column. For example, if you created a mood board, you could write the following: 'I liked the paisley patterns the best and thought the colour scheme of red, blue and purple would look good.' Basically you are describing your early thoughts about the design.	In this column, rewrite your findings from the previous column and include your decisions about the design. For example, you could write: 'My colour scheme will be red, blue and purple and I will develop the paisleys as my theme for the product.'

△ **Table 1.1** Analysis of research: an example of a blank analysis form to help you collate your research

Cont.

Research activity	What did you hope to find out?	What key things did you discover?	How and where will you use this in your designing?
Design task and research planning			
Inspiration – historical/ cultural/designer influences; mood board/trends			
Market research – shop visits, existing products, product analysis and disassembly			
Consumer profile and questionnaire			

△ **Table 1.1** Analysis of research *continued*

What is a design specification?

A design specification provides a detailed list of requirements into which the design ideas must fit.

Key terms

Criteria – a list of key points.

Design specification – an outline that details all the requirements of a product.

Specification criteria

Using your analysis of research summary or chart, you will be able to write your design specification criteria, taking into consideration the points below:

- function/purpose
- appearance
- consumer requirements/target market
- product types
- performance requirements (materials and their properties)
- values issues – social, moral, environmental and sustainability
- details – shape, size and style
- techniques to be used
- health and safety issues (consumer rights and risk assessments)
- cost (scale of production)
- life expectancy of the product.

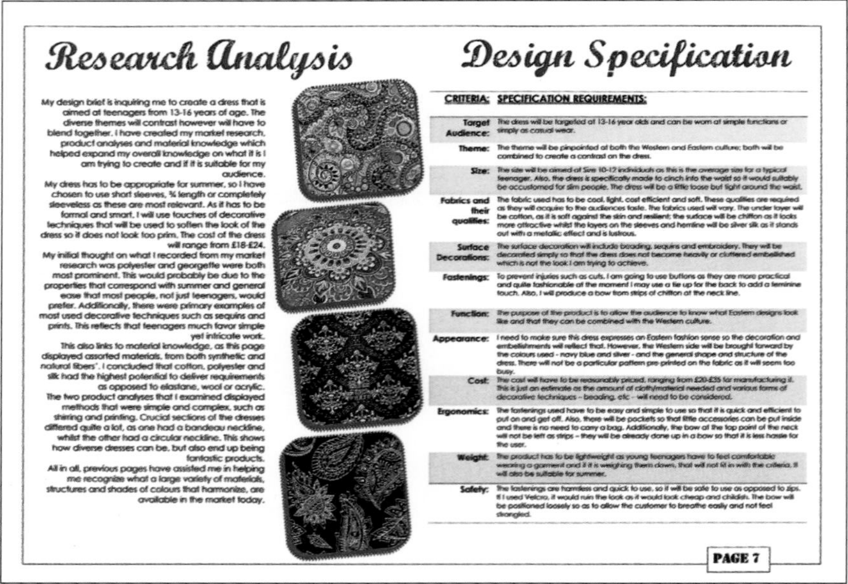

Research Analysis

My design brief is inquiring me to create a dress that is aimed at teenagers from 13-16 years of age. The diverse themes will contrast however will have to blend together. I have created my market research, product analyses and material knowledge which helped expand my overall knowledge on what it is I am trying to create and if it is suitable for my audience.

My dress has to be appropriate for summer, so I have chosen to use short sleeves, ¾ length or completely sleeveless as these are most relevant. As it has to be formal and smart, I will use touches of decorative techniques that will be used to soften the look of the dress so it does not look too prim. The cost of the dress will range from £18-£24.

My initial thought on what I recorded from my market research was polyester and georgette were both most prominent. This would probably be due to the properties that correspond with summer and general ease that most people, not just teenagers, would prefer. Additionally, there were primary examples of most used decorative techniques such as sequins and prints. This reflects that teenagers much favor simple yet intricate work.

This also links to material knowledge, as this page displayed assorted materials, from both synthetic and natural fibers'. I concluded that cotton, polyester and silk had the highest potential to deliver requirements as opposed to elastane, wool or acrylic.

The two product analyses that I examined displayed methods that were simple and complex, such as shirring and printing. Crucial sections of the dresses differed quite a lot, as one had a bandeau neckline, whilst the other had a circular neckline. This shows how diverse dresses can be, but also end up being fantastic products.

All in all, previous pages have assisted me in helping me recognize what a large variety of materials, structures and shades of colours that harmonize, are available in the market today.

Design Specification

CRITERIA:	SPECIFICATION REQUIREMENTS:
Target Audience:	The dress will be targeted at 13-16 year olds and can be worn at simple functions or simply as casual wear.
Theme:	The theme will be pinpointed at both the Western and Eastern culture; both will be combined to create a contrast on the dress.
Size:	The size will be aimed at Size 10-12 individuals as this is the average size for a typical teenager. Also, the dress is specifically made to cinch into the waist so it would suitably be accustomed for slim people. The dress will be a little loose but tight around the waist.
Fabrics and their qualities:	The fabric used has to be cool, light, cost efficient and soft. These qualities are required as they will acquire to the audiences taste. The fabrics used will vary. The under layer will be cotton, as it is soft against the skin and resilient; the surface will be chiffon as it looks more attractive whilst the layers on the sleeves and hemline will be silver silk as it stands out with a metallic effect and is lustrous.
Surface Decorations:	The surface decoration will include beading, sequins and embroidery. They will be decorated simply so that the dress does not become heavily or cluttered embellished which is not the look I am trying to achieve.
Fastenings:	To prevent injuries such as cuts, I am going to use buttons as they are more practical and quite fashionable at the moment I may use a tie up for the back to add a feminine touch. Also, I will produce a bow from strips of chiffon at the neck line.
Function:	The purpose of the product is to allow the audience to know what Eastern designs look like and that they can be combined with the Western culture.
Appearance:	I need to make sure this dress expresses an Eastern fashion sense so the decoration and embellishments will reflect that. However, the Western side will be brought forward by the colours used - navy blue and silver - and the general shape and structure of the dress. There will not be a particular pattern pre-printed on the fabric as it will seem too busy.
Cost:	The cost will have to be reasonably priced, ranging from £20-£35 for manufacturing it. This is just an estimate as the amount of cloth/material needed and various forms of decorative techniques – beading, etc – will need to be considered.
Ergonomics:	The fastenings used have to be easy and simple to use so that it is quick and efficient to put on and get off. Also, there will be pockets so that little accessories can be put inside and there is no need to carry a bag. Additionally, the bow at the top point of the neck will not be left as strips – they will be already done up in a bow so that it is less hassle for the user.
Weight:	The product has to be lightweight as young teenagers have to feel comfortable wearing a garment and if it is weighing them down, that will not fit in with the criteria. It will also be suitable for summer.
Safety:	The fastenings are harmless and quick to use, so it will be safe to use as opposed to zips. If I used Velcro, it would ruin the look as it would look cheap and childish. The bow will be positioned loosely so as to allow the customer to breathe easily and not feel strangled.

PAGE 7

△ **Figure 1.12** A student's research analysis and design specification

Exam tips

- A maximum of eight marks are awarded for this section.
- A maximum of five pages are required to fulfil this section.
- By the end of this section, you should have identified the important points of the design brief, analysed the key areas of research, identified your next steps and completed an initial plan.

Summary

By the end of this section you will:

- have identified the clear areas and important points of the design brief
- know how to accumulate primary information to identify your consumer group and target market
- know how to accumulate secondary information to identify your inspiration and existing products
- understand how to analyse your research.
- have learnt how to write a design specification.

Activities

1. Analysing the task

Analyse one of the design briefs below.

Design brief 1: a well-known toy and educational retailer has asked a group of designers to design and make a product based on stimulating a child's learning. The focus is on traditional, bright colours, with fun and educational imagery. The target market is children with autism, aged between 18 months and 3 years. This will have to be considered when making the product.

Design brief 2: a well-known environmentally conscious company, The People Tree, supplies textile products to people who wish to support fair trade and look after the environment. You have been asked to design and make a range of bags using a Far Eastern country as an inspirational theme. Make up at least one item from your range. You are to design for manufacturing in quantity.

2. Research – product analysis

Find a simple product – garment, accessory or home furnishing. Using Figure 1.13 below, create a product analysis mind map, to carry out a product disassembly. Take photographs or draw the disassembled pieces for the analysis.

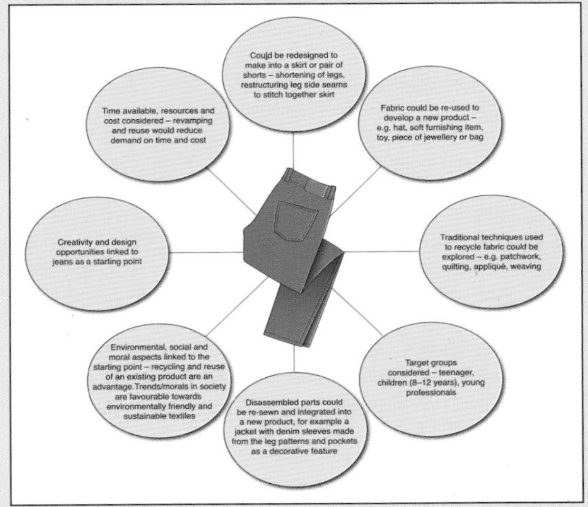

△ **Figure 1.13** Product analysis mind map

3. Research – mood board

Create a mood board using a Far Eastern country as inspiration to assist with Design brief 2 in Activity 1.

Exam practice questions

1. Give two reasons why a designer requires a design brief. **[2 marks]**
2. Designers often study the work of others to give them ideas of new products. Give two advantages of this. **[2 marks]**
3. Explain what a mood board is and how it is used by a designer. **[4 marks]**
4. List three advantages of using product disassembly to analyse a product **[3 marks]**

Stretch yourself

1. Explain why the following types of research are important within the design process:

   (a) trend forecast

   (b) surface decorative technique

   (c) target market. **[6 marks]**

2. Analyse the influences of new technologies used to make fashion and textile products. Give specific examples in your answer. **[5 marks]**

Case study

Case study objective: to show how a designer is commissioned to a contract

Name of designer: Vivien Prideaux

Type of design: self-employed textiles designer (dyer, embroiderer, freelance tutor, lecturer and writer)

Market area: commissioned works to value retailer

Product area: wall hangings for private clients

Profile

Vivien Prideaux is based in Cornwall with its diverse landscapes. Vivien is a highly skilled textiles designer of 25 years and is an experienced dyer, embroiderer, freelance tutor, lecturer and writer, and her work has taken her all over the world. She sources unusual hand-woven, embroidered, natural fabrics and uses traditional dyeing techniques from India, Thailand, New Zealand, Western Samoa and Japan; for instance, the Japanese technique of shibori and hand/machine embroidery. Vivien has received many awards for her work and has written a number of books on various textile dyeing techniques (e.g. indigo dyeing).

Vivien is given commissions with rigid or very open design briefs that vary in length. Being self-employed in other areas of textile design has allowed her career to span so far.

The research process

Vivien is the director for each of her projects. The design processes that are expected when she is commissioned are as follows:

Identifying contexts/starting points/needs → Design brief → Specification → Planning → Personal evaluation → Originating ideas → Personal evaluation → Develop ideas → Personal evaluation → Refining through making → Specification → Personal evaluation → Planning → Making and refining → Formal evaluation

Summary

In order for Vivien Prideaux to meet the client's guidelines, it is important for her to show attention to intricate detail, sensitivity, a wide general knowledge and understanding of the relationship between arts and science, a willingness to take risks and explore, perseverance, resilience, and total commitment with an open mind. The design portfolio collection for presentation has to be carefully analysed and evaluated before being translated into the final commissioned product – a wall hanging.

Website: www.vivienprideaux.co.uk

Resources

Key books

Fitzgerald, T. and Grandon, A. (2009) *200 Projects to Get You into Fashion Design*, Barron's Educational Series.

Hart, A. and North, S. (2005) *Historical Fashion in Detail: The 17th and 18th Centuries*, V&A Publications.

McKelvey, K. and Muslow, J. (2003) *Fashion Design: Process, Innovation and Practice*, Blackwell Science Ltd.

Seivewright, S. (2007) *Basics Fashion Design 01: Research and Design*, AVA Publishing SA.

Tatham, C. and Seaman, J. (2003) *Fashion Design Drawing Course: Principles, Practice and Techniques: The Ultimate Guide for the Aspiring Fashion Artist*, Thames & Hudson.

Udale, J. (2008) *Basic Fashion Design 02: Textiles and Fashion*, AVA Publishing SA.

Websites

National Geographic: www.nationalgeographic.com

iStockphoto: www.istockphoto.com

The Fashion Spot: www.thefashionspot.com/style-trends

V&A, on Vivienne Westwood: www.vam.ac.uk/vastatic/microsites/1231_vivienne_westwood/sketchdress.html

Trendstop: www.trendstop.com

Fashion Trendsetter, colour trends: www.fashiontrendsetter.com

Mode…information: www.modeinfo.de

Zoom magazine: www.zoom-net.com/zoom-magazine.aspx

1.2 Development of design proposals: initial ideas

Learning objectives

By the end of this section, you should have a key understanding of:

- how to start the design strategy
- how to sketch and draw realistic and functional initial ideas clearly
- how to communicate your design ideas to relate to the design specification.

Key points

- Analytical skills
- Innovative ideas
- Creative ideas
- Values

Introduction

This is the section of your design folder that will demonstrate your creative flair. The key focus of the task is to generate initial ideas that are exciting and original. The design specification is the guide to make sure your ideas are focused and appropriate to your target audience. In order for you to remain focused, it is important to always refer to your design content: mood boards, research analysis and design specification.

Your initial ideas must show that you have a free flow of clear thinking. Ideas are best illustrated with quick sketches (drawings), and remember to use notes and annotations alongside your sketches.

Key terms

Annotate – to add notes to each design idea to explain what you are thinking; this includes the good points and bad points of the design and whether you wish to develop ideas.

Design specification – the specific design details that a product has to match.

Initial ideas – basic ideas completed quickly, usually with a pencil or fine liner. These sketches can be developed further or discarded. It is useful to experiment with different colours, patterns, sizes and styles. They are also known as design sketches.

Sketches – a rough outline on paper which illustrates the points of a design. Tools to use for sketching are pencils, crayons and fine liner pens.

Initial ideas (finding your style and how to do working drawings)

Before starting initial ideas, the key areas to focus and explore are:

- colour
- shape
- pattern/texture
- fabrics
- decoration/embellishment
- size/proportion
- construction.

Note: remember to refer to your mood board, research analysis and design specification.

Key terms

Construction – the process of joining or assembling a product.

Embellish – to improve the look of a product using colour, texture and pattern.

Fabric – material that can be knitted, woven or non-woven.

Proportion – relates to size and scale

Shape – provides or defines form.

Surface decoration – applying various stitching and decorative techniques to the surface of fabrics.

Using a basic HB pencil or a black fine-liner pen, sketch a few early ideas to see how the key design themes can be drawn together (focused practice task – FPT). If you get off to a slow start, for motivation, have a look at existing products that appeal to you drawn by fashion designers or students.

The expected number of initial working ideas is 16–20 sketches. These sketches should take up at least two A3 pages of your design folder. You should not use erasers, rulers, coloured pencils or compasses while working on the initial ideas. The design ideas must illustrate a free flow of working. It is important for your creative thinking skills to be demonstrated. Make notes and/or annotations for the working drawings.

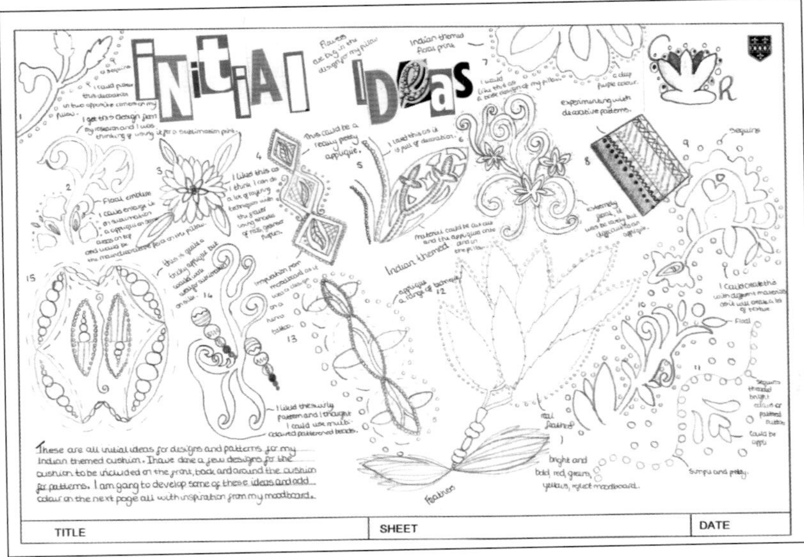

△ **Figure 1.14** A student's initial ideas

You should use a variety of drawing skills and graphical techniques, including ICT and computer-aided design (CAD) software such as SpeedStep®, to present your ideas. Below are a few techniques to try:

- Use cross-hatching, dots and rubbing techniques to illustrate different material textures.
- Practise sketching to get your ideas on paper quickly.
- Use CAD packages to simulate creating different surface decoration and embellishment techniques, repeat patterns, motifs and geometric patterns.
- Use a scanner and digital camera to import and manipulate images.

Exam tips

- Remember to refer to your mood board, research analysis and design specification when practising your sketching technique.
- Make sure your initial ideas meet the criteria on the design specification; if they do not, the ideas will be disregarded.
- The shape and style of initial ideas must be clear and well presented.
- Use notes and annotations alongside your drawings.

Activities

1. Create a design specification for a school bag.
2. Draw as many different ideas on one A3 page as you can, including detailed annotations. Remember to research relevant and appropriate fabrics, their properties and fastenings (see Chapter 4).

Evaluating and analysing design ideas

It is an important element of your design folder to evaluate and analyse your design ideas as they develop. Remember to always match them to the design specification, making sure there is reference to the essential and desirable criteria. Once you have finished your ideas you should highlight which ideas can be further developed.

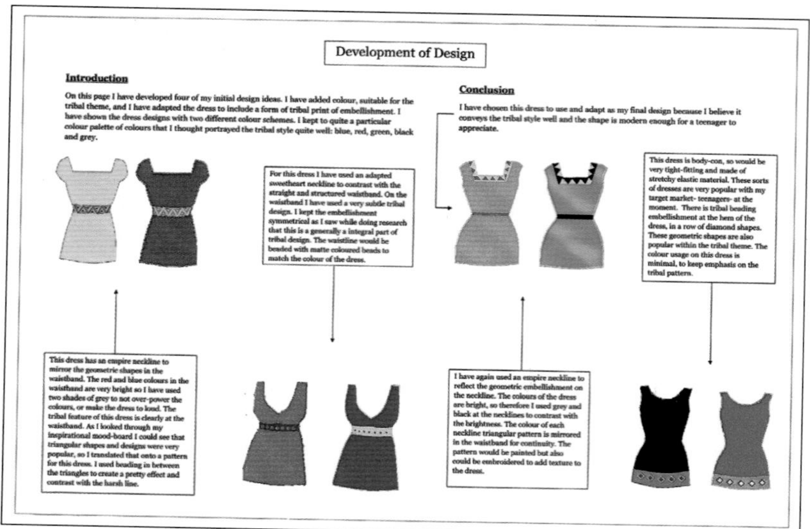

Figure 1.15 A student's colour pattern development

Summary

By the end of this section you should know that:

- you must always refer to your design specification
- you must refer to your mood board for colours, surface pattern and decoration and shapes
- you must practise your product sketches to prepare you for the controlled assessed initial ideas task
- you must collect different types of fabrics and components to broaden your design ideas.

Exam practice questions

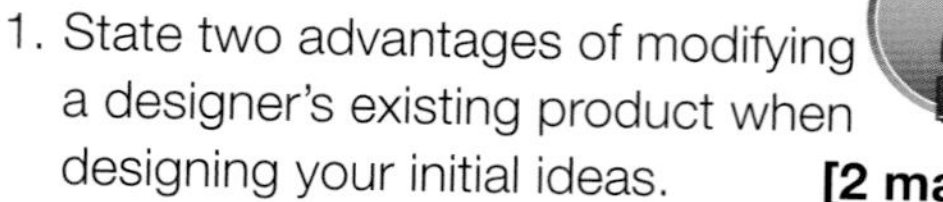

1. State two advantages of modifying a designer's existing product when designing your initial ideas. **[2 marks]**

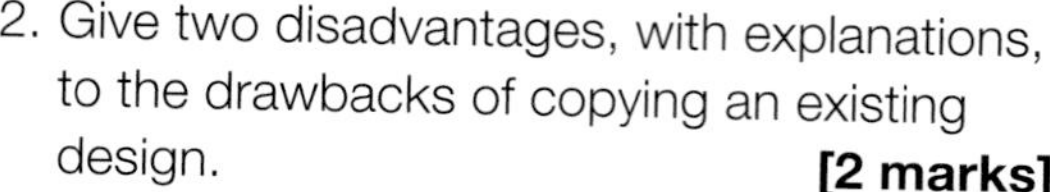

2. Give two disadvantages, with explanations, to the drawbacks of copying an existing design. **[2 marks]**
3. Give three reasons why designers would use ICT to present their ideas to a client. **[3 marks]**

Stretch yourself

You have been asked to illustrate design ideas for a product. The design specification states your product must:

- be based on a famous architectural building
- use hand/machine embroidery technology
- be suitable for mass production (made in large quantities).

1. Draw and label two different design ideas for your product. **[2 × 3 marks]**

Case study

Case study objective: to show how one garment, an A-line skirt, can be developed into a range of different skirts using a variety of different embellished techniques

Name of designer: Alison Willoughby

Type of design: fashion, textiles and art installation

Market area: couture garments, high-end products and value retailer

Product area: fashion garments and commissioned products – art and accessories

Website: www.alisonwilloughby.com

Profile

Alison Willoughby is based in Central London, E1. She is renowned for her intricate and individual, hand-constructed skirts. These were originally created as wall pieces and then became functional garments as viewers wanted to buy to wear. Alison's work has extended from wall pieces and straddled through fashion, art, craft and design.

The research/design process

Alison uses her skirts as a blank canvas to create her art masterpieces. Her inspiration came from taking photographs of domestic and everyday surroundings, and exhibition comments that evoked the feeling to change her construction of her skirt. Alison works with colour, line, shape, proportion, texture and placement studies, which are strongly illustrated in her skirts.

Her gallery pieces can be worn by members of the public. For instance, one skirt had glass replaced with glass beads in order for the skirt to become wearable and function as a piece of art. Alison's clients are used to wearing bespoke couture garments. Alison has published a book called *49 Sensational Skirts: Creative Embellishment Ideas for One-of-a-Kind Designs*, which highlights how to use one garment and combine very different ideas of embellishments on construction.

Summary

In order to get ahead as a designer, you need to be clear about your concepts and directions and be open-minded to criticism. You need to allow your style to be challenged and pushed so your work can transcend into unexpected arenas.

Resources

Key books

Burke, S. (2003) *Fashion Artist: Drawing Techniques to Portfolio Presentation*, Burke Publishing.

Burke, S. (2006) *Fashion Computing Design Techniques and CAD*, Burke Publishing.

Drudi, E. and Paci, T. (2001) *Figure Drawing for Fashion Design*, Pepin Press BV.

Hopkins, J. (2010) *Basic Fashion Design 05: Fashion Drawing*, AVA Publishing SA.

Udale, J. (2008) *Basic Fashion Design 02: Textiles and Fashion,* AVA Publishing SA.

Websites

Fashion-era: www.fashion-era.com

Fashion Templates: www.fashion-templates.com

1.3 Development of design proposals: developing of ideas and evaluated colour illustrations

Learning objectives

By the end of this section, you should have a key understanding of:

- how to illustrate development of ideas
- how to use other mediums (equipment and tools) to develop and present ideas
- how to use research to demonstrate creativity and originality with colour design ideas
- how to evaluate your coloured development ideas clearly against the design specification
- how to product develop (product refine) and choose the final idea.

Key points

- Analytical skills
- Communication skills
- Creative ideas
- Innovative ideas
- Linking technology and design
- Values

Introduction

Within this section you will have to choose one of your completed design ideas. Your ideas will have to be presented in more detail using the colours, fabrics and components from your mood board. Once you have evaluated your designs, you will be able to start the planning of your final idea.

Development of ideas – evaluated colour illustrations

Development of ideas involves experimenting to ensure that the designs are realistic and work as a product and then refining the ideas to make them look aesthetically pleasing and to ensure the product is marketable. In this section, ideas are chosen to be developed in more detail, taking into consideration the following factors:

- scale
- proportion

Key terms

Appliqué – shapes of fabric are applied to the surface or background of another fabric using zigzag (satin) or straight stitch to secure the design.

Beading – machined or hand-sewn on to fabrics to add texture, glamour and decoration. It is placed in an area that does not get much wear. It is an expensive form of decoration.

Components – parts such as buttons, trims and interfacing that are an integral part of a textile and fashion product.

Darts – a method of disposing of fullness and shaping in a garment or textile product.

Development – involves experimenting to ensure the idea works, or refining an idea to make it better and easier to use.

Embroidery – a decorative design or pattern that is applied to a fabric using specific hand or machine stitches.

Materials – fabrics, paper, card etc. necessary for a practical task.

Quilting – layers of fabric that are stitched together to create a 3D decorative finish.

Reverse appliqué – the main fabric has a shape cut out and the appliquéd shape is cut out and stitched on to the back and the colour comes through.

- fabric/s to use and their properties
- appropriate colours or colour combinations
- what properties does your product need to have?
- is it appropriate to add designs, embellishments, surface decoration, etc. onto the fabric?

It is important to think about the key values of your product, the effects and impact on the environment, social and moral issues associated with the design and making of the product, and the cost of making the product. You need to understand the dimensions of your product and show you have considered ergonomic and anthropometrics data. At this stage, you should already have made some key decisions such as the colour, fabric(s), decorative techniques, modelling samples and construction techniques are clearly annotated with further notes on each idea.

Key terms

Anthropometrics – the scientific study and recording of human body sizes that help designers to make products to the correct size for people to use and wear.

Ergonomics – a process of using measurements and data when designing and making products.

Evaluating and testing

Once you have developed your ideas you will have evaluated your designs, taking into consideration how to modify your designs. These include modifications such as adding sleeves, shortening or adding length to the sleeves, changing the pattern size or changing the front or back neck line. It is essential to go back to your client or seek other individuals' opinions on your developed ideas in order to make sure your product suits the design specification. If not, you need to think about improvements you could use to make the product.

Key term

Evaluate – to consider the success of the product, and also what is unsuccessful.

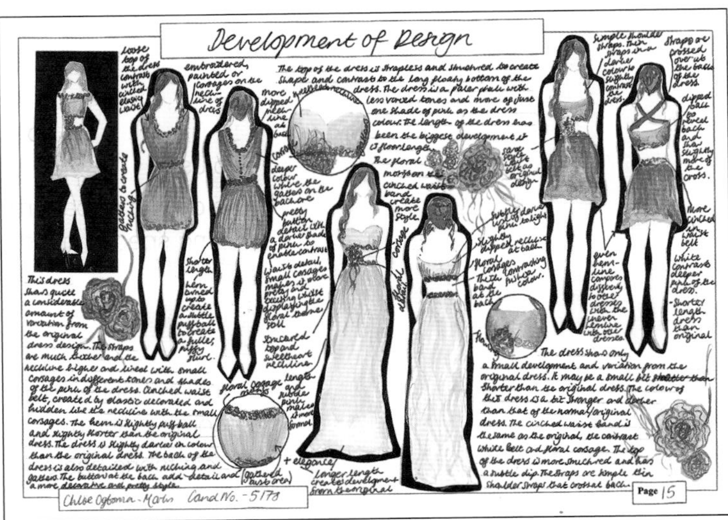

△ **Figure 1.16** A student's developed ideas, with colour illustrations and suggested fabrics and components

Presentation of development ideas

It is essential that you use graphic techniques (CAD software such as Adobe® Photoshop® or SpeedStep®) when presenting your ideas, to ensure that your developments such as colour and fabric variations, shape and size and modelling are illustrated creatively and clearly. You should also show key details of how your product can be constructed in the industrial process.

Knowledge link

For more information on presenting your ideas, see Chapter 11.

Summary

- Development designs need to illustrate modifications to the initial ideas.
- Remember to use your research to demonstrate creativity and originality in your designs.
- Remember to refer to your design specification.
- Design software (CAD) can help create, communicate and present your ideas and work clearly and concisely.

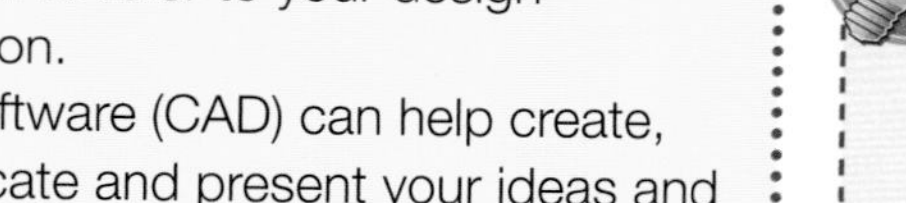

Activities

1. Design as many design ideas as you can for developing a basic 'A' shape skirt – sketch 20 or more ideas on a sheet of A3.

2. Import your ideas (using a scanner or other digital tools) into a software package.

3. Using CAD software add or change the colours and add surface decoration patterns.

Figure 1.17 Modelling a garment

Exam practice questions

1. Give four reasons why your design ideas have to match your design brief and specification. **[4 marks]**
2. Why do designers develop initial designs? **[2 marks]**
3. What is meant by the terms 'ergonomics' and 'anthropometrics'? **[2 marks]**

Knowledge link

For more on CAD/CAM software and processes, see Chapter 11, pages 265–272.

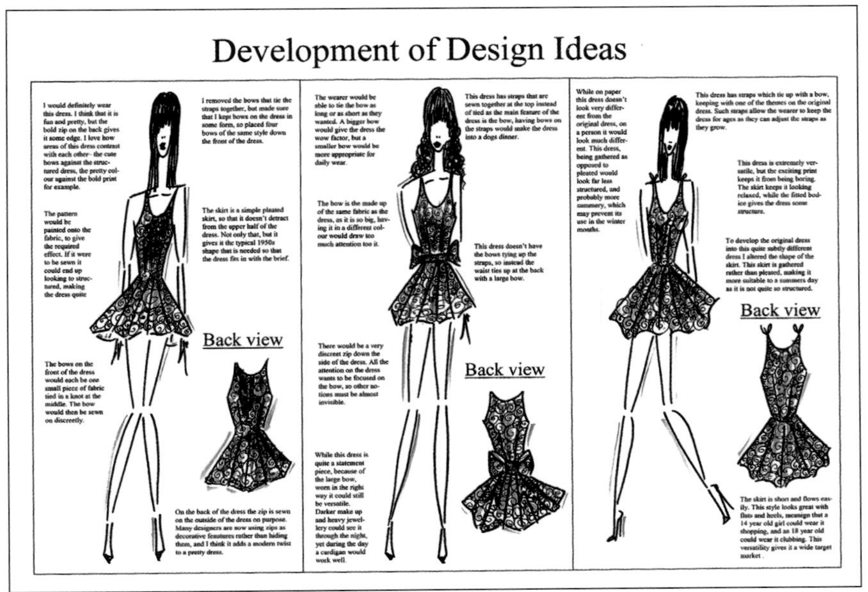

△ **Figure 1.18** You should use ICT skills to create simple and appropriate developed ideas

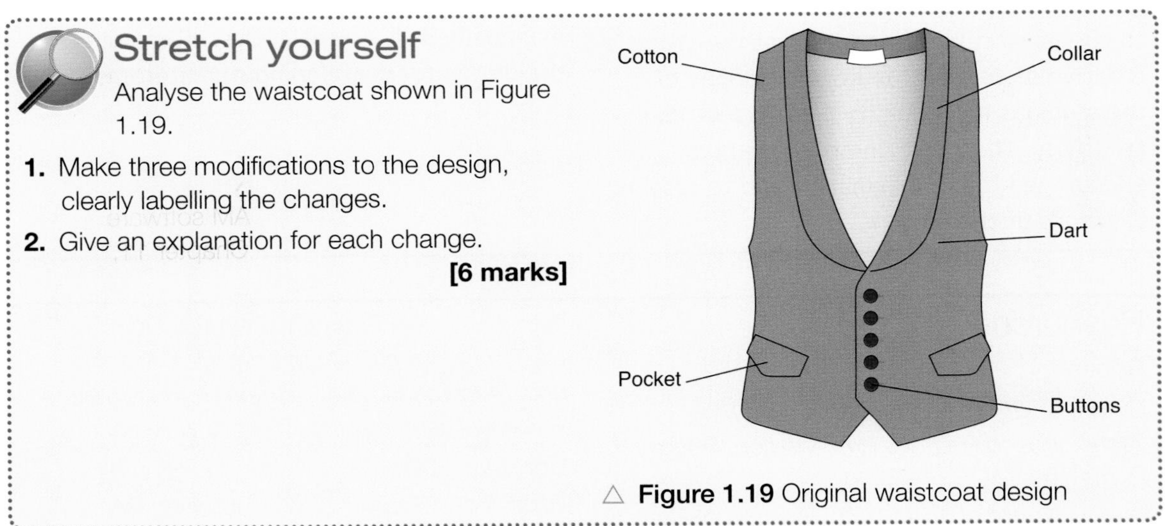

Stretch yourself

Analyse the waistcoat shown in Figure 1.19.

1. Make three modifications to the design, clearly labelling the changes.
2. Give an explanation for each change.

[6 marks]

△ **Figure 1.19** Original waistcoat design

Case study

Case study objective: to illustrate how a design company integrates design software into their design inspiration through to the presentation of the final collection.

Name of company: Lewis and Lewis Design

Type of design: textile design (print, embroidery and weave) for fashion

Market area: high-end couture (appointment to view collection)

Product area: fashion garments and biannual trend books

Website: www.lewisandlewisdesign.com

Profile

The partnership is based in London and develops a biannual trend book that is sold to clients worldwide and informs the studio's creative direction. The key philosophy of the studio is individuality and respect for creativity. The small, in-house team is encouraged to be imaginative and to respond to trends of the season.

The research process

The Lewis and Lewis Design ethos is creativity, individuality and attention to detail, and the head designers, the directors, oversee the design team. Lewis and Lewis Design produces two collections a season, Spring/Summer and Autumn/Winter, which are constantly updated throughout the season. Each collection features a unique mixture of digital print, embroidery, hand-painted print, weave and vintage fabrics. All Lewis and Lewis designs are produced on fabric, and digital designs are available on disc.

Summary

Lewis and Lewis uses CAD design software in order to fulfil their clients' needs for fashion-directional fabrics. Producing trend books biannually, it is essential that all members of the design team are computer-literate.

Resources

Books

Burke, S. (2003) *Fashion Artist: Drawing Techniques to Portfolio Presentation*, Burke Publishing.

Burke, S. (2006) *Fashion Computing Design Techniques and CAD,* Burke Publishing.

Drudi, E. and Paci, T. (2001) *Figure Drawing for Fashion Design*, Pepin Press BV.

McKelvey, K. and Muslow, J. (2003) *Fashion Design: Process, Innovation and Practice,* Blackwell Science Ltd.

Tatham, C. and Seaman, J. (2003) *Fashion Design Drawing Course: Principles, Practice and Techniques: The Ultimate Guide for the Aspiring Fashion Artist*, Thames & Hudson.

Udale, J. (2008) *Basic Fashion Design 02: Textiles and Fashion*, AVA Publishing SA.

Websites

Trendstop: www.trendstop.com

Fashion Trendsetter, colour trends: www.fashiontrendsetter.com/content/color_trends.html

1.4 Development of the design proposal: developing techniques, modelling and product and manufacturing specifications

Learning objectives

By the end of this section, you should have a key understanding of:

- how to present evidence of your planning skills
- how to develop the product's shape and style
- how to make modifications to the product pattern
- how to cost the product
- how to construct and model the product
- how to make colour decisions/choices using the mood board
- how to choose the right materials and components
- the social, moral, environmental and economic issues (sustainability) that are relevant to your product
- how to define the product specification
- how to define the manufacturing specification with flow diagrams
- investigating, experimenting and presenting construction and decorative techniques.

Key points

- Creative ideas
- Innovative ideas
- Analytical skills
- Communication skills
- Linking technology and design
- Values

Knowledge link

For more on understanding software, see Chapter 11.

Key term

Product planning – shows a timeline for the overall construction of the final textile or fashion product.

Introduction

Once you have finished your developed designs you have to think about your development planning to help further your chosen design, keeping in mind how it could be manufactured in a large quantity.

Planning is to know how long each key stage will take and is an important task. You need to understand how to create Gantt charts or simple flow charts, use spreadsheet software, interpret your planning using flow charts and use mind-mapping software to illustrate your planning.

Planning involves the development of 2D design ideas into a 3D functional product. You are expected to show that you can plan and organise tasks throughout the constructing (making) stage, to ensure that the appropriate materials and tools are selected to make the final product successfully. It is essential to record the key stages in the making of the product through a written and photographic diary. The key elements of the planning process are outlined as follows.

Developing and modifying design ideas

- Refer to your research and design specification to properly develop your initial design ideas into evaluated coloured designs.
- Review the shape and style of the product – refine it, alter it and ask the target audience for their opinions and preferences on the different shapes.
- Plan the development stages.
- Choose an idea/ideas that closely meets the specification.

Pattern modifying and modelling

- You must list the equipment and tools required to construct your product and know the health and safety implications when used in mass production.
- Refer to your mood board to look at patterns and decoration – consider adding new components or trying different patterns. Is the overall composition suitable to the specification? Choose a suitable colour(s). Are the colours in trend? Experiment with different colourways using CAD software such as Adobe® Photoshop®, Adobe® Illustrator® and SpeedStep®.

Knowledge link
For more on researching current trends, see Chapter 7, pages 159–60.

- Model the product in paper to see if it is the right size and shape and to enable you to visualise the decoration placement. Will the decorations work together?
- Experiment with different construction techniques.

Knowledge link
For more on researching making techniques, see Chapter 2.

- Create a paper pattern with the correct markings.

Knowledge link
For more on commercial patterns and grading, see Chapter 11, page 268.

- Mock up part of the garment or a complete toile.
- Once you have mocked up the garment, investigate different decorative techniques or adding shape – for example, embellishments, fabric manipulations, shaping techniques and printing techniques.

Knowledge link
For more on surface decoration, see Chapter 5, page 129–135.

- List the characteristics and properties of the fabric(s) that you wish to use. Think about the aftercare of fabric(s).

Knowledge link
For more on fabrics and aftercare, see Chapter 4.

- Investigate components, including fastenings and threads, and their suitability for the job.

Knowledge link
For more on fastenings and components, see Chapter 6.

- Investigate commercial pattern markings and make sure the construction instructions are understandable.

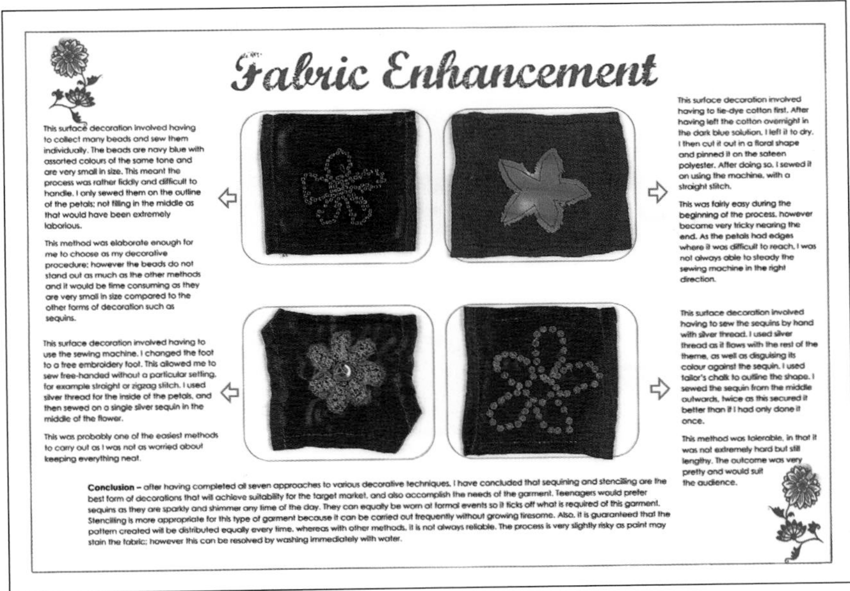

△ **Figure 1.20** A student's surface pattern and decoration using inspiration from a mood board

Pre-development knowledge: understanding product and manufacturing specifications

To carry out the development design and model work you have to start to think how your product will be best made.

This section will help you to have an overview of your product. This can be done by creating a product specification. You will need to be aware of the following to complete your development design section successfully:

- How to make sure the product is within the recorded price range. How much does it cost to make? (See Figure 1.21.)

Knowledge link

For more on product costing, see Chapter 10, page 240.

- What type of modifications are required to make your product feasible for mass production.
- Consider health and safety issues. (You need to illustrate this through the design flow chart.)
- What do you need to consider when designing and making for sustainability and other environmental, moral and social issues?
- Consider how to present the final idea including the target audience's opinions, sustainability factors and issues.

Knowledge link

For more on product and manufacturing specifications, see Chapter 10, page 239.

Once you have summarised your findings with a final design idea, identify and analyse your decisions about materials, components, techniques, skills and processes. You must record and understand the equipment and tools used in the development and making of your product.

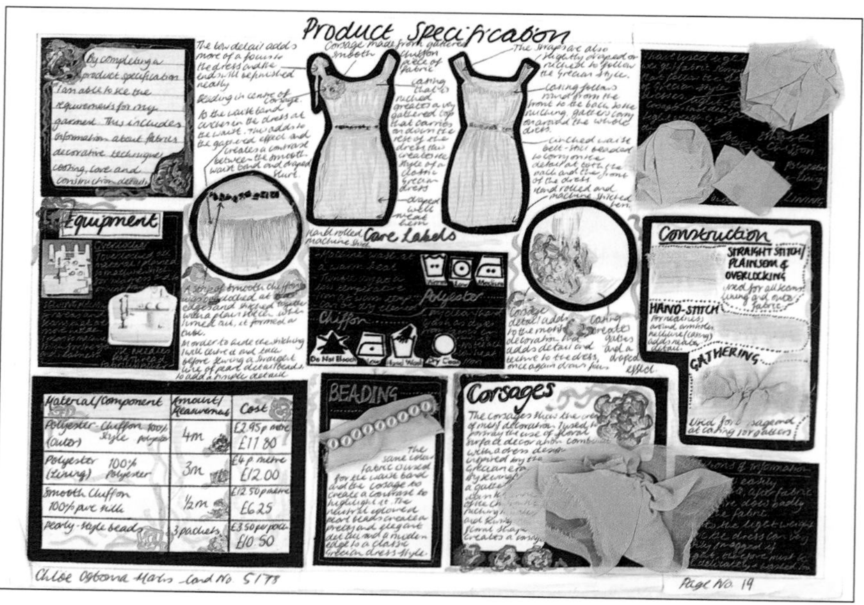

△ **Figure 1.21** A student's product cost of her final design

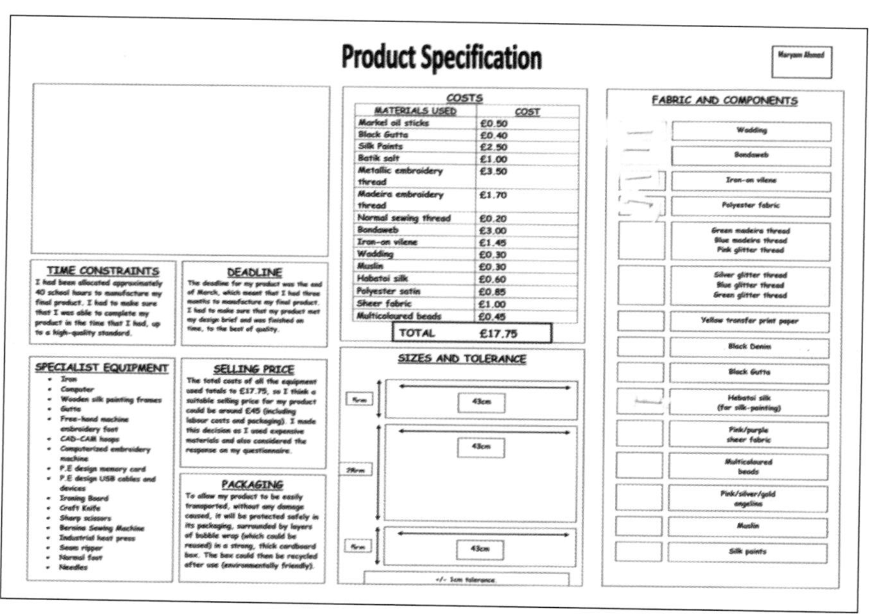

△ **Figure 1.22** A student's product specification of her final chosen product

Tools for developing ideas

The research put together to investigate the design context (see Section 1.1, page 6) is required to help make key decisions, from developing design ideas through to the manufacturing specification. The key areas of research that are required are as follows:

- sketchbook – design journal
- mood board (surface pattern ideas, colour, items for shape)
- trend board (fabric samples, components, trims, thread, textures and colour)
- consumer profile and target audience's preferences
- existing products used within a comparative report
- product analysis (analysing and disassembling products).

A successful design folder illustrates the link between research and developing ideas throughout the work.

Key terms

Sketchbook – can be used for gathering information from a variety of sources – for example, exhibition and show literature, fabric swatches, colour references and sketches.

Style – a form of appearance, design or production.

Exam tips

For the assessment criteria, you are required to use two pages to fully demonstrate your developed ideas.

Activity

You have received a design brief from an environmentally conscious company, The People Tree.

Design brief: the company supplies textile products to people who wish to support fair trade and look after the environment. You have been asked to design a range of bags using Morocco as an inspirational theme and make up at least one item from your range. You are to design for manufacturing in quantity.

Design specification:

- Must have two Moroccan-influenced surface pattern or decoration techniques.
- Must have two different secure fastenings.
- Must be made with donated fabrics.
- Must be colourful.

Design and annotate as many different design ideas for the bags within 30 minutes, using the above design brief and design specification.

Note: the successful folders will include an evaluation of the developed ideas followed by an overall summary of the findings.

Activity

Refer to the design brief and design specification in the first activity on this page. Choose one of your design ideas and illustrate modifications to this idea using the design specification.

Note: have you considered the health and safety issues (British Standards) involved in making your product?

Modelling and pattern development

This section is made up of three distinct areas:

- developing design ideas – style, shape, size and proportion
- investigating and experimenting – colour and decorative ideas
- choosing fabrics and components.

Key terms

Construction techniques (hems, seams pockets, etc.) – use of specific techniques for joining textile products together or making components or a particular part of a product.

Modelling (toiles and models) – involves developing, experimenting and trying out ideas to see what works best; can be done using fabric or computer-based 3D software.

Pattern template – commercial patterns are produced from measurements set by industry professionals and may vary from time to time, depending on what the fashion is at the time.

Surface pattern – to apply, arrange or decorate with a pattern onto a surface.

The product should be fashionable and refined to meet current trends and the needs of the target audience. In industry, the designer would use a basic block pattern and modify this until the product is the right size and shape. For your design, you should make a paper model of the product or buy a commercial pattern and use the same technique – modifying the pattern until the size and shape are suitable. You need to understand pattern markings in order to use them on your own paper pattern or template. You should think how the product's pattern will fit together – practise different construction techniques or scale down the pattern to find the best way to make the product.

Developing design ideas – style and shape

During the development stage, you should adapt and revise your ideas until you find the best possible final garment or product to meet the design specification. The development ideas such as style, size and shape must illustrate improved style and shape when compared with design ideas. The drawings must be more detailed and your knowledge must be illustrated through the use of a wide range of materials, components and construction techniques, as well as specific textiles technology terms.

In this section you should know how the product will work, highlighting front and back views where appropriate and other key details. Your work should include exploded details.

Key elements for development

Once you have put together the research that answers the design context (see Section 1.1 in this chapter), which is required to help make key decisions, from developing design ideas through to the manufacturing specification. The key areas of research required are as follows:

Investigating and experimenting – colour and decorative techniques

This section will help you when testing a range of fabrics and processes to find the most suitable choice/s for your product.

Use your mood board to help you choose suitable colours that follow current trends. Experiment with different colours using either a software paint package or paints such as acrylic or watercolours. Evaluate your colour development choice – ask others what they think and check that the colour choices reflect your research findings.

Refer back to your mood board and look at your ideas for surface patterns and decorations. Once you have decided on the decorative work, choose the best practical techniques to illustrate these ideas. Investigative work has to be carried out to assist you in producing samples to see if the technique(s) work for your design and on the fabrics you are most likely to use. Evaluate your techniques, explaining what the process involves, what the outcomes are and whether you will apply the technique on your final idea.

Choosing fabrics and components

This section builds on your understanding of fabrics and their properties and making the right choices for your product.

Your thoughts on fabrics should have been included at the initial ideas stage, through to your developed designs. Weight of the fabric, texture, and so on. should all be documented. Choosing the most suitable fabrics and components for your product is important. You will have to carry out further research in order to make informed decisions. Below are a few pointers:

- Choosing the fabrics – make a list of all the properties the fabric needs to have to be suitable for your product (e.g. durable, does not burn easily, easy to care for). If you are unsure about the fabric's properties, test it. Know which fibres will be suitable for use and understand that different fibres have different properties. Remember that fabrics can sometimes consist of one or more fibres.
- Components, including threads, trims and fastenings, must be researched for cost purposes and to test whether or not they give the right effect to the product (see Table 1.2).
- Costing – price your fabric/s and components to see if the production costs would be feasible. Seek your target audience's opinion.
- Consider sustainability and other environmental, moral and social issues in your choices.
- Think of the materials' aftercare.

	Ease of use	Ease of fitting	Variety of types	Strength	Ease of care	Cost
Button holes	•	••••	••••	••	••	▲▲
Toggles	•••	•••	•	••	••	▲▲
Zips	•••	•	••	••••	••	▲▲▲
Velcro	••••	••••	•	••••	•••	▲▲
Hooks/ eyes	•	••	••	•	•••	▲
Eyelets and laces	••	•••	••	••••	••	▲▲
Press studs	•••	•••	••	•	•••	▲
Clips/ buckles	••	•••	••	•••	•••	▲▲▲
• – few blobs for worse, •••• – more blobs for better ▲ – cheap, ▲▲▲ – most expensive						

△ **Table 1.2** Choosing the correct components

Source: www.nationalstemcentre.org.uk

> **Activity**
>
> Look back at the design brief for The People Tree in the activity on page 29. Put together a mood board of suitable fabrics and components for your design ideas that meet the brief.
>
> Note: you need to show an awareness of fabric testing. The areas to think about with regard to testing fabrics include strength, colour-fastness and crease resistance, among others.

The chosen final design idea

From your developed and evaluated ideas, there will be one that best meets your design specification criteria. This idea should be further modified and should show a good understanding of the materials, components, processes and construction techniques required for the product. All decisions made regarding the product should be justified.

Remember, it is your responsibility as a designer is to make sure that sustainability and other environmental, moral and social issues have been considered in the chosen final design idea.

> **Knowledge link**
>
> For more information on environmental, moral and social issues, see Chapter 3 and Chapter 8.

At the end of this process, there should be enough information to produce a detailed product specification.

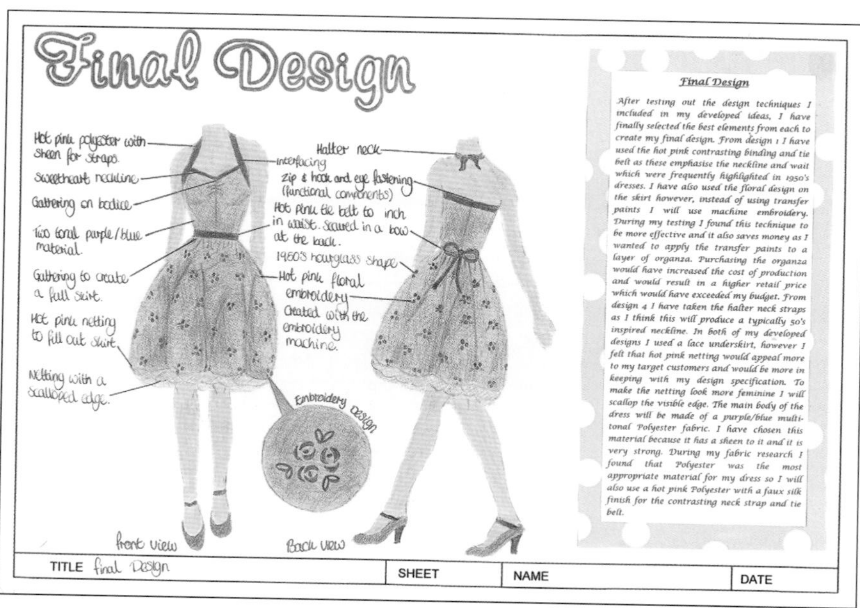

Final Design

After testing out the design techniques I included in my developed ideas, I have finally selected the best elements from each to create my final design. From design 1 I have used the hot pink contrasting binding and tie belt as these emphasise the neckline and wait which were frequently highlighted in 1950's dresses. I have also used the floral design on the skirt however, instead of using transfer paints I will use machine embroidery. During my testing I found this technique to be more effective and it also saves money as I wanted to apply the transfer paints to a layer of organza. Purchasing the organza would have increased the cost of production and would result in a higher retail price which would have exceeded my budget. From design 4 I have taken the halter neck straps as I think this will produce a typically 50's inspired neckline. In both of my developed designs I used a lace underskirt, however I felt that hot pink netting would appeal more to my target customers and would be more in keeping with my design specification. To make the netting look more feminine I will scallop the visible edge. The main body of the dress will be made of a purple/blue multi-tonal Polyester fabric. I have chosen this material because it has a sheen to it and it is very strong. During my fabric research I found that Polyester was the most appropriate material for my dress so I will also use a hot pink Polyester with a faux silk finish for the contrasting neck strap and tie belt.

△ **Figure 1.23** A student's final design idea

Product and manufacturing specifications

This section is divided into three key areas:

- product specification
- costing
- manufacturing specification.

Product specification

A product specification contains instructions and information that are used to make a prototype and sample products.

The product specification should contain the following:

- a working drawing of the product – a technical drawing showing front and back views, measurement details, exploded drawings and highlighting key details of seams, darts, etc.
- a written description of the product, including a list of all the materials and components to be used, quantities needed and fabric swatches and samples for reference
- size details for all the components to be used
- appropriate care label information and instructions for aftercare.

Knowledge link

For more information on testing see pages 249–50.

It is vital for the information to be accurate and clear in order to calculate the cost of the product.

Costing

When costing for a product, you need to consider the key costs of:

- materials – threads, fabrics, trims etc.
- components – zips, buttons, interfacing etc.
- labour – wages and working premises
- energy – electricity used.

Knowledge link

For more information on costing, see Chapter 10, pages 240–43.

You also need to be aware of ethical issues related to fair wages and working conditions.

Knowledge link

For more information on ethical and sustainability issues, see Chapter 8.

Key terms

Product specification – contains instructions and information that will be used to make a prototype and calculate the final cost of your product.

Manufacturing specification – the specific manufacturing details and instructions needed to make a product.

Costing – the process of working out the cost of making a product.

6Rs – recycle, rethink, reduce, reuse, refuse and repair.

Manufacturing specification

The manufacturing specification consists of a list of guidelines to follow during the stages of production. All the materials required for production should be listed and diagrams and flow charts are needed in order to make the product exactly how the designer envisaged during the production process. The manufacturing specification should provide enough information so that anyone could use the specification to make the same product over and over.

The manufacturing specification must include:

- a list of tools and equipment required
- a detailed description of the processes involved (e.g. cutting, machining, finishes)

- the types of fabrics to be used and how they should be treated
- a list of components required
- details of the pattern to be used
- appropriate quality control checks or critical control points for each stage of making
- a detailed production plan (use a flow chart)
- details of matching materials and components with the correct tools, equipment and processes (e.g. use fabric scissors to cut out fabric)
- timelines and guides for each stage (e.g. Gantt chart or simple flow chart)
- details of possible problems (risk assessment) that could occur and how they could be avoided and, if necessary, corrected.

See Figure 1.24 for an example manufacturing specification.

In industry, there will be in-house machinists to work with the designers to advise on the most appropriate method/s to construct the product.

Note: the manufacturing and product specification can be combined together to produce a final product specification.

Key terms

Flow chart – a diagram that uses special symbols to show the sequence of a process.

Gantt chart – a plan that is created to show activities and the time, people and resources required to complete them.

Health and safety – a risk assessment for each production stage should be carried out to ensure you are working in a safe environment and using safe equipment.

Quality assurance – a guarantee given to the customer from the company to assure the quality of the product.

Quality control – tests and inspections carried out to ensure that the products meet the specification criteria.

Risk assessment – identification and minimisation of the potential hazards in the workplace.

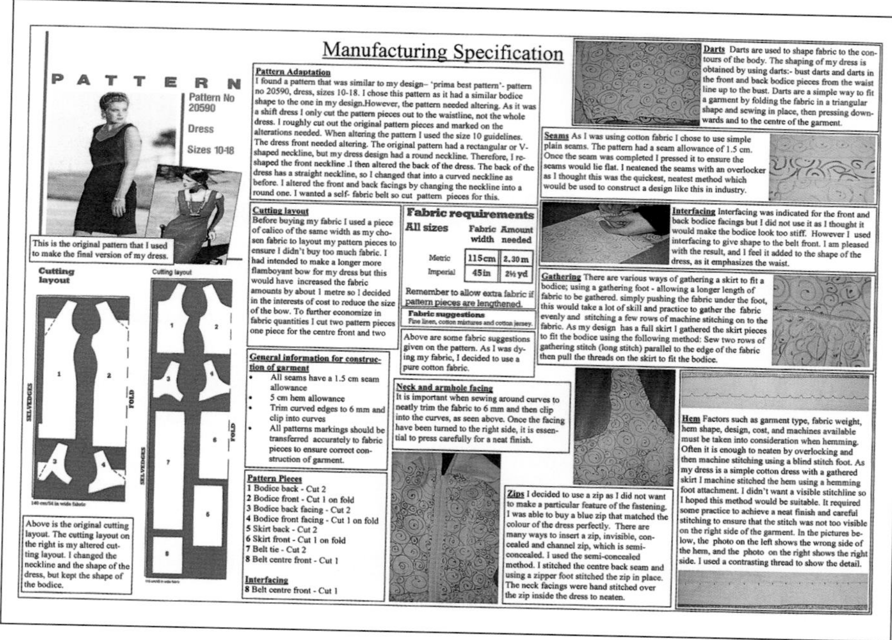

Manufacturing Specification

PATTERN

Pattern No 20590

Dress

Sizes 10-18

This is the original pattern that I used to make the final version of my dress.

Cutting layout

Cutting layout

SELVEDGES

FOLD

140 cm/54 in wide fabric

Above is the original cutting layout. The cutting layout on the right is my altered cutting layout. I changed the neckline and the shape of the dress, but kept the shape of the bodice.

Pattern Adaptation
I found a pattern that was similar to my design– 'prima best pattern'- pattern no 20590, dress, sizes 10-18. I chose this pattern as it had a similar bodice shape to the one in my design.However, the pattern needed altering. As it was a shift dress I only cut the pattern pieces out to the waistline, not the whole dress. I roughly cut out the original pattern pieces and marked on the alterations needed. When altering the pattern I used the size 10 guidelines. The dress front needed altering. The original pattern had a rectangular or V-shaped neckline, but my dress design had a round neckline. Therefore, I re-shaped the front neckline .I then altered the back of the dress. The back of the dress has a straight neckline, so I changed that into a curved neckline as before. I altered the front and back facings by changing the neckline into a round one. I wanted a self- fabric belt so cut pattern pieces for this.

Cutting layout
Before buying my fabric I used a piece of calico of the same width as my chosen fabric to layout my pattern pieces to ensure I didn't buy too much fabric. I had intended to make a longer more flamboyant bow for my dress but this would have increased the fabric amounts by about 1 metre so I decided in the interests of cost to reduce the size of the bow. To further economize in fabric quantities I cut two pattern pieces one piece for the centre front and two

Fabric requirements

All sizes	Fabric width	Amount needed
Metric	115cm	2.30m
Imperial	45in	2½yd

Remember to allow extra fabric if pattern pieces are lengthened.

Fabric suggestions
Fine linen, cotton mixtures and cotton jersey.

Above are some fabric suggestions given on the pattern. As I was dying my fabric, I decided to use a pure cotton fabric.

General information for construction of garment
- All seams have a 1.5 cm seam allowance
- 5 cm hem allowance
- Trim curved edges to 6 mm and clip into curves
- All patterns markings should be transferred accurately to fabric pieces to ensure correct construction of garment.

Pattern Pieces
1 Bodice back - Cut 2
2 Bodice front - Cut 1 on fold
3 Bodice back facing - Cut 2
4 Bodice front facing - Cut 1 on fold
5 Skirt back - Cut 2
6 Skirt front - Cut 1 on fold
7 Belt tie - Cut 2
8 Belt centre front - Cut 1

Interfacing
8 Belt centre front - Cut 1

Darts Darts are used to shape fabric to the contours of the body. The shaping of my dress is obtained by using darts:- bust darts and darts in the front and back bodice pieces from the waist line up to the bust. Darts are a simple way to fit a garment by folding the fabric in a triangular shape and sewing in place, then pressing downwards and to the centre of the garment.

Seams As I was using cotton fabric I chose to use simple plain seams. The pattern had a seam allowance of 1.5 cm. Once the seam was completed I pressed it to ensure the seams would lie flat. I neatened the seams with an overlocker as I thought this was the quickest, neatest method which would be used to construct a design like this in industry.

Interfacing Interfacing was indicated for the front and back bodice facings but I did not use it as I thought it would make the bodice look too stiff. However I used interfacing to give shape to the belt front. I am pleased with the result, and I feel it added to the shape of the dress, as it emphasizes the waist.

Gathering There are various ways of gathering a skirt to fit a bodice; using a gathering foot - allowing a longer length of fabric to be gathered. simply pushing the fabric under the foot, this would take a lot of skill and practice to gather the fabric evenly and stitching a few rows of machine stitching on to the fabric. As my design has a full skirt I gathered the skirt pieces to fit the bodice using the following method: Sew two rows of gathering stitch (long stitch) parallel to the edge of the fabric then pull the threads on the skirt to fit the bodice.

Neck and armhole facing
It is important when sewing around curves to neatly trim the fabric to 6 mm and then clip into the curves, as seen above. Once the facing have been turned to the right side, it is essential to press carefully for a neat finish.

Zips I decided to use a zip as I did not want to make a particular feature of the fastening. I was able to buy a blue zip that matched the colour of the dress perfectly. There are many ways to insert a zip, invisible, concealed and channel zip, which is semi-concealed. I used the semi-concealed method. I stitched the centre back seam and using a zipper foot stitched the zip in place. The neck facings were hand stitched over the zip inside the dress to neaten.

Hem Factors such as garment type, fabric weight, hem shape, design, cost, and machines available must be taken into consideration when hemming. Often it is enough to neaten by overlocking and then machine stitching using a blind stitch foot. As my dress is a simple cotton dress with a gathered skirt I machine stitched the hem using a hemming foot attachment. I didn't want a visible stitchline so I hoped this method would be suitable. It required some practice to achieve a neat finish and careful stitching to ensure that the stitch was not too visible on the right side of the garment. In the pictures below, the photo on the left shows the wrong side of the hem, and the photo on the right shows the right side. I used a contrasting thread to show the detail.

Figure 1.24 A student's manufacturing specification

Summary

- Your research should be clear, concise and relevant to the chosen design task.
- Planning is the most important part of the development stage within the coursework.
- The planning stage can be time-consuming, but time is limited – no more than six hours should be spent on this section.
- Maintaining a sketchbook throughout your design folder is important.
- You should remember to illustrate technical drawings, focusing on the product's detail.
- It is important to gain client feedback on modifications to your ideas.
- You need to give explanations for your choices of materials, components, processes and construction techniques.
- You need to be aware of sustainability and ethical issues.
- You need to cost for materials and labour (linked to values and ethical issues).
- You need to be able to read and understand a commercial pattern.
- You need to be able to modify your commercial pattern using a mannequin to record your modifications.
- You need to be able to apply a surface pattern, a surface decoration (embellishment) or both techniques to your fabrics.
- You need to choose the most appropriate fabric/s and components for your design specification.
- You should aim to include photographic images to record the key stages in the making of the product.
- You need to write a product and manufacturing specification.
- You should aim to present your work on eight A3 sheets of paper.

Activities

1. Write a product specification for a unisex waistcoat for the autumn/winter season. The waistcoat should be for children aged 11–14 years and reflect the urban street style culture. **[15 marks]**
2. Create a flow chart to show the production plan for making the waistcoat, using the specific symbols for each stage of the process. **[10 marks]**

Exam practice questions

1. Draw the following construction techniques for seams and joins:
   (a) flat fell seam
   (b) French seam
   (c) overlocker seam
   (d) slip stitch for hand stitching. **[12 marks]**
2. Draw the following pattern markings:
   (a) notch
   (b) lengthwise grain line
   (c) cutting line
   (d) shortening and lengthening line. **[12 marks]**
3. Why are quality control checks and critical control points important within the production plan? **[2 marks]**
4. List four advantages of using computer-aided manufacture (CAM). **[4 marks]**

Stretch yourself

1. How does the production of different fabric finishes – dyeing, calendaring and mercerising – have an impact on the environment? **[6 marks]**
2. What does CIM mean? Why do manufacturers use CIM in their manufacturing processes? **[5 marks]**

Case study

Case study objective: To understand why the designer has to provide intricate details to every participant involved in the design process.

Profile

Anne Kyyö Quinn is a textile designer whose sculptural view has pioneered a new direction for interior textiles based on a three-dimensional structure. Her products are inspired by organic shapes with a twist on Scandinavian simplicity. Anne Kyyö Quinn is a London-based designer who is a leader in manufacturing handcrafted interior textiles. She provides a consultancy service for special residential or contract projects, working with architects, contractors and interior designers to create bespoke products for a wide range of interior environments.

Anne Kyyö Quinn's original approach to interior products allowed one of her products to feature in the film *Sex and the City 2* – the Lola Ottoman.

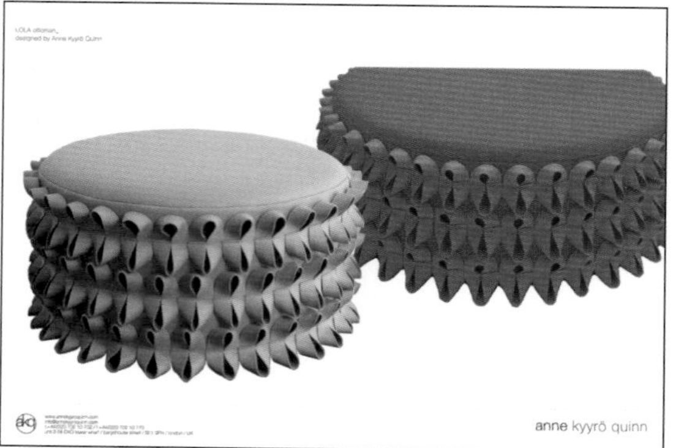

△ **Figure 1.25** The Lola Ottoman in *Sex and the City 2*

The decorative ottoman, upholstered with a blue wool felt, is part of the main character Carrie Bradshaw's (Sarah Jessica Parker) stylish home interiors.

For Anne Kyyö Quinn to fulfil requests for this product once the film was released must have evoked frenzy at her studio. It is extremely imperative for designers to have all their collection material to hand.

Website: www.annekyyroquinn.com

Resources

Inhabitat: www.inhabitat.com

The Fashionoclast: www.fashionoclast.com

Terra Plana: www.terraplana.com

Make Cotton Sustainable: www.makecottonsustainable.com

Fashion-era: www.fashion-era.com

Fashion Templates: www.fashion-templates.com

CAD/CAM

Computerised fabric cutting/etching: www.lasercutfabric.com

CAD/CAM embroidery: www.projecttextiles.co.uk/cadcam

Computerised embroidery: www.bernina.co.uk

Ethical/environmental textiles

Ethical/recycled textiles: www.traid.org.uk

Recycled products: www.greenhouseonline.co.uk

Barley Massey: www.fabrications1.co.uk

www.junkystyling.co.uk

www.enamore.co.uk

Safety

British Standards Institution: www.bsigroup.com; www.bsieducation.org

chapter 2 Making skills

2.1 Making

Learning objectives

By the end of this section, you should have a key understanding of:

- the evidence you need to show to meet the assessment criteria for making
- what types of textile products are appropriate for the controlled assessment tasks provided
- the skills required to make your product with a level of accuracy and quality finish
- the level of demand in making your product (modifying the product according to design and product specifications)
- how to use tools and equipment correctly, safely and following the appropriate health and safety guidelines
- the benefits of technology (ICT) to your coursework and product
- how to present your final idea successfully.

Key points

- Creative ideas
- Innovative ideas
- Analytical skills
- Communication skills
- Values

Introduction

In this chapter, you will find out how to focus your making skills to your best ability. Making your chosen product in three dimensions demands a high level of understanding and commitment. This is the most exciting and fulfilling part of the course. The examining board gives you credit for any making skills that are involved in producing the finished product. These are:

- **the modification of paper pattern; development of mock-up and toiles**
- **the development samples of surface pattern decoration**
- **the development samples of construction and finishing-off techniques**
- **the use of components, including fastenings and trims.**

The examining board requests that the 'final outcome(s) shows a high level of making/modelling/finishing skills and accuracy'. This means that you are required to produce a product that is adequately complex and well made in order to gain the highest marks. See Figures 2.1, 2.2 and 2.3 for examples of finished products.

Assessing your making skills

Your project and the development of your design folder will be monitored constantly by your teacher. Your teacher will guide you through the assessment for making and explain what type of textile products are expected in conjunction with the design tasks. Your assessment is not just based on the finished product; it is also based on your production processes and techniques. To gain the highest marks, you should remember the following pointers, which designers have to adopt throughout each project:

- You should be an independent worker.
- The product must demonstrate a high level of skill.

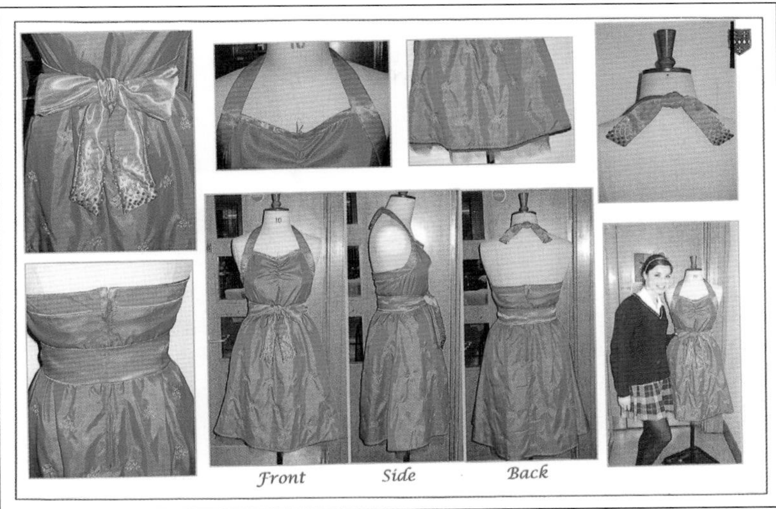

△ **Figure 2.1** A student's finished product inspired by 1950s new look

- The fabric/component/technique choices must present a challenge to handle.
- You must choose the correct tools, materials, components, equipment and techniques.
- Your product must have a quality finish.
- You must adopt safe working practices.
- You should know where and when to apply quality control checks and risk assessments.
- The product must be of high quality, meet the design and product specification and suit the target market.
- You must illustrate awareness of possible modifications for making the product suitable for mass production.
- You should demonstrate and illustrate how working errors are corrected and modified as you go along.
- You should use modern technology that is available at your school – for example, computerised sewing machines, scanner cutters for stencils, sublimation printers and computerised embroidery machines.
- You should support your product making with photographic evidence.

Designers working within a team have to keep to a strict plan. The team contains different levels of designers, both in-house and freelance. The head designer will have the assistance of the project/design manager, who should have the collection outlined, from ideas and inspiration to the manufacture of the prototype. Working in a team involves making sure that each individual carries out their responsibilities thoroughly and to schedule, in order not to disrupt the flow of the plan and to prevent any financial hiccups. You will need a good understanding of how a team works in industry, including the different jobs, and why it is important to plan ahead.

Key terms

Planning – a set of detailed instructions created and followed for the duration of a task, enabling you to know what needs to be done when and by whom.

Prototype – a full-scale model of a product design. It is also known as a mock-up, and in fashion it is called a toile.

Controlled assessment tasks

AQA provides a variety of design tasks; two examples and the types of finished products that could be made from these tasks are shown on page 40.

Example design task 1

This task relates to environmental issues – highlighting sustainable textile products has become fashionable in design. The task focuses on a company called People Tree, who supply textile products to environmentally conscious consumers who wish to support international fair trade. A home furnishing product should be designed using a cultural influence from a developing country.

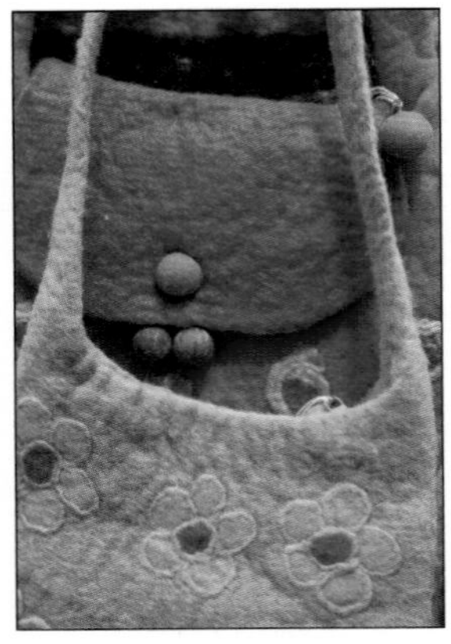

Figure 2.2 A student's finished product – fashion accessories

Example design task 2

This task relates to sustainability and how to save money and be good for the environment by reusing materials. Good-quality children's clothing and fabric toys are often treasured and handed down to other children in the family. The task focuses on creating a new, innovative and unique children's educational toy for the 0- to 5-year age bracket, commissioned by an exclusive craft shop.

Figures 2.2 and 2.3 show exemplar textile products for the two controlled assessment design tasks.

Figure 2.3 A student's finished product – educational soft toy

Case study

Case study objective: to show how a textile designer finds the simplest solution to minimise waste

Name of company: Riedizioni

Type of design: recycled textiles/accessories (textile and plastic waste)

Product area: accessories – bags, holdalls, purses and toiletry bags

Website: www.riedizioni.com

Profile

Riedizioni, owned by Luisa Cevese, is a textile and research-based company in Italy. Riedizioni creates products made out of natural or man-made fibre scraps and various innovative materials. Luisa Cevese was concerned about the enormous amount of waste coming from the textiles industry. Riedizioni's ethos is not to discriminate between natural and man-made fibres. The company is able to make new material from discarded silks and other textile by-products. Each time a new design is created it produces a unique material, so no two products are alike. This is due to the nature of the process that Riedizioni employs.

Summary

Riedizioni continues to look for strategies to reduce waste after their production process. Ethical designers have to be knowledgeable in their specialist, sustainable areas in order for their concerns and beliefs to touch the mass market.

Activities

1. Research and create a mood board on recycling, repairing and reusing. Include fair trade products. **[8 marks]**
2. Design a pattern using one of the following traditional textile techniques – appliqué, quilting, patchwork and hand embroidery. **[8 marks]**
3. Create a mind map, choosing one of the exemplar design tasks from page 39. **[6 marks]**

Making demands

What does a designer do?

The designer meets the client to establish the design brief, including the concept, performance and production criteria. They will brainstorm as part of a team or develop design concepts using dedicated design software (CAD) to produce a design specification, including a parts list and costing. AQA advises that you consider the level of demand in the product before you start making, and you have to complete no more than three design sheets to illustrate your making skills.

Investigation of the design context section strongly influences the direction of the development of the proposal section. Within these sections, you need to ask yourself certain key questions in order to fulfil the assessment criteria. These questions fall into four areas, as outlined in the following sections.

The shape and style of the product

- Is it simple or complicated?
- Are there any special features, and, if so, how many?
- How long will the product take to make?

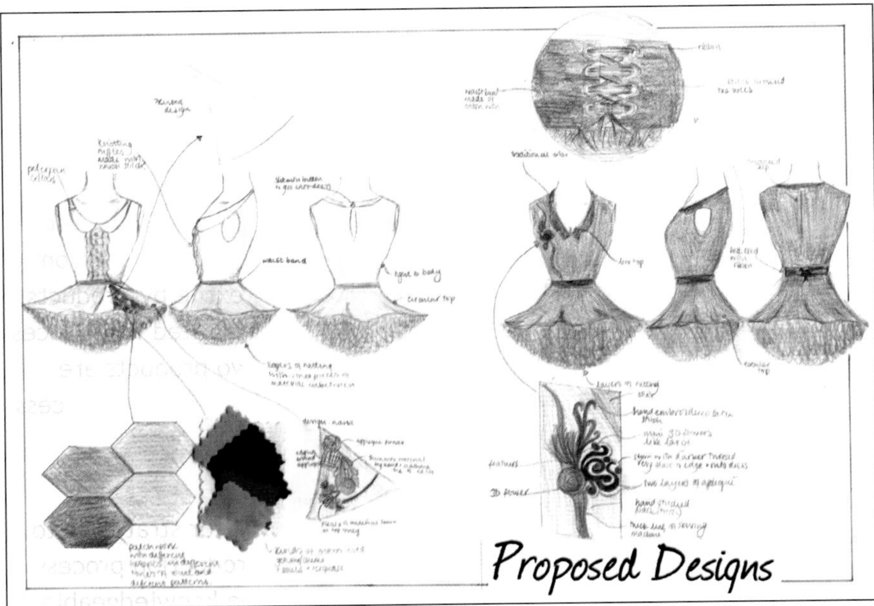

△ **Figure 2.4** A student's range of proposed designs

Key terms

Embellish – to add to the look of a product using colour, texture and pattern, using embroidery and/or beading.

Toile – a fabric version of a pattern, which is altered to get the desired look and fit.

Colour, surface pattern and decoration

- Will the fabric be dyed or purchased already dyed?
- How many techniques are needed to construct the garment?
- Are the techniques complicated, challenging or time-consuming?
- Are the techniques carried out by hand or on a machine?
- What will the quality of the finished techniques be like?

Fabric and component choices

- Have a few fabrics and components been used?
- How difficult are the fabrics to handle and sew?
- Do the fabrics need particular finishes?
- How difficult are the components to stitch? Do they buckle/pucker?

Construction techniques

- How many techniques are used in the construction of the product?
- How demanding and complicated is the construction?

To gain the highest marks, you should review the above questions throughout the modelling and making of your product.

Activity

Use your development of product shape and colour page from your Development section and answer the questions. Refer to the Making demand section. Assess how complicated or simple your product is to make. Discuss your comments with your teacher(s).

This task can be repeated with the other development page and discussed with your teacher(s).

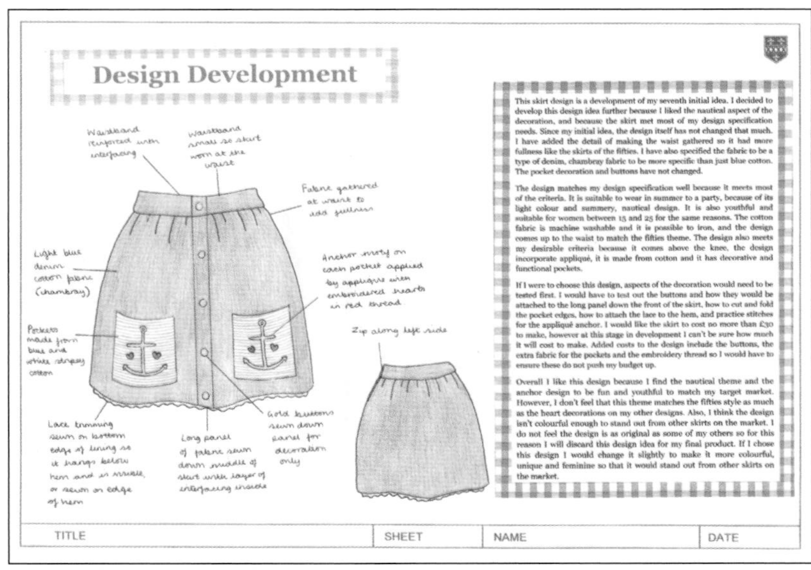

Design Development

This skirt design is a development of my seventh initial idea. I decided to develop this design idea further because I liked the nautical aspect of the decoration, and because the skirt met most of my design specification needs. Since my initial idea, the design itself has not changed that much. I have added the detail of making the waist gathered so it had more fullness like the skirts of the fifties. I have also specified the fabric to be a type of denim, chambray fabric to be more specific than just blue cotton. The pocket decoration and buttons have not changed.

The design matches my design specification well because it meets most of the criteria. It is suitable to wear in summer to a party, because of its light colour and summery, nautical design. It is also youthful and suitable for women between 15 and 25 for the same reasons. The cotton fabric is machine washable and it is possible to iron, and the design comes up to the waist to match the fifties theme. The design also meets my desirable criteria because it comes above the knee, the design incorporate appliqué, it is made from cotton and it has decorative and functional pockets.

If I were to choose this design, aspects of the decoration would need to be tested first. I would have to test out the buttons and how they would be attached to the long panel down the front of the skirt, how to cut and fold the pocket edges, how to attach the lace to the hem, and practice stitches for the appliqué anchor. I would like the skirt to cost no more than £30 to make, however at this stage in development I can't be sure how much it will cost to make. Added costs to the design include the buttons, the extra fabric for the pockets and the embroidery thread so I would have to ensure these do not push my budget up.

Overall I like this design because I find the nautical theme and the anchor design to be fun and youthful to match my target market. However, I don't feel that this theme matches the fifties style as much as the heart decorations on my other designs. Also, I think the design isn't colourful enough to stand out from other skirts on the market. I do not feel the design is as original as some of my others so for this reason I will discard this design idea for my final product. If I chose this design I would change it slightly to make it more colourful, unique and feminine so that it would stand out from other skirts on the market.

TITLE	SHEET	NAME	DATE

△ **Figure 2.5** A student's development page

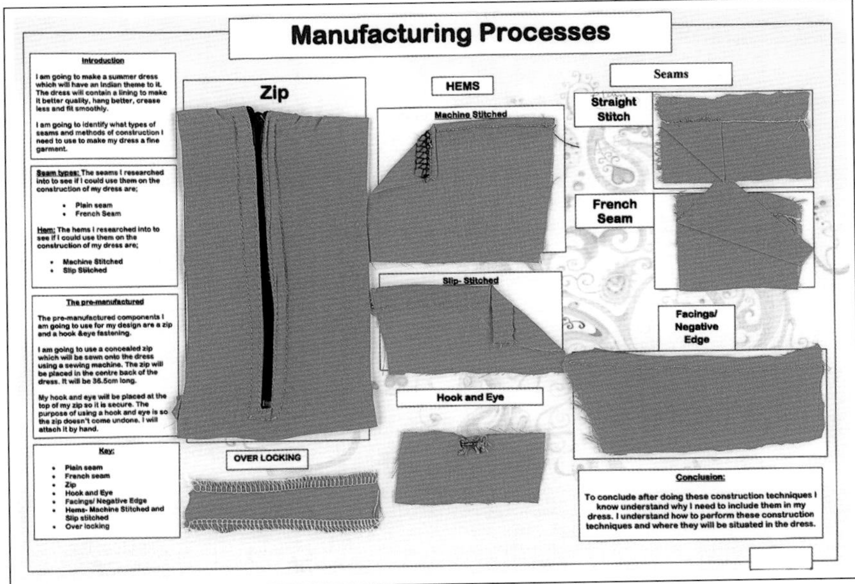

△ **Figure 2.6** A student's production and construction techniques

The production diary/plan (evidence in the design folder)

In industry, the designer's objective is to sell their ideas. One way to impress the client is to present them with presentation boards that illustrate the product in full colour, with alternative colour ideas and fabric/component choices to show the product's best features.

Your product should be able to be made by a third party using the detailed information you provide in your product and manufacturing specifications; a production flow chart must be included.

Key terms

Batch production – a production where small numbers of identical items are made.

Cell production – a process used in manufacturing a specialised product.

Manufacturing specification – the specific manufacturing details and instructions needed to make a product.

Mass production – a system where large numbers of items are made on a continuous basis.

One-off (bespoke) production – the production of a unique product for a specific brief.

Knowledge link

For more information on production flow charts, see Chapter 10, pages 237–240.

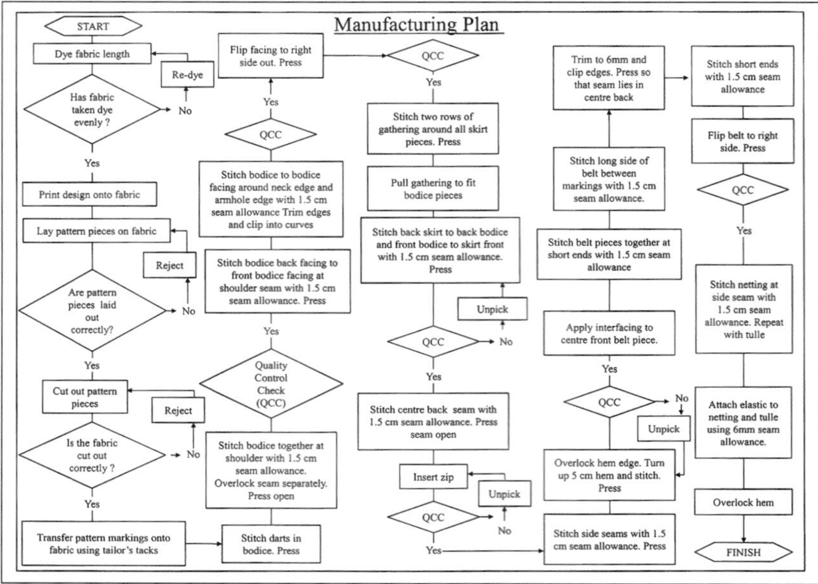

△ **Figure 2.7** A student's production plan

Within your design folder, you must show evidence of producing plans to ensure an efficient production flow chart that illustrates how the product would be made. Remember to include the following:

- the quality assurance of whether the product would meet the criteria on the design and product specification – setting and meeting standards
- what quality control checks are expected and when; critical control points – raw materials, production samples and prototype.

This section requires a maximum of three pages. It is advisable to either put all your information on one sheet or present it as a manufacturing specification with photographic evidence to illustrate the process, or you might prefer to produce the maximum number of pages and include the following information:

- working or technical drawings
- production diary, including photographs to illustrate how you made your product
- manufacturing production plans – flow charts, input and output layouts.

The expectations of working or technical drawings are as follows:

- These should be detailed drawings, often drawn to scale with the correct measurements and sizes.
- Front and back views should be included with exploded diagrams of special features if needed.
- A black fine-liner pen is the best drawing tool to create clear and clean lines to provide the best illustration for the drawings.

Production diary with recorded evidence

This section involves the modelling carried out in your development section and should give you a good understanding of how to make your product and enable you to produce a simple plan to show how you will make your product.

Normally, it is recommended that you use flow charts and other planning charts, such as a Gantt chart or simple flow chart. This information is best complemented with photographic evidence of your making skills and the finished product outcome.

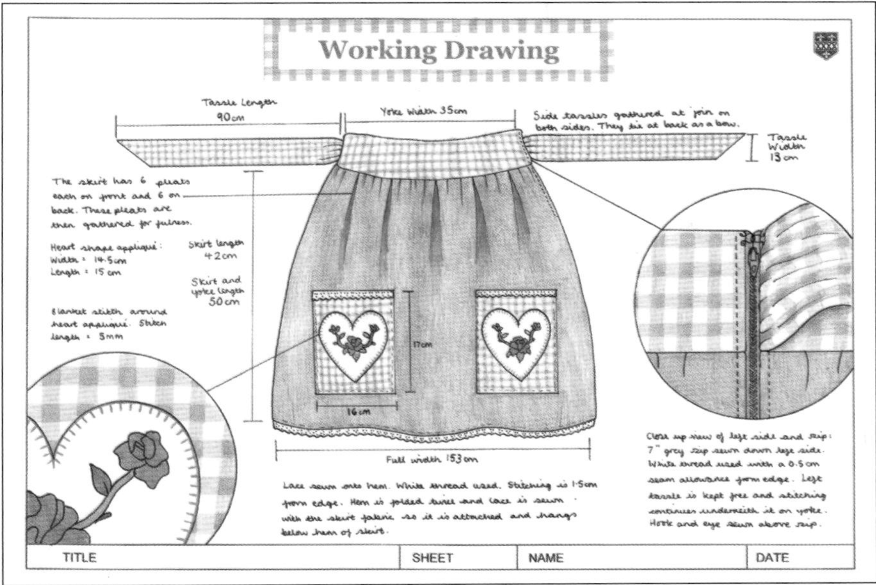

△ **Figure 2.8** A student's working drawing

Creating detailed records will be helpful when you come to evaluate your work at each stage, when you are writing a detailed manufacturing specification and when you need to give suggested modifications for mass production products.

Activity

Write a production plan for a simple shopper bag.

The use of hand tools and equipment

Knowing how to use the right tools, equipment and machinery correctly makes it easier to fulfil a design-and-make task, and can make a difference to the speed, accuracy and safety of producing a quality textile product.

Tools and equipment can be divided into three groups:

- essential tools (measuring, marking, cutting, sewing and pressing) and equipment
- specialist tools and equipment
- machinery.

Essential tools

Measuring tools

In order to work accurately and ensure a good shape to a product, it is essential that you use the correct tools for the job (e.g. for measuring long lengths of fabric or shortening a sleeve). Measuring tools include:

- tape measure
- metre (yard) stick
- ruler.

Knowledge link

For explanations of how to use the tools, see Chapter 9, page 227.

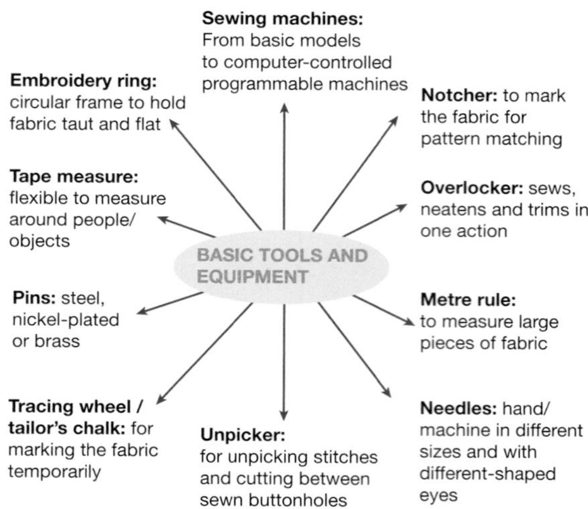

△ **Figure 2.9** Tools

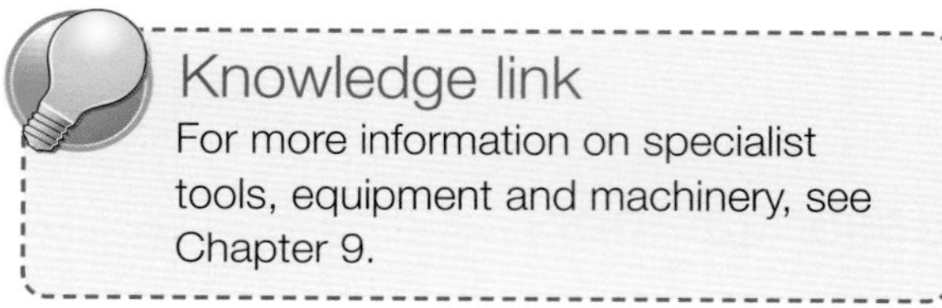

Knowledge link

For more information on specialist tools, equipment and machinery, see Chapter 9.

Cutting tools

There is a wide variety of cutting tools available for use in textiles; you need to choose the most appropriate for the task. Cutting tools include:

- shears (large blades – for cutting fabric quickly)
- pinking shear (neatening edges)
- serrated shears (sheer fabrics)
- needlework/embroidery scissors
- paper scissors
- craft knives
- rotary cutters
- seam rippers (seam unpickers).

Sewing and pressing tools

For sewing tasks, pins and needles are essential tools to assist the making of a textile or fashion product. Pins are used to hold the fabric together before either tacking in place with a needle and thread or stitching with a sewing machine.

Dry steam irons are different pressing tools to give the product a quality finish at each stage of the construction.

Essential equipment

Sewing machines increase sewing speed. They produce neat and even stitches to provide a quality finish.

Overlockers are especially used to sew seams and finished edges, at the same time as providing a high quality finish.

Specialist machinery

The use of computerised embroidery machines allows you to add polished decorative stitching and patterns. Additional specialist machines, such as computerised knitting and weaving looms, allow you to create fabric, garment pieces and textile products.

Marking tools

Marking tools are used to transfer lines and position marks onto fabric – for instance, to position darts and pockets accurately. There are different types of chalk (e.g. Tailor's chalk is usually in triangular pieces, pencils and rollers) and marking pens (e.g. wash away and fade away).

Manufacturing safely

Health and safety

Health and safety in textile and fashion production is essential. Designers need to be aware of what is involved in the making of their prototypes. Manufacturers need to carry out risk assessments and follow the health and safety regulations that have been put in place.

In the workplace, all employees should be fully trained to use their machines safely. Manufacturers need to identify all possible risks in the workplace and put systems in place to ensure a safe working environment. For example, cutting blades must be protected by a guard and the operator needs to wear chain-mail gloves as protection; when screen-printing, the room needs to be well ventilated to avoid inhalation of fumes.

Employers are obliged to ensure a safe working environment for all their employees and abide by the Health and Safety at Work Act 1974.

Key terms

Quality control – tests and inspections carried out to ensure that the products meet the specification criteria.

Quality assurance – a guarantee given to the customer from the company to assure the quality of the product.

The risk assessment

Risk assessments should take place to ensure safe working practices. There are three main areas to consider:

- **Input** – all materials and components should be checked thoroughly.
- **Work in process** – look at each stage of production. What has the potential to go wrong?
- **Outcome** – what checks should be carried out (e.g. loose threads, straight seams, correct seam allowance)?

The key areas to be checked during a risk assessment are:

- tools and equipment
- materials and chemicals
- protective clothing
- working practices.

Identifying and minimising risks to the environment

Manufacturers need to be aware of the damage that the textile industry can have on the environment. The main principles of conserving the environment are as follows:

- Avoid using materials that damage the environment (e.g. some dyes and bleach). Chemicals are used in many aspects of production (e.g. fertilisers are used when cotton is grown).
- Reduce the consumption of materials.
- Recycle materials.
- Use fabrics that are biodegradable.

Some manufacturers now use eco-labelling. If you buy a product with this label, you can guarantee it has been manufactured in a way to help protect the environment. These items will cost more, just as it costs more to produce organic foods.

The use of technology (design folder and product)

Designers use technology in three phases to enhance their ideas and collections:

- the design phase
- the production phase
- the post-production phase.

Design phase

- Research design ideas on the internet, present mood boards, and so on, using graphics programs.
- Use graphics packages to present first ideas.
- Design fabric using CAD software.
- Put designs onto fabric using 2D mapping or 3D image-draping system.

Key terms

CAD – computer-aided design. Computer-aided designs are designs created using a computer.

CAM – computer-aided manufacture. Computer-aided manufacture is where computers are used in the manufacturing process.

Costing – the process of working out the cost of making a product.

Just-in-time – a form of stock control when goods are delivered just in time to use on the production line.

Production phase

- Technology used by the testing department to test relevant parts of an item (e.g. seam strength).

- Costing of items carried out using product data management (PDM) software. PDM systems track materials and components before production starts.
- Product specification sent to pattern-making department, who create the pattern using pattern-generation software.
- Computerised lay plan created, which calculates the best way of laying pattern pieces for the least wastage.
- Fabrics can be cut out on a specialised cutting table.

Post-production phase

- Sales and marketing use virtual design systems, which give ways in which the product can be shown on in-store display systems.
- Product can be launched on the web with a virtual fashion show.
- Once the product is sent to the shop, it can be tracked using a computerised bar code system called EPOS.
- All products can be put onto website for sale (online retailing).

Knowledge link

For more information on CAD/CAM packages, see Chapter 11.

Being aware of the different production processes and being able to choose the right production method is essential to your making skills and design folder.

Exam practice questions

1. Name the main three critical control points (CCP) during production. Explain why the quality control checks are necessary within each point. **[6 marks]**
2. How might fabric be cut in industry? **[2 marks]**
3. Describe the process of sub-assembly and name three products that might incorporate this process. **[6 marks]**

Stretch yourself

1. Describe three ways that denim fabrics can be produced to reduce their impact on the environment. **[3 marks]**
2. Describe three symbols that might be found on a textile product's label. **[3 marks]**
3. Design an environmentally friendly product's care label and give explanations as to why you have included certain information. **[3 marks]**

Summary

- You need to refer to your specifications to make sure you have fulfilled the criteria.
- Choosing the correct fabrics and components and carrying out modelling tasks helps towards gaining the highest mark.
- You need to be able to understand the level of demand expectations for the assessment criteria.
- You should be able to modify your product accordingly to what best suits your product specification.
- You should know what quality checks are required and the health and safety issues that may arise from your own production plan and identify the techniques that will be used in the manufacturing process.
- You should know how to use the appropriate tools and equipment safely and correctly in the designing and manufacturing stages throughout your design folder and product.
- Accuracy and efficient use of tools and equipment will assist with producing a high-quality product.
- You should be able to understand how to use a design package to develop your design ideas.
- You should know the advantages of using CAD and CAM throughout the design phase to the post-production phase.

Case study

Case study objective: to show how a designer's instinct and emotion towards their design process allows their creations to have an impact on their audience

Name of designer: Rei Kawakubo, owner of Comme des Garçons

Type of design: fashion, couture to collaborative work with H&M, extending their range to the mass market

Profile

Comme des Garçons was created by Rei Kawakubo, who worked in textiles and as a stylist. The company has been going strong for over 40 years. Rei Kawakubo has several flagship stores, in Paris, Milan, London, New York and Japan. Her ethos is strongly based on an intellectual approach. Rei Kawakubo states that 'creation takes things forward. Without anything new, there is no progress. Creation equals new.'

Summary

In order for a designer to meet the guidelines to create a collection, they have to make sure the collection tells a story or has a meaning/message to express their cause or passion. Rei Kawakubo sees herself more as a journalist than as an artist, which is why the contents of your coursework also involves the skills of a journalist.

www.interviewmagazine.com/fashion
www.commedesgarcons.org

Resources

Books

Fischer, A. (2009) *Basics Fashion Design 03: Construction*, AVA Publishing SA.

Hollahan, L. (2010) *How to Use, Adapt and Design Sewing Patterns*, A&C Black Publishers.

Knight, L. (2008) *The Dressmaker's Technique Bible: A Complete Guide to Fashion Sewing Techniques*, Quarto Publishing.

Renfrew, C. and Renfrew, E. (2009) *Basics Fashion Design 04: Developing a Collection*, AVA Publishing SA.

2.2 Testing and evaluation

Learning objectives

By the end of this section, you should have a key understanding of:

- how to evaluate research
- how to write final evaluation reports
- how to test and evaluate the product against the design criteria and product specification
- the testing and evaluating methods for each stage
- how to carry out target audience trials and record findings
- how to write your final product evaluation.

Key points

- Creative ideas
- Innovative ideas
- Analytical skills
- Communication skills
- Linking technology and design
- Values

Introduction

Once you have completed the making of your product, you will have to:

- **critically evaluate and test the designing and making process, taking account of client/user or third-party opinion**
- **test the final outcome against all the specifications**
- **compare the final product to a commercial product**
- **produce a product analysis report, presenting improvement and modification suggestions.**

In industry, during the development of a product, designers are constantly testing and evaluating their ideas to identify and suggest areas for improvement and refinement. There are a variety of techniques and methods to achieve throughout the process of designing and making (e.g. paper models, patterns, mock-ups and prototypes). These are tested regularly against the requirements of the specification. Designers also have to consider physical tests, such as the size, strength and durability of fabric, construction, weight, fabric colour and texture combinations.

You should test your final product for performance and quality, ensuring it meets the criteria on your original design specification.

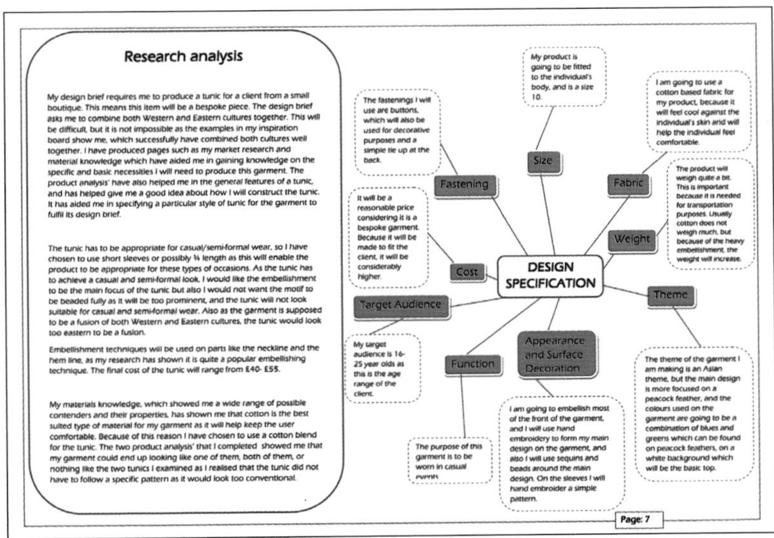

△ **Figure 2.10** A student's research analysis and design specification

Key terms

Comparative – a comparison of a similar, existing product against your final product.Were there any similarities? Which garment was made better?

Evaluate – to consider the success of the product.

Modify – to change the form or quality of something; usually only slightly – 'we had to modify the original design'.

Reflect – to give evidence of other individuals' or groups' opinions or views on the final product.

Study – to analyse and evaluate information and ideas.

Test – a process to ensure that standards are met.

Evaluation should be carried out throughout your project/design folder. The examining board states that 'in order to design and make a textile product that meets the requirements of the design brief and will sell well to the public, you have to keep checking that your ideas will work through the project'.

It is important to comment on how well you have worked throughout the project.

Testing and evaluating throughout the project

In order to make a textile product of the highest quality, you must evaluate your design folder and improve the product at every stage. There are a number of ways you will be able to do this:

- Evaluate your design ideas against the specifications.
- Test and evaluate the appropriateness of materials, components, techniques and processes.
- Test and evaluate through sampling and prototypes; this information helps the intended users to give their feedback.
- Compare you own product to an existing commercial product.

Evaluating your research section (investigating the design context) is vital. In this section, you would have looked at information to inspire and inform you before presenting your ideas. The information that you are likely to collect and evaluate in this section would have come from a wide range of sources. The appropriateness of the information should have been evaluated against your chosen design task and presented in your design folder. Mood board images should also be evaluated and the colour schemes, patterns, shapes, and so on. tested for their suitability. Existing designs and products should also be analysed and evaluated by visiting retail shops and disassembling products to gain a clear understanding of how the product is assembled.

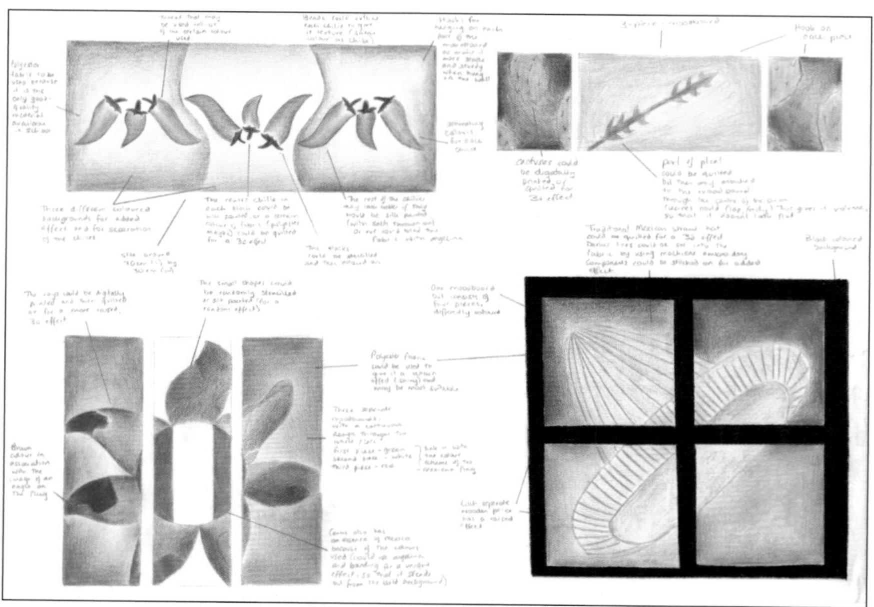

△ **Figure 2.11** A student's evaluated developed ideas

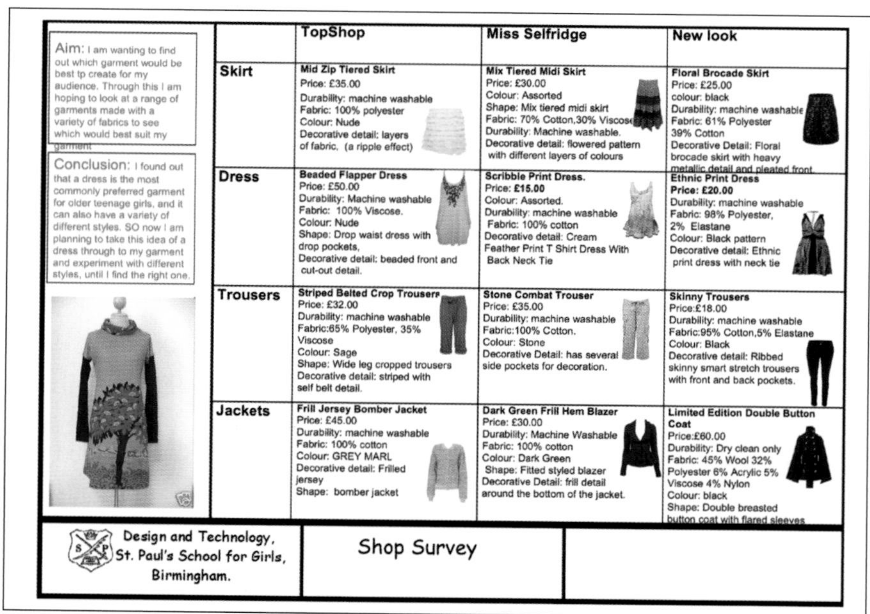

Aim: I am wanting to find out which garment would be best tp create for my audience. Through this I am hoping to look at a range of garments made with a variety of fabrics to see which would best suit my garment

Conclusion: I found out that a dress is the most commonly preferred garment for older teenage girls, and it can also have a variety of different styles. SO now I am planning to take this idea of a dress through to my garment and experiment with different styles, until I find the right one.

	TopShop	Miss Selfridge	New look
Skirt	**Mid Zip Tiered Skirt** Price: £35.00 Durability: machine washable Fabric: 100% polyester Colour: Nude Decorative detail: layers of fabric, (a ripple effect)	**Mix Tiered Midi Skirt** Price: £30.00 Colour: Assorted Shape: Mix tiered midi skirt Fabric: 70% Cotton,30% Viscose Durability: Machine washable. Decorative detail: flowered pattern with different layers of colours	**Floral Brocade Skirt** Price: £25.00 colour: black Durability: machine washable Fabric: 61% Polyester 39% Cotton Decorative Detail: Floral brocade skirt with heavy metallic detail and pleated front.
Dress	**Beaded Flapper Dress** Price: £50.00 Durability: Machine washable Fabric: 100% Viscose. Colour: Nude Shape: Drop waist dress with drop pockets, Decorative detail: beaded front and cut-out detail.	**Scribble Print Dress.** Price: **£15.00** Colour: Assorted. Durability: machine washable Fabric: 100% cotton Decorative detail: Cream Feather Print T Shirt Dress With Back Neck Tie	**Ethnic Print Dress** **Price: £20.00** Durability: machine washable Fabric: 98% Polyester, 2% Elastane Colour: Black pattern Decorative detail: Ethnic print dress with neck tie
Trousers	**Striped Belted Crop Trousers** Price: £32.00 Durability: machine washable Fabric:65% Polyester, 35% Viscose Colour: Sage Shape: Wide leg cropped trousers Decorative detail: striped with self belt detail.	**Stone Combat Trouser** Price: £35.00 Durability: machine washable Fabric:100% Cotton. Colour: Stone Decorative Detail: has several side pockets for decoration.	**Skinny Trousers** Price:£18.00 Durability: machine washable Fabric:95% Cotton,5% Elastane Colour: Black Decorative detail: Ribbed skinny smart stretch trousers with front and back pockets.
Jackets	**Frill Jersey Bomber Jacket** Price: £45.00 Durability: machine washable Fabric: 100% cotton Colour: GREY MARL Decorative detail: Frilled jersey Shape: bomber jacket	**Dark Green Frill Hem Blazer** Price: £30.00 Durability: Machine Washable Fabric: 100% cotton Colour: Dark Green Shape: Fitted styled blazer Decorative Detail: frill detail around the bottom of the jacket.	**Limited Edition Double Button Coat** Price:£60.00 Durability: Dry clean only Fabric: 45% Wool 32% Polyester 6% Acrylic 5% Viscose 4% Nylon Colour: black Shape: Double breasted button coat with flared sleeves

Design and Technology,
St. Paul's School for Girls,
Birmingham.

Shop Survey

△ **Figure 2.12** A student's coursework page on existing products – shop report (market research)

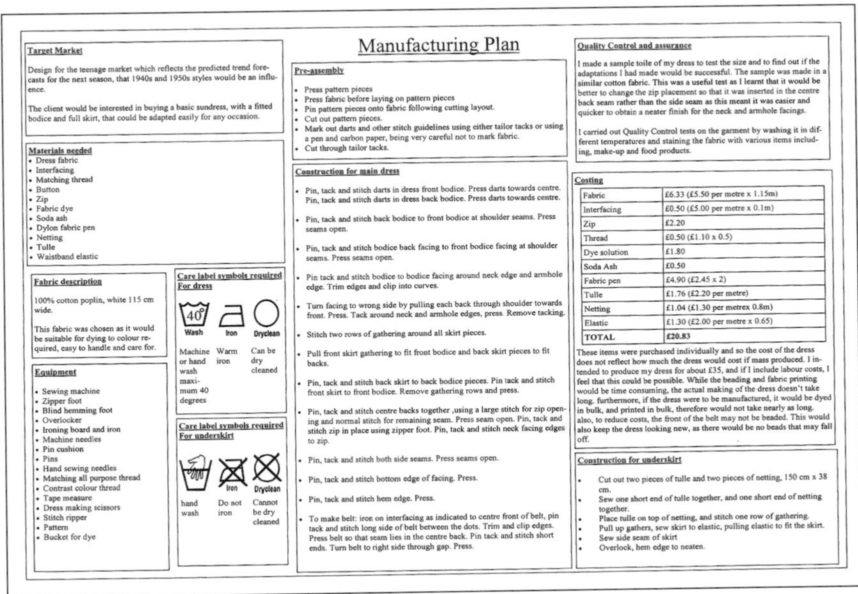

Manufacturing Plan

Target Market

Design for the teenage market which reflects the predicted trend forecasts for the next season, that 1940s and 1950s styles would be an influence.

The client would be interested in buying a basic sundress, with a fitted bodice and full skirt, that could be adapted easily for any occasion.

Materials needed
- Dress fabric
- Interfacing
- Matching thread
- Button
- Zip
- Fabric dye
- Soda ash
- Dylon fabric pen
- Netting
- Tulle
- Waistband elastic

Fabric description

100% cotton poplin, white 115 cm wide.

This fabric was chosen as it would be suitable for dying to colour required, easy to handle and care for.

Care label symbols required For dress

Wash	Iron	Dryclean
Machine or hand wash maximum 40 degrees	Warm iron	Can be dry cleaned

Equipment
- Sewing machine
- Zipper foot
- Blind hemming foot
- Overlocker
- Ironing board and iron
- Machine needles
- Pin cushion
- Pins
- Hand sewing needles
- Matching all purpose thread
- Contrast colour thread
- Tape measure
- Dress making scissors
- Stitch ripper
- Pattern
- Bucket for dye

Care label symbols required For underskirt

	Iron	Dryclean
hand wash	Do not iron	Cannot be dry cleaned

Pre-assembly
- Press pattern pieces
- Press fabric before laying on pattern pieces
- Pin pattern pieces onto fabric following cutting layout.
- Cut out pattern pieces.
- Mark out darts and other stitch guidelines using either tailor tacks or using a pen and carbon paper, being very careful not to mark fabric.
- Cut through tailor tacks.

Construction for main dress
- Pin, tack and stitch darts in dress front bodice. Press darts towards centre. Pin, tack and stitch darts in dress back bodice. Press darts towards centre.
- Pin, tack and stitch back bodice to front bodice at shoulder seams. Press seams open.
- Pin, tack and stitch bodice back facing to front bodice facing at shoulder seams. Press seams open.
- Pin tack and stitch bodice to bodice facing around neck edge and armhole edge. Trim edges and clip into curves.
- Turn facing to wrong side by pulling each back through shoulder towards front. Press. Tack around neck and armhole edges, press. Remove tacking.
- Stitch two rows of gathering around all skirt pieces.
- Pull front skirt gathering to fit front bodice and back skirt pieces to fit backs.
- Pin, tack and stitch back skirt to back bodice pieces. Pin tack and stitch front skirt to front bodice. Remove gathering rows and press.
- Pin, tack and stitch centre backs together ,using a large stitch for zip opening and normal stitch for remaining seam. Press seam open. Pin, tack and stitch zip in place using zipper foot. Pin, tack and stitch neck facing edges to zip.
- Pin, tack and stitch both side seams. Press seams open.
- Pin, tack and stitch bottom edge of facing. Press.
- Pin, tack and stitch hem edge. Press.
- To make belt: iron on interfacing as indicated to centre front of belt, pin tack and stitch long side of belt between the dots. Trim and clip edges. Press belt so that seam lies in the centre back. Pin tack and stitch short ends. Turn belt to right side through gap. Press.

Quality Control and assurance

I made a sample toile of my dress to test the size and to find out if the adaptations I had made would be successful. The sample was made in a similar cotton fabric. This was a useful test as I learnt that it would be better to change the zip placement so that it was inserted in the centre back seam rather than the side seam as this meant it was easier and quicker to obtain a neater finish for the neck and armhole facings.

I carried out Quality Control tests on the garment by washing it in different temperatures and staining the fabric with various items including, make-up and food products.

Costing

Fabric	£6.33 (£5.50 per metre x 1.15m)
Interfacing	£0.50 (£5.00 per metre x 0.1m)
Zip	£2.20
Thread	£0.50 (£1.10 x 0.5)
Dye solution	£1.80
Soda Ash	£0.50
Fabric pen	£4.90 (£2.45 x 2)
Tulle	£1.76 (£2.20 per metre)
Netting	£1.04 (£1.30 per metrex 0.8m)
Elastic	£1.30 (£2.00 per metre x 0.65)
TOTAL	**£20.83**

These items were purchased individually and so the cost of the dress does not reflect how much the dress would cost if mass produced. I intended to produce my dress for about £35, and if I include labour costs, I feel that this could be possible. While the beading and fabric printing would be time consuming, the actual making of the dress doesn't take long. furthermore, if the dress were to be manufactured, it would be dyed in bulk, and printed in bulk, therefore would not take nearly as long. also, to reduce costs, the front of the belt may not be beaded. This would also keep the dress looking new, as there would be no beads that may fall off.

Construction for underskirt
- Cut out two pieces of tulle and two pieces of netting, 150 cm x 38 cm.
- Sew one short end of tulle together, and one short end of netting together.
- Place tulle on top of netting, and stitch one row of gathering.
- Pull up gathers, sew skirt to elastic, pulling elastic to fit the skirt.
- Sew side seam of skirt
- Overlock, hem edge to neaten.

△ **Figure 2.13** A student's manufacturing specification for the final product

Key terms

Research – Using a series of activities to investigate, study, find out and discover information to support your studies.

This research activity will illustrate that you have a clear understanding of how to make the product: what types of fabrics, components and special features are required, what the aftercare of the product will be and what the price is likely to be.

Testing the final outcome

Throughout modelling and making, you must always refer back to your original design specification to the product. Check each statement and think about how that requirement can be tested. Some points may be very easy to test, while others might require you to ask an intended user from your target group. For instance, you could ask your intended consumer to test the product for its intended use, or ask a specialist/expert in the field or your teacher to test it and give their opinion.

You need to make sure the users who test your product give you either written or verbal comments. In addition, taking photographs of your product being tested is essential to your final product outcome and provides the evidence required to attain the highest marks. Involving your intended user in the testing process is also what would happen in the fashion and textile industry.

Recording the results of your tests is vital. Table 2.1 on page 54 shows an example of how you could record your data.

Designers carry out a variety of tests in order to make a flawless prototype. Examples of the questions that designers may face are as follows:

- Are the colours and patterns coordinating or contrasting?
- Do the different fabrics complement each other in colour, textile and weight?
- Does the use of the same colour in different fabrics work together?
- Are the components of the outfit varied in the intensity of their detail?

Criterion	Testing method	To what extent was the criterion met?

△ **Table 2.1** Recording the results of your tests

Key terms

Commercial product – an item created for sale to the general public through different retail and online outlets.

Consumer – a person who buys products; the end user of a product.

Criteria – a list of key points.

Target group/target markets – a range of people at whom a product is aimed.

User trials – getting sample users from your target market to try out a prototype product, in return for feedback. The feedback is used to assist with making modifications to your design, to make the product fit for its purpose.

The models, mock-ups and prototypes are often made in different sizes and materials to the final product. Sometimes only certain parts of a product are modelled in order to test out specific parts of the design. ICT is used a great deal to analyse and present information.

There is a variety of techniques and methods that can be used to achieve a quality outcome. Physical tests, such as size, strength of the fabric, weight, ergonomics, are constantly evaluated. These results are recorded and compared against the set standards, making it possible to assess the efficiency of the materials and products chosen.

In industry, testing and evaluating enables the designer to made definitive decisions on the materials, components and colour ranges. Alterations can reduce the product cost after extensive evaluation. The designer can also decide on the best construction methods at this stage. Lastly, the care (wearing), aftercare (washing and ironing) and ergonomics of the product can be tested.

Evaluating the final product

Once you have completed all tests, you need to make an overall evaluation of the final product outcome. You will also need to review the way your design has developed throughout the project. You will have to present meaningful conclusions, leading to proposals for modifications to improve the product. You will have to ask yourself the following questions:

- How successful was the making?
- What changes did you make and why?
- Did the product turn out as expected? If not, why not?

Use photographs to explain your answers.

The final evaluation is a comprehensive summative evaluation; it completes the story to your design folder. It explains how successful your final product is and if it matches the specifications. Remember, you need to refer back to your design brief/task and to your specification in order to see how well your product matches them. You should have tested your product to ensure it matches your criteria. For example, if your specification states that your product has a hand-painted floral panel on the middle of the dress, state whether the product has and, if not, say why not. Is the fabric suitable? Have you kept within the costing? What do other people think of your product, especially potential consumers?

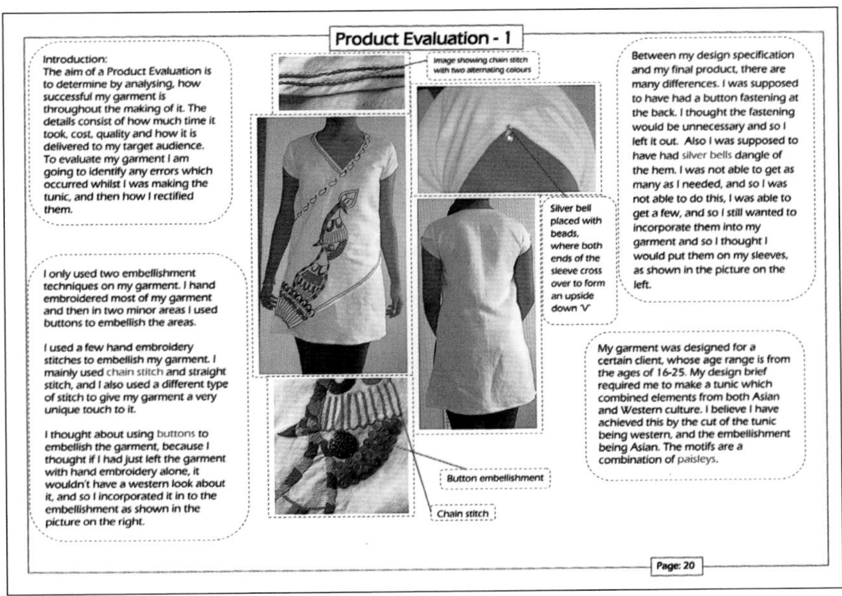

△ **Figure 2.14** How a student evaluated their final product

Commenting on how well you planned your work is essential to the evaluation. Ask yourself questions such as:

- Did you spend too long or not long enough on your investigating, designing, planning or making?
- How closely were you able to keep to your planning chart (Gantt chart or simple flow chart) during the making process?

List the things you could improve if you were to do it again (see Table 2.2).

Evaluating your planning, whether you have been rigid or generous, is a required contribution to the story of your final evaluation.

Strengths and weaknesses	Areas for improvement
Overlocking to neaten edges	Need to practise more in order to overlock straight with a steadier pace
Pattern worked really well	Could have drawn more working sketches as I tended to go straight to the final product
	Need to evaluate my research material more thoroughly

△ **Table 2.2** Evaluating the final product

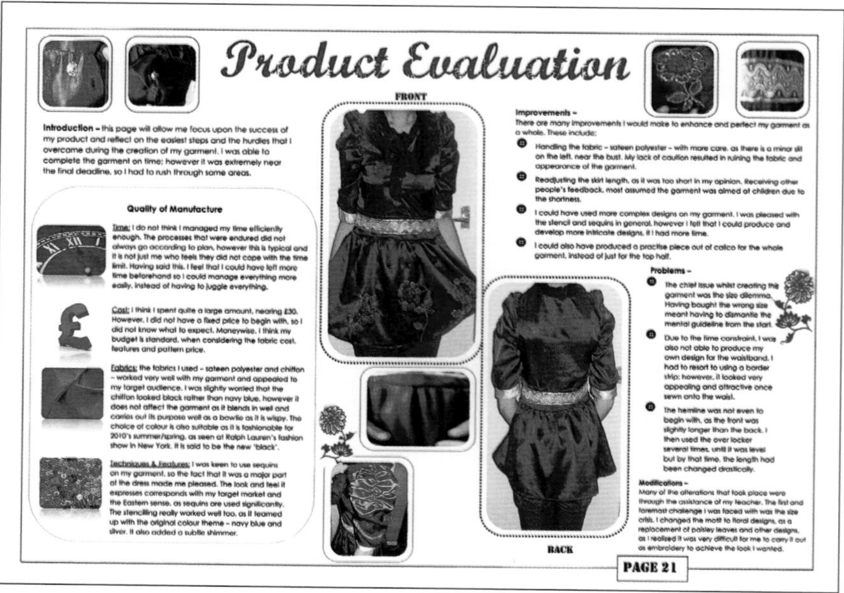

Product Evaluation

FRONT

Introduction – this page will allow me focus upon the success of my product and reflect on the easiest steps and the hurdles that I overcame during the creation of my garment. I was able to complete the garment on time; however it was extremely near the final deadline, so I had to rush through some areas.

Quality of Manufacture

Time: I do not think I managed my time efficiently enough. The processes that were endured did not always go according to plan, however this is typical and it is not just me who feels they did not cope with the time limit. Having said this, I feel that I could have left more time beforehand so I could manage everything more easily, instead of having to juggle everything.

Cost: I think I spent quite a large amount, nearing £30. However, I did not have a fixed price to begin with, so I did not know what to expect. Moneywise, I think my budget is standard, when considering the fabric cost, features and pattern price.

Fabrics: the fabrics I used – sateen polyester and chiffon – worked very well with my garment and appealed to my target audience. I was slightly worried that the chiffon looked black rather than navy blue, however it does not affect the garment as it blends in well and carries out its purpose well as a bowtie as it is wispy. The choice of colour is also suitable as it is fashionable for 2010's summer/spring, as seen at Ralph Lauren's fashion show in New York. It is said to be the new 'black'.

Techniques & Features: I was keen to use sequins on my garment, so the fact that it was a major part of the dress made me pleased. The look and feel it expresses corresponds with my target market and the Eastern sense, as sequins are used significantly. The stencilling really worked well too, as it teamed up with the original colour theme – navy blue and silver. It also added a subtle shimmer.

Improvements –
There are many improvements I would make to enhance and perfect my garment as a whole. These include:

- Handling the fabric – sateen polyester – with more care, as there is a minor slit on the left, near the bust. My lack of caution resulted in ruining the fabric and appearance of the garment.
- Readjusting the skirt length, as it was too short in my opinion. Receiving other people's feedback, most assumed the garment was aimed at children due to the shortness.
- I could have used more complex designs on my garment. I was pleased with the stencil and sequins in general, however I felt that I could produce and develop more intricate designs, if I had more time.
- I could also have produced a practise piece out of calico for the whole garment, instead of just for the top half.

Problems –

- The chief issue whilst creating the garment was the size dilemma. Having bought the wrong size meant having to dismantle the mental guideline from the start.
- Due to the time constraint, I was also not able to produce my own design for the waistband. I had to resort to using a border strip; however, it looked very appealing and attractive once sewn onto the waist.
- The hemline was not even to begin with, as the front was slightly longer than the back. I then used the over locker several times, until it was level but by that time, the length had been changed drastically.

Modifications –
Many of the alterations that took place were through the assistance of my teacher. The first and foremost challenge I was faced with was the size crisis. I changed the motif to floral designs, as a replacement of paisley leaves and other designs, as I realised it was very difficult for me to carry it out as embroidery to achieve the look I wanted.

BACK

PAGE 21

△ **Figure 2.15** Product evaluation

Summary

- You need to produce a detailed evaluation of your product as well as the processes involved in making the final prototype. You should show how you have thought about the needs of the end user and evaluate your strengths and weaknesses.
- You should consider how your materials, components and processes have 'combined' to form a quality product that is fit for purpose. Refer to the working properties of the materials to support your decisions.
- You need to outline realistic and detailed modifications to your work. Use sketches with notes, as well as modelling, to support your points. Any improvements you make should be creative and refer to innovation, environmental and sustainability issues.

Activity

Take a photograph of a textile product you have designed and made and an existing product used for the same purpose. Compare the two products, commenting on the following:

- appearance/aesthetic qualities
- anthropometric qualities – size, ease of use
- ease of care – materials, components used
- cost
- environmental and sustainability issues – can the products be recycled?
- innovation.

Present your results in an interesting and informative way. You must make sure that your report includes a digital photograph of the two products. **[15 marks]**

Exam practice questions

1. Define 'evaluating' and explain its purpose in creating a new product. **[3 marks]**
2. Why do designers evaluate their making process in detail at each stage? **[2 marks]**
3. Explain why it is important for a designer to provide a comprehensive manufacturing specification for their manufacture. **[2 marks]**
4. List four problems a manufacturer could encounter with a new designer's first manufacturing specification. **[4 marks]**

Stretch yourself

Look at the garment in Figure 2.16. List four ways in which the garment design shown could be adapted/changed or improved. Give reasons for your choice. **[8 marks]**

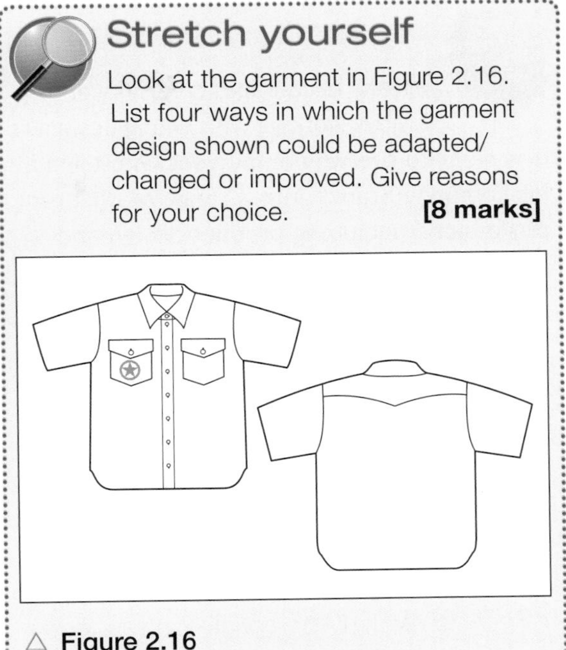

△ **Figure 2.16**

Case study

Case study objective: to show how a renowned designer has incorporated science, technology and ethical beliefs into creating many new innovative and forward-thinking fabrics and products

Name of designer: Issey Miyake

Type of design: fashion and textiles engineering using science and cutting-edge technology packages

Market area: couture to high-end fashion and interior products

Profile

Issey Miyake set up his design studio in Tokyo in 1970. He works with the same manufacturers and traditional craftsman that he originally struck a dialogue with in the 1970s.

Miyake is one of the leaders in the fashion arena. In 1982, he was the first fashion designer ever to be featured on the cover of the American magazine *Art Form*, which included a model wearing a bodice in rattan and bamboo (designed by a craftsman on Sado Island). In 1993, his range 'Pleats Please' was launched using a pioneering new manufacturing technique – a pleating machine. The A-POC creations were launched in 1997, using a revolutionary process that enabled customers to cut different garments from a single, continuous roll of cloth woven on computerised looms. The creations were first made in a factory that manufactured fishing nets.

Miyake is keen to introduce new and innovative fibres onto the textiles market. His creations start with a yarn and he is interested in the new – invention: he prefers evolution to look towards the future.

Cont.

Case study *continued*

Miyake encourages creativity and enjoys working with young designers. It is clear to see why employees who train at his company branch into a range of different professions, including product design and architecture.

Summary

Miyake's ethos is to be an innovator, creative and resourceful within the design field. He says, 'it is important to make clothes for longer-term use, not just for one season. Society cannot keep throwing things away.'

www.isseymiyake.com

2.3 Communication

Learning objectives

By the end of this section, you should have a key understanding of:

- how to communicate fully (lay out clearly) your design folder's contents
- how to use ICT appropriately in your design folder
- how to clarify your design thinking, using fluent, coherent language and showing a good grasp of grammar, punctuation and spelling.

Key points

- Creative ideas
- Analytical skills
- Innovative ideas
- Communication skills
- Linking technology and design

Introduction

The most essential part of being a fashion designer is the ability to communicate ideas. The key is being able to transfer what is in your head onto paper, so the third party, the manufacturer, can clearly see and understand your ideas.

The design folder needs to tell the story of the chosen design project. The sections should be ordered sensibly, showing clearly what will happen next and explaining why. The design folder should consist of 20 A3 pages.

Key terms

Communicate – to convey gathered information, other opinions and views in a clear, written format.

Concise – to express your point by being brief but comprehensive; a clear statement.

Focused – to direct towards a particular point or conclusion; to focus your attention on finding a solution to the problem.

Relevant – to highlight something important about what is being discussed, asked and collected.

Assessment criteria number	Assessment criteria name	Maximum mark	Suggested no. of pages	What this might include (this is not an exhaustive list)
1	Investigating the design opportunity	8	4	Analysis of task, research plan, design brief, client profile, mood board, review of existing products/ comparative shop report, designer/company research, evaluation of research, cultural and historical issues, disassembly, analysis of research, design specification/criteria
2	Development of design proposals (including modelling)	32	8	Initial ideas, development work planning, trends, colour and colourways, selection of appropriate components, fibre/ fabric information, construction and modelling/prototyping techniques, environmental/ social/ethical/sustainability concerns, evaluation of development and final design, flowchart/planning chart, pattern/pattern information, layplan, manufacturing specification, care labelling, application of CAD/CAM, product costing
3	Making	32	4	Diary of making, production plan, quality control, finished product and photographs, appropriate selection of tools/equipment and components, appropriate use of technologies e.g. CAM, high-quality making skills
4	Testing and Evaluation	12	4	Testing against the design specification, testing against manufacturing specification, consumer trials/feedback, evaluation/production evaluation, suggestions for modifications and/or changes, suggested modifications for commercial production

△ **Table 2.3** Controlled Assessment criteria

Cont.

Assessment criteria number	Assessment criteria name	Maximum mark	Suggested no. of pages	What this might include (this is not an exhaustive list)
5	Communication	6		Check for good use of grammar and communication skills throughout folder, use of appropriate textile technology terms, legible text.
		TOTAL: 90 marks	TOTAL: 20 pages	

△ **Table 2.3** Controlled Assessment criteria *continued*

Ways to present the design folder

There is no uniform way to present your coursework pages; this section will give you some guidance on the best ways to do so.

Key terms

Appropriate – to set apart gathered information for a specific outcome.

Coherent – an orderly, logical and aesthetically consistent relation of sections – 'a coherent coursework folder'.

Critical – being able to construct careful or analytical evaluations – 'constructive critical conclusions'.

Planning

Planning how to layout each page is necessary in order not to waste space. Aim to have a good mixture of text and visual images. Images could be produced by hand and/or on a design package. Remember to include evidence to demonstrate your understanding of the time required to complete the coursework. Your teacher will be able assist you with initial planning (see Table 2.4).

Appearance

Making sure the appearance of your pages is clearly presented is important. Think about the design – font type, font size, appropriate headings for each page and borders are all elements that demonstrate a high standard of work. Remember, however, that **no marks** are given for decorating pages.

Contents

The contents can include different types of illustrations (mixed media and ICT) to present your research, such as mood boards, statistical results, graphs, flow charts, images, photographs, sketches, drawings and developments, as appropriate.

Key terms

Comprehensive – to have every necessary point, step and opinion included throughout your design folder.

Specific – details that best describe your product.

	July	Sep	Oct	Nov	Dec	Jan	Feb	Mar	Apr	May	June	July
Investigating the design opportunity												
Development of design proposal												
Making												
Testing and evaluating												
Revision											Study leave	

△ **Table 2.4** A simple planning chart used as a guideline at the beginning of the Controlled Assessment

Use of ICT and CAD/CAM

Using CAD, you can change or develop design ideas (e.g. colours). Designs can be developed, templates can be created and specification sheets with flat designs can be produced.

Digital photography is useful for visually modifying your modelling process, and adaptations drawn on the photographs can be used to document your plan of making. This would provide a clear illustration of your modelling development.

Knowledge link

For more information on video/audio documenting, see Chapter 9, page 258.

Use of additional design techniques

Using art materials is optional and depends on your ability (e.g. for creating fabric textures, using on working and technical drawings).

Evaluating – textile technology terms and literacy awareness

Remember to check carefully through your design folder. Correct any spelling, punctuation and grammar mistakes and use the correct terminology at all times. If your language is not clear, you may lose marks.

Remember to give reasons why you have chosen particular fabric(s), components or seams, for example.

Refer back to your design task and design specification to ensure that you have remained focused on the task – whenever you make a change, you need to justify the change.

Additional suggestions

- Check with your teacher that you are using a variety of appropriate skills in the practical work presented.
- Make sure that you understand what you need to include in order to gain maximum marks. The clearer and more organised your work, the higher your grade is likely to be.
- Bind all your pages together securely. Use treasury tags or a slide binder.

Ensure that you present and communicate your research, ideas, developments, testing and evaluating clearly within your design folder, this will help you to gain the maximum six marks (see Table 2.3). Therefore, it is important to choose the appropriate design packages, equipment and materials to achieve this successfully.

Summary

- Your design folder should be focused, concise and relevant, and demonstrate an appropriate selection of material for inclusion.
- All decisions should be communicated in a clear and coherent manner, with appropriate use of technical language.
- The text should be legible, easily understood and show a good grasp of grammar, punctuation and spelling.

Activity

Using one of your group member's coursework, review and assess a few layout pages against the assessment criteria to see what is required.

Exam practice questions

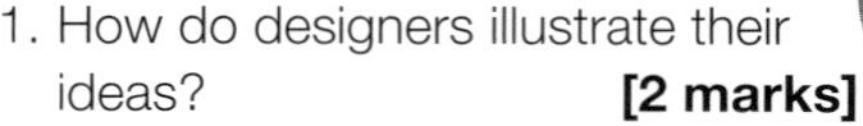

1. How do designers illustrate their ideas? **[2 marks]**

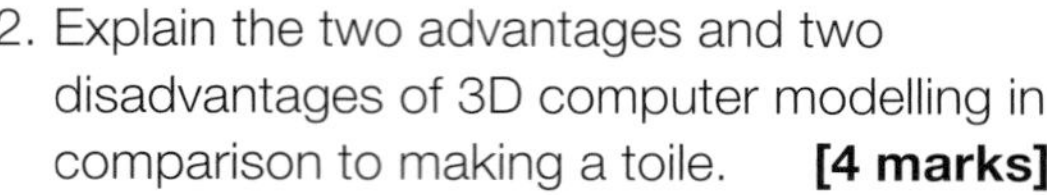

2. Explain the two advantages and two disadvantages of 3D computer modelling in comparison to making a toile. **[4 marks]**

Stretch yourself

Textile technology is forever changing. What types of changes does the future hold for new creators? **[5 marks]**

Resources

Seivewright, S. (2007) *Basics Fashion Design 01: Research and Design*, AVA Publishing SA.

Case study

Case study objective: to show how flexible you can be in fulfilling a design brief using CAD/ICT and traditional materials to present to a client

Name of company: Alex Russell Creative Services

Type of design: print design, pattern, graphics and illustration

Product area: fashion and furnishing/interiors print, print design and trend/styling books

Profile

Alex Russell Creative Services is a freelance design studio providing a wide range of textile design, surface pattern and illustration services. Alex Russell is given a range of open and closed design briefs. It is important for them to keep to deadlines and completely fulfil the client's needs.

Summary

Having versatility in design allows you to have your finger on the pulse in the market and enables the studio to be constantly on a contract.
www.alexrussell.com

2.4 Working efficiently

Learning objectives

By the end of this section, you should have a key understanding of:

- the importance of planning your work
- how quality control can improve your work
- how and when to carry out quality control checks.

Key points

- Analytical skills
- Communication skills
- Linking technology and design

Key terms

Quality – the overall or total characteristics of a product and how it meets the end user's needs. It guarantees the product has been made to a certain standard.

Standards – the level a product must meet to be usable for a particular purpose.

Quality control – tests and inspections carried out to ensure that the products meet the specification criteria.

Quality assurance – a guarantee given to the customer from the company to assure the quality of the product.

Test – a process to ensure that standards are met.

Introduction

Every product that you purchase has to go through a range of quality control tests to ensure that it meets the requirements of the client and that it is safe to use by the consumer. These tests are a critical part in the manufacture of a product.

Quality control

Quality control is one aspect of the quality assurance system and is used to ensure that the product you create is of a good quality, is safe to use and meets certain standards.

Knowledge link

For more information on quality assurance, go to page 245.

Quality control also ensures that manufacturers test textile products as stated in the law or legislation, at a local level, national level and also as stated in EU regulations. In quality control, the use of the feedback process helps to ensure that the faults can be located and systems put in place to solve the problem.

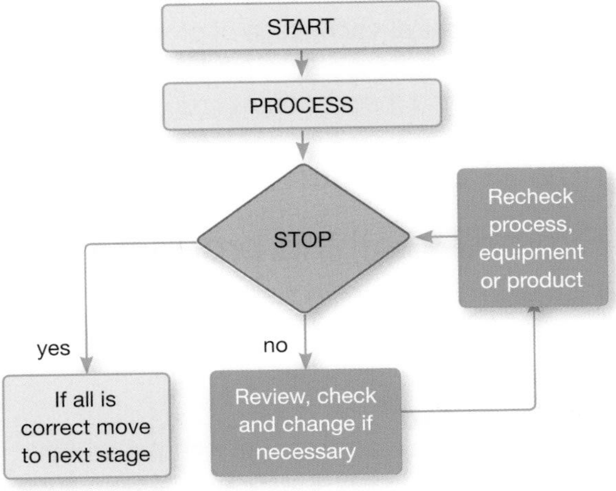

Figure 2.17 Feedback loop, showing critical control points

In the textiles and fashion industry, companies use a range of quality control tests to do the following:

1. Make sure that all parts and components of a product are of the right quality and fit for purpose.
2. Make sure that all the components are the correct ones for the product.
3. Make sure that, when put together, the product is safe to use.
4. Ensure that the product meets the level of quality required.
5. Make sure that tolerance levels are acceptable. Tolerances are guidelines that state what is acceptable in a product and what is not acceptable for it to go through the production process.
6. Ensure that products are the correct colour.

Key terms

Fit for use – a product is made to a certain quality level, for the end use for which it is made.

Tolerance levels – the amount (maximum and minimum levels) of small defects in the product.

Quality control points, also called critical control points, operate at each stage of production, from fibre and raw materials, through to fabrics and prototypes, and then the final product.

How is a test carried out?

Example clothing product

1. The gold seal or manufacturing sample is matched against the sample product taken from the production line. One or more samples are tested.
2. The samples are compared with the design and manufacturing specification.
3. All aspects of the garment are checked and key measurements taken.

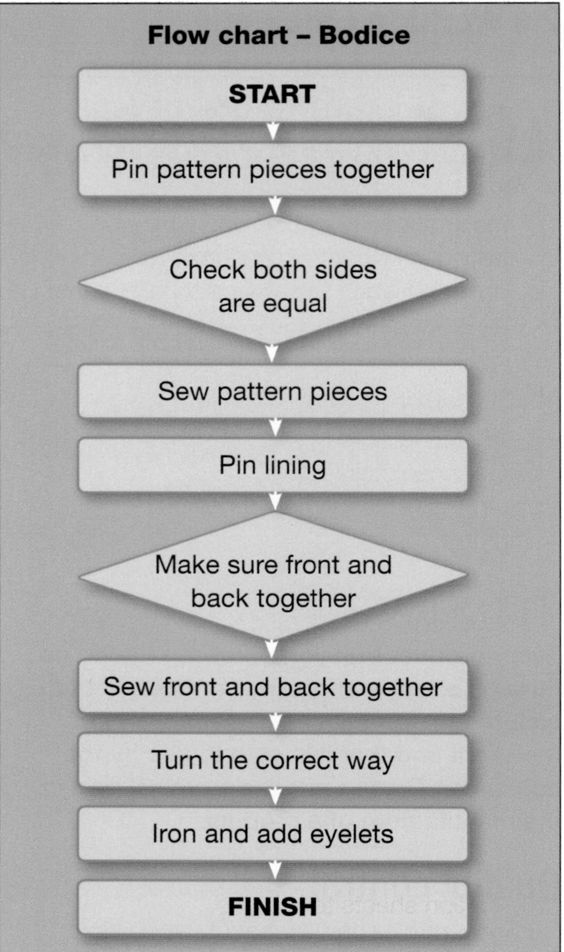

△ **Figure 2.18** Quality control points for textile products

4. Details of all the checks are recorded.
5. If the samples pass inspection, then production continues as normal. If the sample fails the inspection, steps are taken to check where the faults are. The information gathered from quality control checks result in products being the same quality all the time, leading to higher customer satisfaction and lower customer returns.

Quality control checks allow companies to evaluate systems and processes and to put in place any amendments to the system, should they be needed.

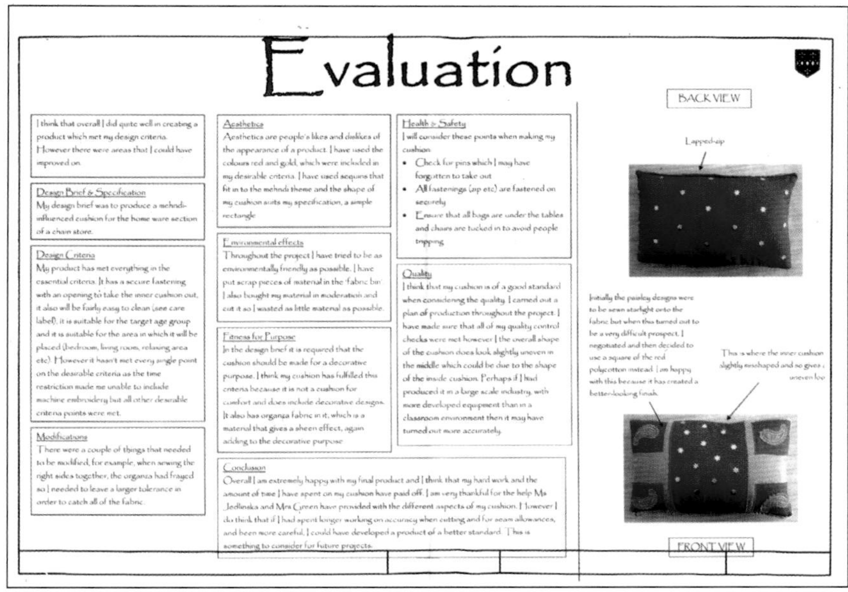

△ **Figure 2.19** A student's evaluation for quality control

Specification sheets

Specification or technical sheets are documents that provide key information about a product and all the components needed to make it, along with any additional technical information. Quality control will use the information on the specification sheets to identify critical control checkpoints.

The specification sheets need to:

- be clearly laid out and show all the components of a product
- give clear diagrams showing all views of the product and highlighting key details
- give special instructions or highlight key points using certain colours or text.

To make sure that products are safe to be used, they need to be tested. Some of the tests that are carried out help the manufacturers to check the following:

- that the component is fit for use by the end user
- that the component is safe to use
- that the product conforms to the correct standards as laid down in law or by standards documentation
- size of product
- appearance of product
- colour of product and colour application
- durability of product
- flammability of product
- overall performance of product
- fitness for purpose.

In addition, tests can be carried out on specific aspects of a product, such as perspiration/sweat or pilling (i.e. bobbles on the surface of fabric – this is an important test for knitted products).

Key terms

BSI (British Standards Institution) – professional organisation that sets the standards for industry and decides the tests needed to be applied on different products.

Specification – an outline that details all the requirements of a product.

Trading standards – an association established to protect the customer.

The quality control department uses different tests and statistics as the tests are carried out. The data gathered are then used to update specification sheets and tolerance guidelines. The guidelines and data are then used by manufacturers to see which products from the production line should be accepted and which rejected as they are tested.

Tolerances are used not only during the production phase, but can also be highlighted in the following areas:

- initial client specification
- design research/design specification
- manufacturing plan
- size of product.

When making one-off products, you may find that the accepted tolerances are different from those made in large volumes. In large-scale production, hundreds or thousands of products are made, so manufacturers will set a limit on the number of products being tested – this is called a sample. The results of the sample will inform the company of whether they need to do further tests, change the way in which a product is being made or allow production to continue.

To make sure that testing is carried out correctly, companies will need to:

- plan when the tests will be carried out and at what stage in the design process
- know how to prevent faults in lay planning, making or distribution
- have clear specifications for all products and components
- have systems in place for monitoring products on an ongoing basis.

Defects that can be seen in production

Below are some of the key defects that can be found during production of a product.

- **Pattern defects**
  - Incorrect number of pattern pieces or wrong size of pattern pieces.
  - Laying or spreading the fabric on a cutting table incorrectly can result in pattern pieces that are not the correct shape.
  - Cutting out the garment shapes incorrectly can lead to misshapen pattern pieces.
- **Sewing defects**
  - For example, needle damage, skipped stitches.
  - Seam defects – twisted seams or seam pucker.
  - Assembly defects – the product is incorrectly put together or with the wrong fastenings.
- **General faults**
  - General faults – stains, holes.
- **Pressing/ironing faults**
  - Pressing defects (during manufacture) – underpressing incorrect, scorches or burns to fabrics.
  - Fusing defects – wrong interfacing added to product, or interfacing comes away from product.
  - Pressing defects (final pressing and checking) – broken buttons or zips, watermarks.
- **Packing faults**
  - Folding, packing and storing in the warehouse – for example, incorrect folding of the garment/product, attack of pests on the product, damage caused in storage.

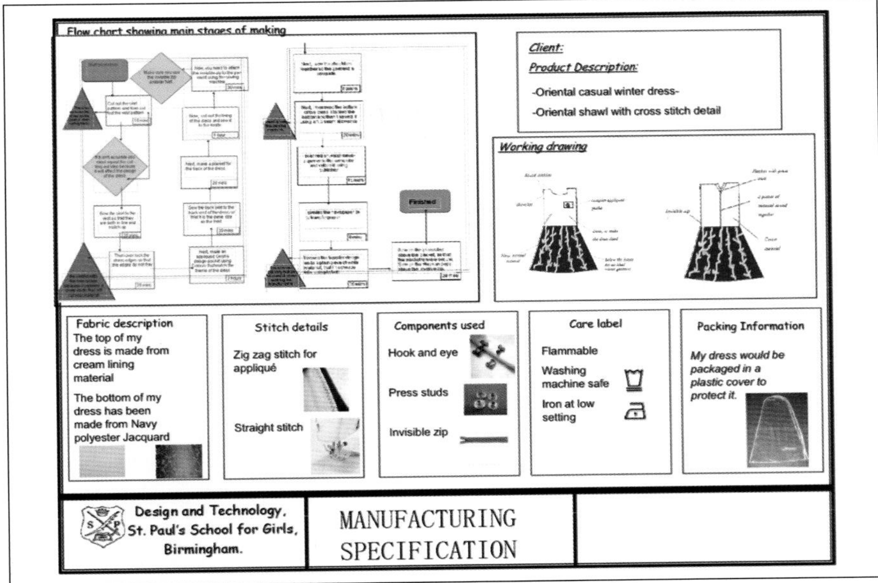

△ **Figure 2.20** Specification

Summary

- Quality control is a key part of the process in product making. Without it, you cannot guarantee that your product has been made to the correct standard and is fit for purpose.
- All products need to be tested thoroughly before the general public can use them. There are standard tests that all products undergo.
- Testing provides key information about a product that will allow you, the designer, to create information for product maintenance.
- In your own work, you will set up a system to check that your product is well made, and then evaluate your outcome.
- Feedback loops and critical control points provide key places for checking how well products are being made.

Exam practice questions

1. What does quality control mean? **[2 marks]**
2. Why do companies have to use quality control? **[2 marks]**
3. At which points in the production of a product will checks be carried out? **[4 marks]**
4. Why are critical control points or feedback loops important for checking products? **[4 marks]**
5. Why are specification sheets important? **[3 marks]**

Stretch yourself

Look at the pictures and the descriptions of the following products.

A child's sun hat for 3- to 5-year-olds). This is a woven hat with ties to hold the hat in place.

△ **Figure 2.21** Child's hat

Trousers for a boy (up to 6 years old): combat trousers with a nylon zip and drawstring ties.

△ **Figure 2.22** Trousers for an infant

Rucksack cover for a cyclist: a rucksack cover with reflective strip details and reflective print.

△ **Figure 2.23** Rucksack

Cushions for a sofa in a living room: a cushion with multi-button design detail.

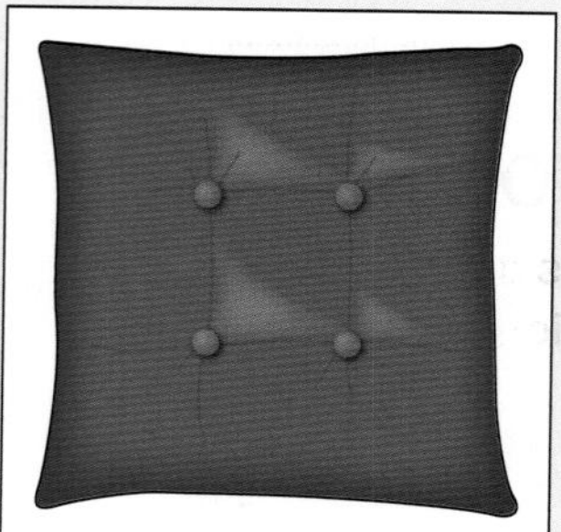

△ **Figure 2.24** Cushion

1. Identify three key tests that need to be carried out on each product, giving reasons. **[6 marks]**
2. Look at each product. How would you remake or adapt these products to ensure that they are safe for use? In your answer you should consider the following: manufacture, materials and processes and components. **[16 marks]**
3. Choose one product and redesign it, taking into consideration the safety issues. Illustrate your answer with sketches and notes. **[15 marks]**

Resources

Websites

Trading Standards: www.tradingstandards.gov.uk

Consumer Protection: www.consumerdirect.gov.uk

Citizens Advice Bureau: www.citizensadvice.org.uk

British Standards: www.bsieducation.org

chapter 3 Values

3.1 Ethical, social and environmental values, and diversity

Learning objectives

By the end of this section, you should have a key understanding of:

- what values are
- ethical values
- social values
- environmental values
- diversity and culture
- values in fashion and textiles
- how values are incorporated into the design process
- the application of values to consumer goods
- how this might be applied to your own designs and coursework (Design and Make practice).

Key points

- Analytical skills
- Communication skills
- Values

Introduction

Values and cultural issues are linked to traditional and modern methods of making products or are related to the way we live and the traditions that are a part of our everyday lives. Many cultures have traditions that are an important part of their identity. These may be linked to the clothes they wear or to the textiles techniques they practise.

Key terms

Culture – A range of beliefs and way of life that are attributed to a particular society or civilisation.

Values – Moral principals or beliefs that you think are important.

Many traditions and crafts are linked to a range of other social practices or events, such as the passage from teenager to adulthood, or getting married.

Textile products can be created to showcase and document particular events in history. The Bayeux Tapestry is one such famous textile product that shows a historical event: the Battle of Hastings in 1066.

△ **Figure 3.1** The Bayeux Tapestry

Techniques such as quilt-making can be used to tell stories or they can be used as symbols of an event, such as the HIV/Aids

Global Quilt, which was created in 1985, or the commemorative Millennium Quilt, which celebrated our entry into the year 2000.

In the eighteenth and nineteenth centuries, young girls and women used to make textile samplers to showcase their understanding of various stitches, as well as design techniques. Women of the South African Ndebele tribe produced angel dolls and computer dolls in the 1990s to illustrate the number of children who were suffering due to Aids.

Ethical values

Today's designers need to review the way in which they design and how the products that they make are used by consumers in the wider society. This broader understanding of the place of design in society covers issues such as:

- ensuring the right pay or living wage for a day's work
- protecting workers' rights
- making sure that working conditions are clean and safe
- caring about the people who make the products that we use.

Key terms

Consumer choice – the range of products that buyers can choose from.

Consumer legislation – Legal protection for consumers when they purchase goods.

Ethical values are also linked to consumer law/ rights. These are laws or legislation that protect the consumer when they purchase goods. They are in place to ensure that the manufacturer produces goods that are correct and safe to use. Information should be provided on product labels to tell us how to care for and use the products safely. However, health and safety is not only about the products that we buy, but also about the places where we work.

Key term

Ethical values – an issue or something that is morally right or morally acceptable.

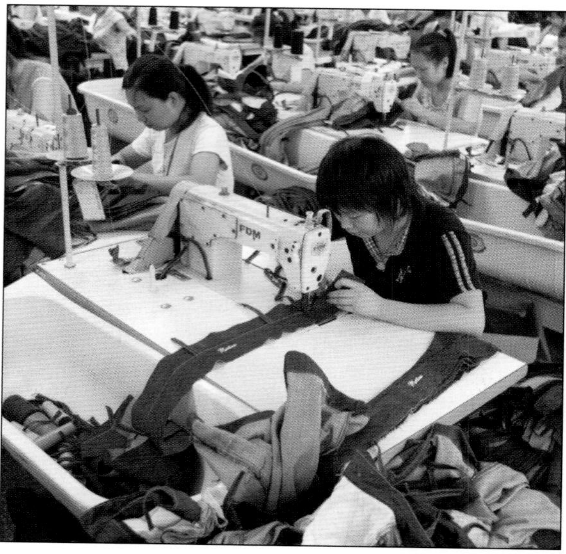

△ **Figure 3.2** Designers should consider working conditions

Fair trade

In recent years, companies such as the Fairtrade Foundation have been promoting ethical issues related to the products we purchase. The aim of Fairtrade is to promote products that have been fairly and ethically produced and provide workers with a fair wage. Much of the work is involved in ensuring that workers get paid fairly for their products or raw materials, which then enables them to invest in other areas, such as education and equipment, to become more productive.

In order for a product to be recognized as 'fair trade', it has to pass through a series of special checks known as certification. Fairtrade operates awareness of its work through events such as Fairtrade week. The Fairtrade symbol is instantly recognisable to the consumer and assures them that the product has followed the appropriate checks and guidelines.

Social values and diversity

Social values means an awareness of both your own social issues and those of others. This is related to such things as:

- colours that are worn or used
- the style of the outfits (e.g. modesty)
- religious ideals
- gender issues
- medical issues
- rituals associated with dying
- age
- disability.

In society, we are conditioned to view certain ways of wearing clothes as being acceptable or unacceptable. In many countries, the way that women and men dress is dictated by religious organisations or acceptable cultural values.

Key terms

Diversity – understanding how people live in different social and cultural contexts.

Social values – preserving or enhancing consumer-related benefits.

Many teenagers belong to different social tribes. Members of these groups may wear particular colours and styles of clothes.

△ **Figure 3.3** Different social tribes may have particular ways of dressing

The use of the Hijab (head covering traditionally worn by Muslim women) has provided talking points related to freedom, but has also led to new designs – for example, sportswear, allowing Muslim women to participate in a variety of sports.

◁ **Figure 3.4** The Hijab

Scotland is renowned for its woven fabrics called tartans. The colours used in the tartans denote tribes or clans that the wearer belongs to. The popular garment worn in Scotland that shows off the weaves is called the kilt. Today, the woven fabrics from Scotland are also used in fashion products.

Disability is one area in which design companies are now engaging, by developing products for the physically disabled. This requires specialist knowledge – for example, designers need to know how clothes will fit when worn by someone who uses a wheelchair. Designers also need to take into consideration the use of easy-close fastenings.

Environmental values

Environmental values are related to the following:

- the ways in which textiles and fashion companies input environmental processes into the production and disposal of their products
- the ways in which we, as consumers, purchase or dispose of products
- the ways in which designers consider environmental issues in the design of textiles products

- the availability of textile and fashion products that have environmental credentials.

Key terms

Environmental issues – issues related to the condition of the environment – for example, reducing pollution, understanding waste and reducing waste.

Environmental values – actions, policies or beliefs connected with protecting or preserving the environment.

◁ **Figure 3.5** 'Make Do and Mend'

Both textiles and fashion have contributed to pollution on a large scale. Textiles is one of the largest users of pollutants, in both the processing and the manufacturing stages, as well as the aftercare of products.

Fashion, because of its emphasis on rapid change and new styles, has been accused of encouraging us to waste products by replacing our garments on a regular basis.

Through such policies as the Kyoto Agreement, countries have agreed to develop strategies to reduce the world's carbon footprint, as well as agree certain controls on environmental waste. In fashion and textiles, companies and social groups are now developing ways to reduce our textiles waste. They are also using past movements, such as 'Make Do and Mend', which was popular during the Second World War and encouraged people to reuse materials and mend textile products. Other textile movements, such as 'Slow Design', encourage us to review how we make products and the energy we use.

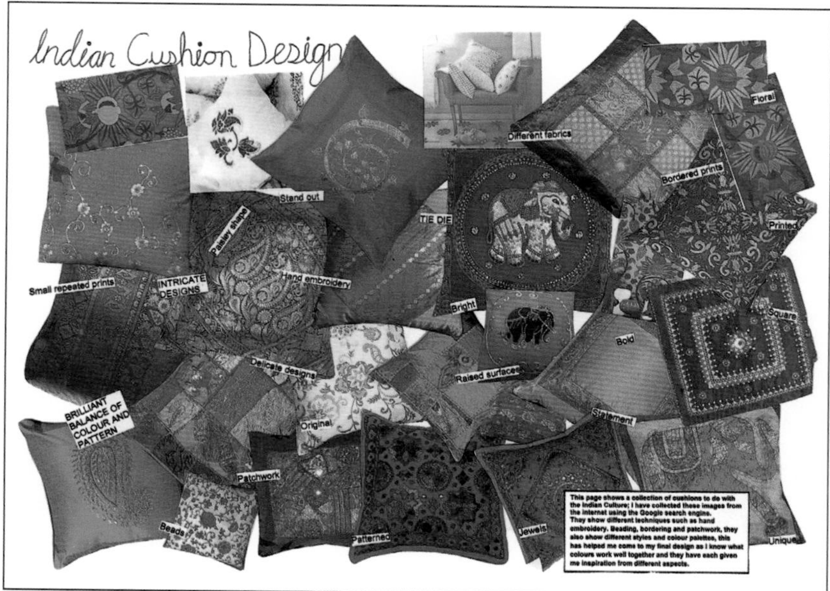

△ **Figure 3.6** Student consideration of social and cultural issues

Customising clothes is a good way to reuse clothing and textile products and avoid having to purchase new ones. They make the products unique (one of a kind) and give them added value.

Knowledge link

For more information on reusing textiles, see Chapter 8.

The impact of modern technologies

Modern technologies allow small- and large-scale producers to reduce waste and materials. Digital printing is one such technology that allows designers to engage with making bespoke products and only print 'on demand', or as much as they need. Digital printing technologies reduce the following:

- energy use
- water use
- fabric wastage
- print and dye disposal.

Key term

Bespoke – individual made-to-measure tailoring for men's suits.

Knowledge link

For more information on how digital printing works, see pages 268–69.

Values in the fashion and textiles industry

Many fashion manufacturing companies will now have what is called a 'corporate and social responsibility' (CSR) document, which covers ethical design and manufacturing. This is related to treating workers fairly and paying them a living wage.

△ **Figure 3.7** Student use of CAD/CAM digital printing

Key term

CSR (corporate and social responsibility) – company policies related to how they will tackle environmental issues, such as pollution or reducing waste. This also covers how companies will treat workers or those that manufacture products for them – for example, ensuring that the supply chain supports ethical issues.

This is important, as many products, although they might be designed in the UK, are manufactured abroad for a range of reasons. Designers and retailers (shops) are now more aware of the need for products that have been made using labour where people are paid a proper wage and have good working conditions.

The CSR will also highlight issues to do with the environment and showcase how a company might reduce its carbon footprint, by looking at the use of products, processes and services that reduce the impact on the environment.

Summary

- Values are an essential aspect of the textiles chain.
- Cultural values and diversity are displayed in textiles products in different forms, such as use of colours, or designs, or methods of making.
- Many modern textile and fashion companies incorporate aspects of culture into their designs.
- As a designer, there is a responsibility to the consumer to design a range of products that meet their cultural needs, are good in design and are made ethically.
- In fashion and textiles, there is a place for both traditional and new technologies.

Exam practice questions

1. Design companies often design products in one country and manufacture them in another country. Describe one benefit and one disadvantage of this method. **[2 marks]**
2. Designers working for eco companies often work with local craftspeople in developing new products. Give two advantages of doing this. **[2 marks]**
3. What does the term fair trade mean? List three reasons why a company might want to use the FAIRTRADE Mark on their products. **[3 marks]**
4. Why are digital technologies such as digital printing a good method for creating new fabrics? Give reasons for your choice. **[4 marks]**
5. Name two textile techniques that can be used to tell stories or describe historic events. **[2 marks]**
6. Give two reasons why a designer has to consider environmental issues when developing new designs. **[2 marks]**

Stretch yourself

1. For this activity, you will need:
   - a map of the world
   - a coloured pen.

Find a map of the world in a book or on the internet and photocopy it/print it off. Create a data collection sheet, like the one shown below.

Textile product	Where it is made	Fibre composition	Fabric type	Retailer	CSR (Yes or No)
T-shirt	India	100% cotton	Knitted		

(a) Look at the care labels of at least 20 textile products that you either wear or use. Using the coloured pen, indicate on the map where your textile products are made. What do your results show? **[5 marks]**

(b) Using any research method, find out if the company has a CSR policy/document. If the answer is yes, what does this tell you about the values of the company? If the answer is no, what does this tell you about the company? **[5 marks]**

(c) Review your answers and your research: will your results make you change your shopping habits? If so, how? **[5 marks]**

2. Choose a country and a specific area and see what information you can find out about its textiles or fashion traditions. Write a short report. Your report should include information on traditional skills and also how those skills or traditions have been modernised. **[10 marks]**

Resources

Books

Black, S. (2008), *Eco-chic: The Fashion Paradox*, Black Dog Publishing.

Brown, S. (2010), *Eco Fashion*, Laurence King.

Fletcher, K. (2008), *Sustainable Fashion and Textiles: Design Journeys*, Earthscan.

Fuad-Luke, A. (2005), *The Eco-design Handbook: A Complete Sourcebook for Home and Office*, Thames and Hudson.

Harrison, R. (2005), *The Ethical Consumer*, Sage.

Barbero, S. and Cozzo, B. (2010) *Eco Design* H.F. Ullmann.

Websites

Labour behind the label: www.labourbehindthelabel.org

Fashioning an ethical industry: http://fashioninganethicalindustry.org

The Fashion Roadmap: www.fashionroadmap.com

Ethical Fashion Forum: www.ethicalfashionforum.com

Aids quilt: www.aidsquilt.org.uk

Practical Action: http://practicalaction.org

chapter 4 Fibres and fabrics

4.1 Properties and characteristics 1

Learning objectives

By the end of this section, you should have a key understanding of:

- the key types of fibres, including natural fibres (wool, cotton, silk, linen), regenerated fibres (viscose, Tencel®, lyocell), synthetic fibres (elastomeric, nylon, polyester, acrylic) and other types of fibres (bamboo, Ingeo™, microfibres)
- the properties of fibres
- the physical and aesthetic characteristics of fibres
- how fibres are processed
- how fibres can be combined through mixing or blending to enhance their properties (poly-cotton, elastomerics)
- the development of new fibres with the environment in mind
- key textile terminology.

Key points

- Critical analysis
- Evaluation
- Values

Introduction

All textile and fashion products start off as fibres. It is essential to understand that each fibre has its own properties and characteristics, and these determine where and how the fibre may be used and processed to manufacture a product.

What is a fibre?

A fibre is defined as a fine, hair-like structure, which can be either short or long. Short fibres are known as **staple fibres** and long fibres are known as **filament fibres**. Filament fibres, because they are long and slim, tend to give a smooth finish to fabrics. Staple fibres, because they are shorter, tend to be more hairy and not as smooth.

Key terms

Characteristics – the key or unique things about a product/fabric/fibre.

Fibres – fine, hair-like structures that can be natural, synthetic or regenerated and can be long (filament) or short (staple).

Properties – the characteristics of a fibre (e.g. absorbency, strength).

Sustainable – combines theories and practices in design that review economic, ecological, environmental and cultural issues. It is a process of looking at the design and manufacture of products and how the impact of the products can be reduced, to have little or no negative impact on either the environment or people that may be employed to make the product. It also includes reviewing the life cycle of the product and how it can be made better or how it can be reused.

Where do fibres come from?

Fibres come from one of three sources:

- natural – plants or animals
- synthetic or man-made – developed through the use of science and other technical advances
- regenerated – a mixture of chemical and natural elements.

Textiles, fibres, the environment and sustainability

A growing awareness of the environmental impact of the products that we use has led to the development of textiles that are either more environmentally friendly or organic. Textile companies are developing 'sustainable' or CSR (corporate and social responsibility) approaches with regard to the manufacture of textile fibres and products.

Knowledge link

You can find more information on textiles and the environment in Chapter 8.

Natural fibres

Natural fibres come from two key sources: plants or animals. The main plant- or vegetable-based fibres are cotton, linen, jute, hemp and ramie. The main animal-based fibres are wool and silk.

Key terms

Cotton – a natural cellulosic plant fibre.

Natural fibres – fibres that occur naturally and are obtained from plants and animals.

Silk – A protein-based natural filament fibre, which comes from the cocoon of the silkworm.

Wool – an animal fibre from the fleece of sheep.

Plant-vegetable-based fibres

Cotton

Cotton fibres are produced by the seed boll (pod) of the cotton plant. Cotton is a cellulose-based fibre. The fibres produced are short (staple) fibres. The fibres are picked by hand or machine, cleaned to remove the seeds or other

Natural fibres

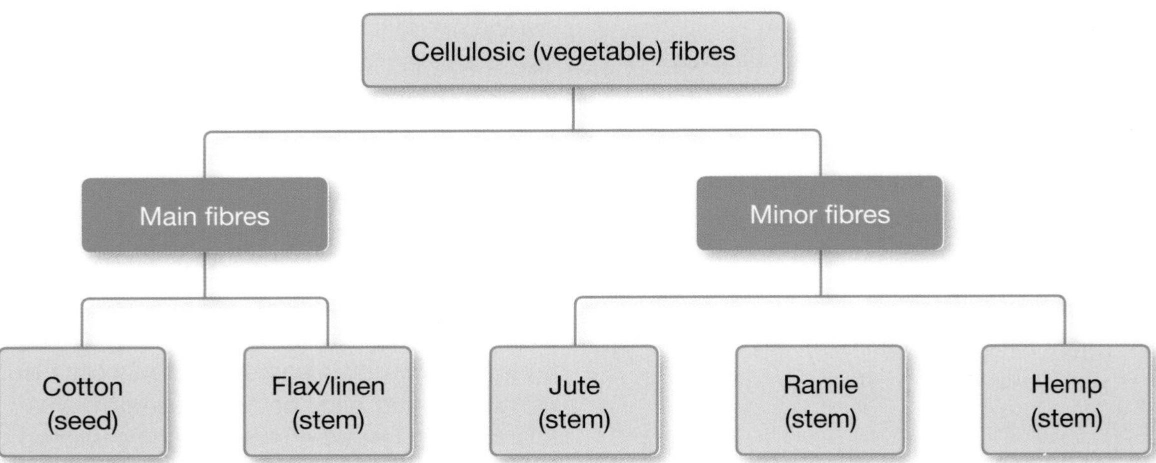

△ **Figure 4.1** Plant-vegetable-based fibres

matter (called **ginning**), then dried. The fibres are then put in a machine for a process known as **carding** and **combing** – this enables the fibres to be laid straight before being made into long ropes, called **roving**. The roving is then sent to the final process, spinning, which converts the roving into yarn – this is the basis for making cloth.

Cotton yarn is used to make all sorts of products, such as for clothing and furnishings and in industrial applications. Products made from cotton are cool to wear. Cotton fabrics such as flannelette are brushed, which makes them warm.

Key term

Yarn – a length of fibres and/or filaments with or without a twist.

Linen

Linen, also known as **flax**, comes from the stem of the flax plant. Linen is a cellulose-based fibre. The fibres of the flax are harvested, then soaked in a chemical mixture that rots away the unwanted plant matter. The long fibres that remain are cleaned and dried, then processed further before being spun into yarn. The fibres produced are long, smooth, straight, lustrous and very strong. Linen yarns are used for clothing and furnishings. Linen products are cool to wear.

Other plant/vegetable-based fibres

Although they are not used every day, other, alternative, natural fibres are:

- **jute** – very coarse and not very strong; used mainly for large bags and coarse rugs
- **hemp** – a very durable fabric; used mainly for rugs, carpets and rope
- **ramie** – can be mixed with other fibres, such as wool and silk; used mainly for rope, nets and some cloth
- **kapok** – a soft yarn, very short fibres and very soft; used as fillings and stuffing, soundproofing and insulation; it can also be used in mattresses, cushions, furniture and life preservers
- **sisal** – a linen-like fibre; used for ropes and bristles for brushes, as well as a filling for upholstery
- **coir** – comes from the outer husk of the coconut and is very coarse; used for ropes, sailcloth and matting
- **pina** – a pineapple fibre, very soft with a high lustre; used for mats, bags and clothing.

All these fibres are cellulose-based.

Animal-based fibres

Wool

A major textile fibre that can be sourced from sheep and other animals, such as goats and rabbits. Wool comes from fleeces, which are shorn from the animals. The fibres produced from wool are short (staple) fibres. Wool has a protein base known as keratin. Once the fleece is removed, it is graded and then has to be washed (**scoured**) to remove oils and other substances. The fibres are processed through carding and combing, which smoothes them out. The fibres are then processed into roving (long ropes) before being spun and twisted into yarn.

Woollen yarns can be created by two spinning processes: **worsted** or **woollen**. Worsted yarns are fine, smooth and strong, so can create strong and fine fabrics. Woollen yarns are short, staple fibres, which are bulkier and thicker.

Identifying wool

Wool fibres are identified by their crimp or waviness and they have natural overlapping scales. The crimp and scales of the woollen fibres can be altered using heat or stream, which causes the fibres to felt. Care should always be taken when washing woollen garments because using water that is too hot will cause garments to shrink and felt. Wool allows air to be trapped between the fibres, making the fabric warm to wear. Generally, wool products can be relatively

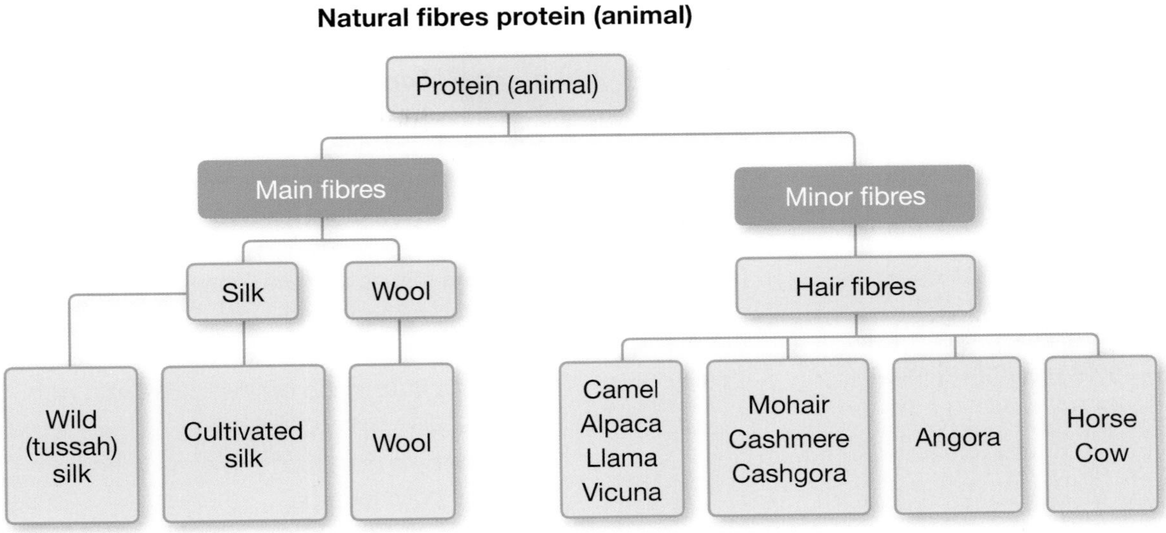

Natural fibres protein (animal)

Protein (animal)

Main fibres

Silk

Wool

Wild (tussah) silk

Cultivated silk

Wool

Minor fibres

Hair fibres

Camel
Alpaca
Llama
Vicuna

Mohair
Cashmere
Cashgora

Angora

Horse
Cow

△ **Figure 4.2** Animal-based fibres

inexpensive. However, products made from specialty wools, such as Merino and Cashmere, are very expensive.

Other sources of wool fibres are:

- **camel** – hair-based fibre; very fine; used for products such as jackets and coats
- **alpaca** – tends to be fine, silky and very strong; used mainly for cloth and suiting fabrics
- **mohair** – a goat hair, which is very fine and long; used in jumpers and suits
- **cashmere** – a luxurious, hair-based fabric, very light and soft; used for suits, scarves and garments
- **rabbit** – angora is the best known of the rabbit hairs; it is very fine, long, silky and warm; used for baby clothes, gloves and hats.

Many of these wools can be mixed or blended together.

Silk

Silk is a protein-based fibre that comes from the cocoon of a moth caterpillar, known as the silkworm. The silk cocoon is spun from the spinneret (mouth) of the worm. While the silk is being spun, it is held together with gum known as sericin, or silk gum. Silk can come from cultivated silk or uncultivated silk (known as wild or tussah silk). Cultivated silk is very fine, lustrous and expensive; wild silk is much coarser and cheaper.

The silk can be gathered in one of two ways:

1. The cocoons are heated to suffocate the worm. This loosens the silk gum and also kills the worm, allowing the silk filament to be unwound to it full length.
2. The moth is allowed to break out of the cocoon. However, doing this breaks the yarn, resulting in short fibres, which are not easy to spin or process.

The silk cocoons are sorted into sizes and then softened in a series of hot and cold baths before being unwound or reeled. After reeling, the silk is dipped into warm water with soap and oil before being dried and wound onto bobbins, ready for twisting.

Silk is cool to wear and is used for products such as clothing, upholstery and furnishings.

Synthetic fibres

Synthetic fibres are made using a range of chemicals, including oil-based ones. This means that it is easy to make or modify the fibres for specific end uses for both the consumer and the

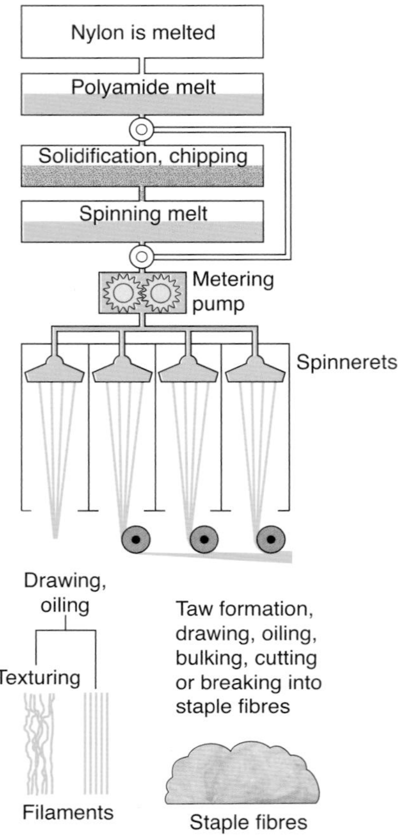

△ **Figure 4.3** The yarn-making process for synthetic fibres

industrial market. The most well-known of the synthetic fibres are polyester and nylon.

How are synthetic fibres made?

Synthetic fibres are made by combining simple chemicals called monomers to create polymers. This conversion process is called polymerisation. The polymers, in liquid or pellet form, are made into yarns by being forced through spinnerets, and then cooled.

Key terms

Acrylic – the generic term for a man-made, synthetic fibre produced from acrylonitrille, which can be cut into short, staple fibres. When crimped, acrylic has a wool-like texture with low moisture absorbency and dries quickly. It produces fabrics that are lightweight, soft, warm and resilient, and it can be used for knitwear, upholstery and carpets.

Nylon – a man-made synthetic fibre with high strength; also called polyamide.

Polyester – a man-made fibre made from synthetic polymer.

Synthetic fibres – manufactured from chemicals.

Polyester

Polyester is the most well-known of the synthetic fibres and one of the most widely used. It is a versatile fibre and can be blended with other fibres, such as cotton. Awareness of the environmental impact of polyester fabrics on the environment means that a lot of work has been carried out on the methods for recycling different types of polyester. Companies such as Polartec and Patagonia now recycle polyester, either in garment or bottle form, by converting it into pellets and reusing it as yarn to make garments.

At the 2010 Football World Cup in South Africa, Nike, the sportswear manufacturer, used recycled PET (polyethylene terephthalate) bottles to make the football kit for more than15 teams taking part in the tournament.

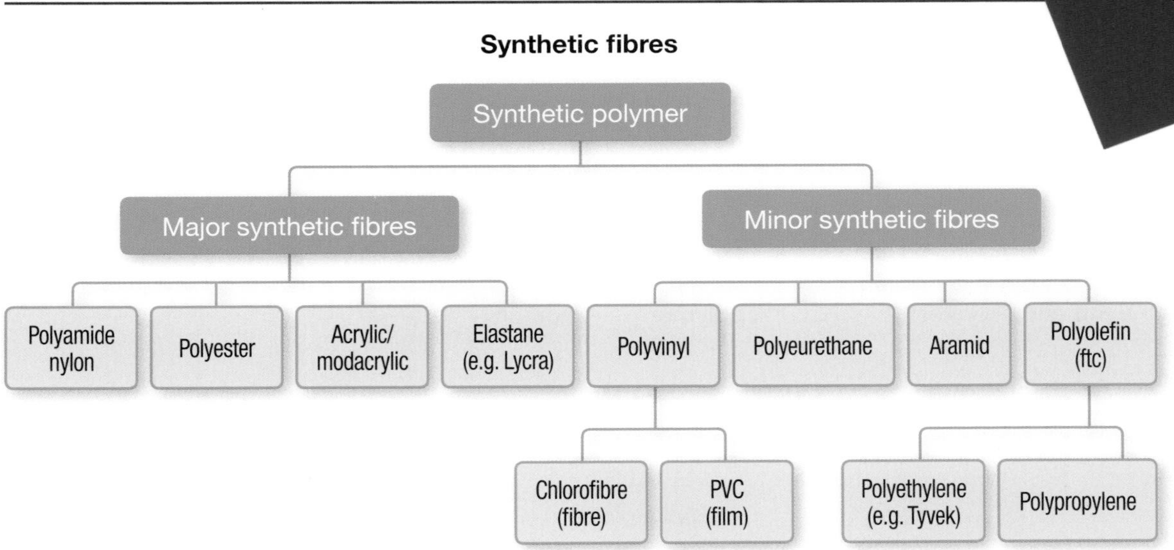

△ **Figure 4.4** Synthetic fibres

Nylon (polyamide)

Regarded as a modern fibre, it is very strong and robust. It can be easily mixed with other fibres and can be manufactured as long filaments or short, staple fibres, depending on its end use.

Acrylic

Acrylic is a soft, warm fabric that emulates wool in its handle and feel.

Elastane

Elastane is a rubber base material that can be used to add stretch and elasticity to products. The addition of elastane to clothing adds what is known as the 'comfort factor'. The best known of the elastane fibres is Lycra®.

Aramid

Aramid fibres are very strong and are used for a variety of protective products. The most well-known of the aramid fibres are Kevlar® and Nomex®.

Key terms

Acetate – one of the families of man-made cellulosic fibres, made from wood pulp or cotton. Acetate fabrics have a luxurious and lustrous appearance. They are fast-drying and can be either crisp or soft to touch, depending on the end use. Used to line garments, in lingerie and in fashion garments.

Lyocell – a man-made regenerated fibre that is environmentally friendly.

Rayon – regenerated fibre, also known as artificial silk. It is made up of the wood pulp of eucaplytus/southern pine/spruce trees and a chemical solution. It is known as a regenerated fibre.

Regenerated fibres – fibres manufactured from natural substances and chemicals.

Tencel® – a staple or filament fibre that is made using an 'environmentally friendly' manufacturing process (recycling).

Viscose – regenerated fibre that is cellulose based.

Other synthetic fibres

Synthetic fibres			
Synthetic polymer	Natural polymer	Other	
Carbon	Textile glass	Metal	Ceramic

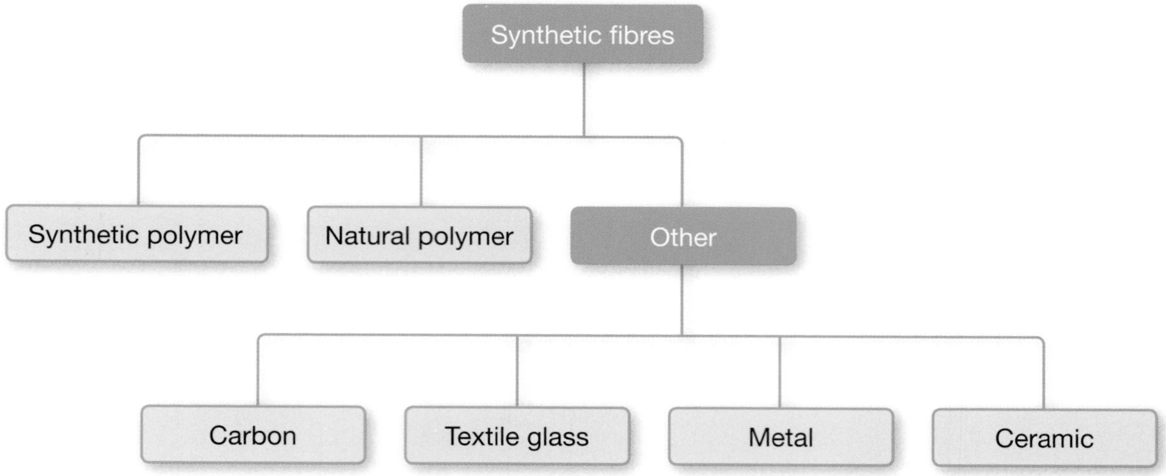

△ **Figure 4.5** Other synthetic fibres

Regenerated fibres

Natural polymer: Viscose | Modal | Cupro | Lyocell (Tencel®) | Acetate | Diacete | Triacetate

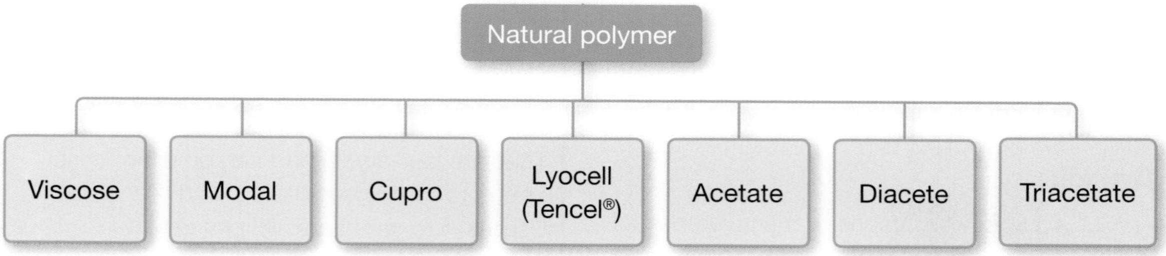

△ **Figure 4.6** Regenerated fibres

Regenerated fibres

Regenerated fibres are also known as manufactured or man-made cellulosic fibres. They are either made from cotton linters, short cotton fibres too short to spin, or pine wood. The cellulose base is mixed with a chemical mixture, which is then converted into a fibre.

To convert this mixture into a yarn, the spinning solution has to be forced through a spinneret. Warm air is then added to solidify the mixture, which can then be made into a continuous filament yarn or staple fibre. The main regenerated fibres are **viscose**, **rayon**, **acetate** and **modal**.

Fibres such as **Tencel®** and **Lyocell** are known more for their environmental approaches to manufacture. They are made using a closed-loop system. This means that all the waste created during the manufacture of the fibre can be reintroduced into the production process.

Fibres such as Tencel® and lyocell are known more for their environmental approaches to manufacture. They are made using a 'closed-loop' system. This means that all the waste created during the manufacture of the fibre can be reintroduced into the production process.

Knowledge link

For more information on environmental issues, see Chapter 8.

Identifying fibres – fibres under the microscope

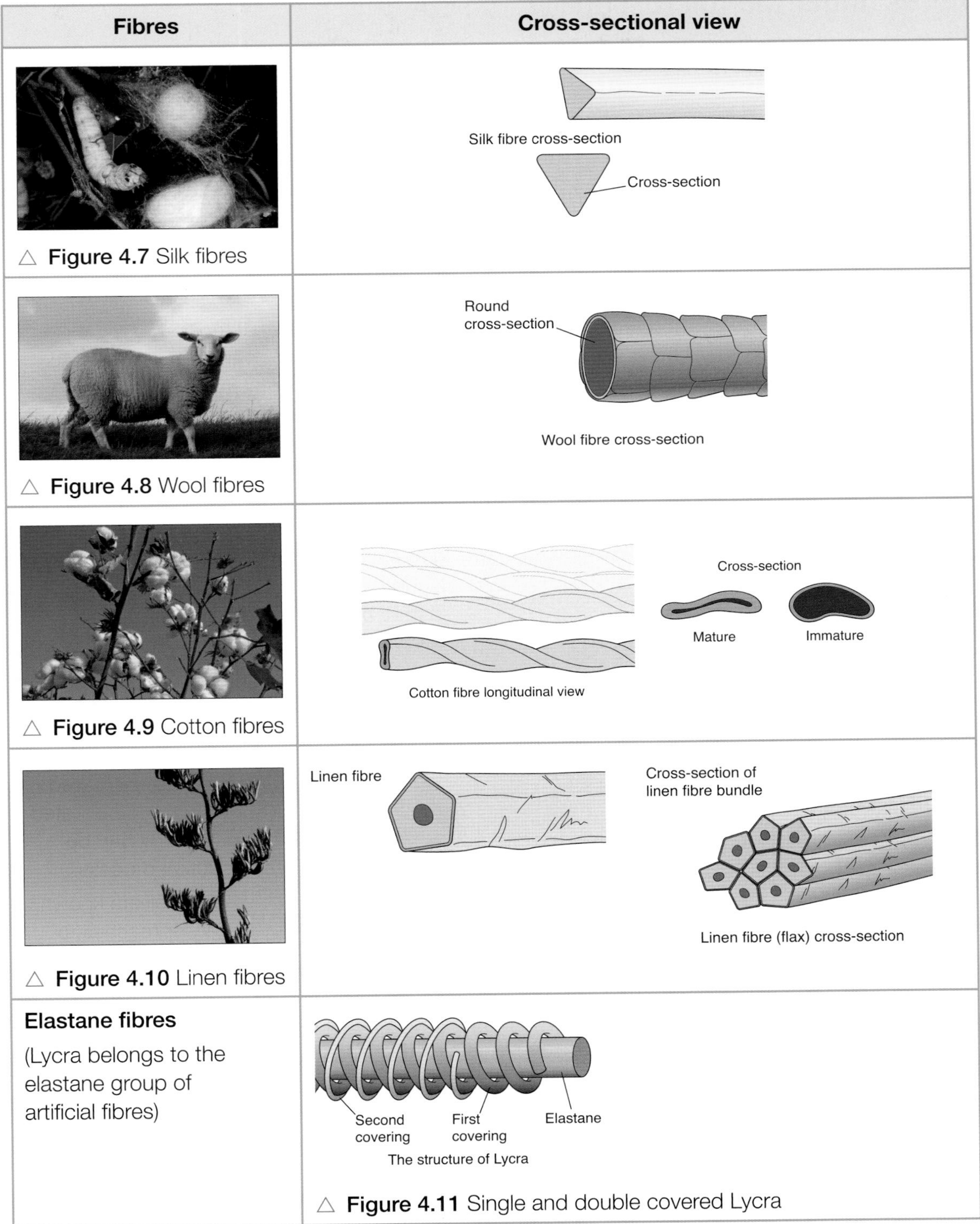

△ **Figure 4.7** Silk fibres

△ **Figure 4.8** Wool fibres

△ **Figure 4.9** Cotton fibres

△ **Figure 4.10** Linen fibres

△ **Figure 4.11** Single and double covered Lycra

Identifying fibres – fibres under the microscope

Fibres can be identified by a series of trade symbols, which indicate they are real.

△ **Figure 4.12** Example trade symbol for fibres

Other fibres

Organic fibres

Organic fibres are marketed as an alternative to conventional fibres. The most well-known organic fibre is cotton, but organic cotton accounts for only between 1 and 3 per cent of overall cotton production. In order for a fibre to be called organic, it must fulfil the following criteria:

- Organic farming processes must have been in place for more than three years.
- No synthetic or commercial pesticides or herbicides must have been used.

There are, however, several issues related to organic cotton:

- It is expensive to produce.
- It has a lower yield than conventional cotton.
- It has higher processing costs.
- It is difficult to qualify as an organic cotton producer.

There is no physical difference between organic and conventional cotton. Their performance is also the same.

Wool can also be classed as organic as long as the farmer uses no synthetic hormones, the sheep receive only organic feed and they are not be dipped in toxic insecticides.

PLA

Since 2002, fibre manufacturers have been developing new yarns made from other source materials, such as corn and sugar beets. These yarns are created by combining the natural carbons and sugars found in these plants to create a polymer called PLA (polyacide). As the fibre comes from a crop that is already grown, it offers manufacturers an alternative source of raw material and environmental benefits, such as being biodegradable. The latest of the PLA fibres are Ingeo™ and Sorona®. PLA fibres can be used for fashion products, as well as pillows, mattresses and other interior products. Key properties of PLA fibres are that they are:

- flame-retardant
- 100 per cent biodegradable
- very strong
- very hydrophilic (attract water) and therefore good at keeping moisture away from the skin
- highly resistant to UV light
- able to be blended with cotton or wool
- cheap to produce.

PLA products such as Ingeo™ are well-suited for interior upholstery due to their very good flame-retardant properties.

Key term

Ingeo™ – Ingeo™ is a high-performance biopolymer fibre that is made from corn.

Microfibres

Recent textile technology has resulted in the development of minute fibres known as microfibres. Microfibres are very fine, hair-like structures and can be manufactured from nylon, acrylic, polyester, polypropylene, Lyocell and rayon. The resulting yarns can be knitted or woven and are used primarily in specialist fabrics, such as those used in outerwear, sportswear and underwear. They offer a range of properties to the end products, such as breathability, water repellancy and being lightweight. They are more expensive to produce because they have to be woven at a slower rate. The cost of dyeing is also higher as more dye is needed.

The best known of the microfibres are Tactel® and Coolmax®.

Key term

Tactel® – a high-tech polyamide fibre.

Microfibres can be formed by extruding very fine filaments into spinnerets, making the yarn finer each time.

◁ **Figure 4.13** Attributes of microfibres

Properties of microfibres

Microfibres carry the properties of the fibres they are made from. In addition, as fabrics, they have the following properties:

- They are softer.
- They have excellent drape.
- They possess excellent wicking qualities.
- Colour is enhanced when printed because of the additional fibres over a surface area.

Blending microfibres

Microfibres can be blended together. The popular blends are wool or cotton with other synthetic fibres.

Popular microfibre trade names include:

- acetate-based: Celenese®, Microsafe®
- nylon-based: Invista®, Supplex®
- polyester-based: Microspun®, Microtherm®
- rayon-based: Modal®, Micro Modal®.

Bamboo

Bamboo comes from fibre that is made from bamboo pulp. The production process for bamboo is similar to that for rayon. Bamboo is a quick-growing plant (unlike cotton) needs no pesticides, and is able to absorb carbon dioxide. Bamboo has good sustainable and eco credentials: during growth, it reduces greenhouse gas emissions and adds nutrients to the soil in which it is grown.

Bamboo is known as 'the air-conditioning fabric' as it has the ability to reduce the wearer's body temperature by one or two degrees. Bamboo is commonly blended with cotton and is being developed for underwear, babywear, sportswear and household cleaning cloths.

Bamboo can now be made 100 per cent eco-friendly. Today, over 95 per cent of bamboo production comes from China, which is also the main area for research into the use of bamboo.

Key properties of bamboo

- It is very soft.
- It is very fine, so great for wearing next to the skin.
- It has high lustre and sheen.
- It has excellent wicking properties.
- It has good elasticity.
- It accepts dye easily and so requires less dye in the dyeing process.
- It is antimicrobial.
- It is very strong and durable
- It blocks ultraviolet rays.
- It is antistatic.

- It naturally neutralises odours.
- It has high absorbency.
- It has low abrasion, so is often blended with cotton or polyester and Micro Modal®.
- It is naturally biodegradable.

Bamboo: a sustainable fibre of the future

The search for more sustainable fibres to support our clothing needs has led to research being developed to explore other fibres that come from more sustainable resources and rely less on water and pesticides to aid growth.

Bamboo is one of the fibres that emerged in the early twenty-first century as a potential fibre for use in clothing. There are two common types of bamboo fibre:

1. Natural bamboo also known as bamboo linen – this has excellent handle and drape properties and is extracted directly from the 'bamboo culms' (stem).
2. Bamboo viscose – this uses beech pulp in production, and the processing is the same as that for viscose.

Bamboo is one of the fastest-growing plants, taking about four years to reach maturity. There are over 1,000 types of bamboo. Bamboo used for textile production is not harvested from tropical forests, but is commercially grown from a bamboo called Moso Bamboo (also called phyllostachys).

There are two methods for extracting the bamboo fibre:

1. The stems (culms) are crushed and converted into cellulose then processed into fibre.
2. Bamboo linen: the bamboo is chemically processed, which extracts the natural bamboo cellulose (called Kunh). This is made into fibre using a process similar to that of the manufacture of viscose.

There are some issues related to the 'ecological processing' of bamboo, and more environmentally high-tech processing methods are being developed. Companies such as the Swiss manufacturer Litrax are pioneering the development of bamboo as 100 per cent environmentally friendly, and also creating a bamboo biofibre.

△ **Figure 4.14** Bamboo

Key term

Antimicrobial (also known as antibacterial or antiseptic) – a finish or property in a fibre that inhibits the growth of bacteria or other germs.

Designers such as Anna Cohen and Ada Zanditon are already using bamboo in their high-end couture ranges.

Specialist babywear retailer Mothercare already stocks products made from bamboo, such as nappies and buggy liners.

Other natural fibres

In the textile industry, there is research into other types of products that could be used to create fibres.

Since the 1930s, there has been research into the development of industrial hemp, which can be used for clothing and other products. Hemp is harvested and processed in a way similar to linen. The leading area for research into the use of hemp for textile products is the Ukraine. Other hemp-producing regions are China, India, North Korea, Hungary and Romania.

Hemp is regarded as a very important fibre because of its ecological and sustainable profile. Its key properties are as follows:

- It is non-toxic while in use.
- It comes from a renewable resource.
- It is non-polluting for the duration of its life cycle.
- It needs very few pesticides to grow.
- Its growth time is 100 days.
- It leaves the soil replenished with nutrients after harvesting.
- It is good at controlling topsoil erosion.
- Oil can also be harvested and converted into a biofuel called biodiesel.
- It is used in the development of bioplastics.
- It requires no bleaching during processing.

Other fibres being explored for their potential use in clothing are Nettle, which produces a very strong, fine fibre, and Kenaf, a fibre similar in appearance to jute. Kenaf's traditional uses have been limited to rope, coarse cloth, fuel and food. Like nettle and hemp, it has strong sustainability and eco-credentials. In production, it requires few or no pesticides and fertilisers. It is being further developed for the areas of engineering, cloth and vegetable oil. Unlike other fibres, kenaf is a naturally white fibre, so needs no bleaching. Kenaf is grown in Africa, Thailand and India. Soy is also being developed as an alternative textile material.

Elastomeric yarns

Elastomeric fibres are also known as spandex or synthetic rubber. The description 'elastomeric' is given to fibres that can be stretched repeatedly to twice their original length, and then revert to their original shape. Spandex is a synthetic rubber that can be given different properties:

- Power stretch gives a garment power and a high hold factor, and is found in swimwear, athletic wear, underwear or foundation garments, and surgical stockings.
- Comfort stretch only adds elasticity and is found in general garments, lingerie, leggings, stockings, athletic wear and fitted sheets.

Elastomeric yarns are available in three key forms:

1. Bare filament – this is the elastomeric fibre on its own.
2. Core-spun – this has an elastomeric core covered with a staple fibre.
3. Covered yarn – this consists of a spandex core wrapped with another yarn.

Mixtures and blends

What is a mixture?

A fibre mixture is where two or more different strands of yarns are twisted together, and then used to make either a knitted or a woven cloth. Fabric mixtures are created to achieve design or colour effects known as cross-dyeing. Mixtures are also created to lower the overall cost of the finished fabric by combining less expensive and more expensive yarns. Common mixtures include rayon and acetate.

What is a blend?

A blend is where two or more different fibres are blended together at the fibre stage before being spun into a yarn. This is done to combine the desirable properties of the fibres to create a better end fabric for a particular purpose. A common blended yarn is cotton and polyester, also known as polycotton. Some popular blends include cotton+wool, made famous by the Viyella brand, a high-quality woven fabric for clothing; wool+nylon, for carpets; and wool+nylon+cashmere, for coats. Other blends are:

- polyester/viscose
- polyester/nylon (polyamide)
- wool/acetate
- wool/acrylic
- wool/viscose
- bamboo/cotton.

Key terms

Blend – to mix together two different fibres. A blended fibre is one that has been mixed to a specified recipe at the spinning stage, before being made into spun yarn. Two or more staple fibres can be blended, such as polyester and cotton, to alter the properties of a yarn. In addition, blending is used to ensure consistency in a yarn – for example, in using cotton from different sources, either for commercial or availability reasons.

Mixture – fibres that are spun into yarn and mixed together during the weaving process.

Why are fibres mixed or blended?

Reasons for mixing or blending fibres include:

- to reduce costs
- to add desirable properties
- to create design effects
- to increase profitability
- to improve appearance
- to improve durability.

Blends can also enhance the following properties of fabrics:

- handle
- weight
- feel
- performance
- draping
- appearance
- lustre
- comfort.

Physical and aesthetic properties of fibres

All fibres have particular properties and characteristics that make them suitable for certain end uses. It is important to understand the key properties of fibres because this will help you to choose the correct fibres for particular end uses.

Key properties of fibres are:

- strength
- elasticity
- absorbency
- crease resistance
- durability
- warmth
- flammability.

Key term

Aesthetic – the look of a product.

Fibre	Strength	Elasticity	Absorbency	Crease resistance	Durability	Warmth	Flammability	General fibre/fabric description	Environmental and sustainable issues
Natural fibres									
Cotton	••••	•	••••	•	••••	••	•	One of the cheaper fibres, strong, cool, creases easily	Uses a lot of water in production Is reusable, can be recycled
Wool	••	••••	•••••	••••	••	•••••	•••	Soft, hard-wearing, low-crease.	A renewable resource Can be recycled Virgin fibres can be mixed with recycled Is biodegradable
Silk	••••	••••	•••••	•••	••••	••••	•••	Expensive, smooth, drapes well, cool	A renewable resource
Linen	••••	•	••••	•	••••	•	•	Stronger when wet, cool, creases easily	A renewable resource

△ **Table 4.2** Fibre properties. Other performance benefits to consider are wearability, comfort, launderability, safety, handle (feel), aesthetics and antibacterial properties. Key • = poor, •• = standard, ••• = good, •••• = very good, ••••• = excellent. When choosing fabrics for products, the characteristics of the fibre and the fabric composition have to be considered together

Fibre	Strength	Elasticity	Absorbency	Crease resistance	Durability	Warmth	Flammability	General fibre/fabric description	Environmental and sustainable issues
Regenerated fibres									
Viscose	••	•	•••••	••	••	••	••	Cheap, lightweight, not very strong	Pulp from renewable resources, but not chemicals used in production
Acetate	•	••	••	••	•	••	••	Cheap, lightweight	A non-renewable resource
Rayon	•••	•	••••	•••	••	•	•	Lightweight	Pulp from renewable resources, but not chemicals used in production
Synthetic fibres									
Polyester	••••	••••	•	••••	••••	••	••	Dries quickly, strong, crease-resistant	Not from a renewable resource Certain PET can be recycled

△ **Table 4.2** Fibre properties. Other performance benefits to consider are wearability, comfort, launderability, safety, handle (feel), aesthetics and antibacterial properties. Key • = poor, •• = standard, ••• = good, •••• = very good, ••••• = excellent.
When choosing fabrics for products, the characteristics of the fibre and the fabric composition have to be considered together. *Cont.*

Fibre	Strength	Elasticity	Absorbency	Crease resistance	Durability	Warmth	Flammability	General fibre/fabric description	Environmental and sustainable issues
Synthetic fibres									
Nylon	••••	••••	•	••••	••••	••	••	Strong, crease resistant	From a non-renewable resource
Acrylic	•••	••••	•	•••	•••	••••	•	Warm, absorbent	From a non-renewable resource
Elastane (elastomeric)	•••	•••••	•	•••••	••••	••	•	Good extension, high elasticity, high durability	The raw material is from a renewable resource. However, synthetic elastane, is from a non-renewable resource

△ **Table 4.2** Fibre properties. Other performance benefits to consider are wearability, comfort, launderability, safety, handle (feel), aesthetics and antibacterial properties. Key • = poor, •• = standard, ••• = good, •••• = very good, ••••• = excellent. When choosing fabrics for products, the characteristics of the fibre and the fabric composition have to be considered together.

continued

Summary

- Fibres can be divided into three categories: natural, synthetic and regenerated.
- Fibres are processed before being twisted and made into yarns.
- Fibres all have particular characteristics, properties and aesthetic qualities.
- They can be mixed or blended together to enhance their properties and reduce costs.
- New fibres are being developed that are more environmentally friendly and need less processing.

Exam tips

- Learn the key fibre names.
- Understand the key properties of each fibre type.
- Know the difference between mixed and blended fibres.
- Understand why different fibres are used for different textile products.
- Understand why new fibres that are environmentally friendly are being developed.

Exam practice questions

1. From where do the following fibres originate?
   (a) wool
   (b) nylon
   (c) viscose **[6 marks]**
2. Identify six key properties of wool fibres. **[3 marks]**
3. Briefly explain how the following fibres are processed to make yarns:
   (a) raw wool
   (b) nylon
   (c) viscose. **[6 marks]**
4. Why are nylon fibres often blended with wool fibres? **[2 marks]**
5. Name three textile products that could be made using a wool/nylon blend. **[2 marks]**

Stretch yourself

You have been asked to suggest a range of garments that would be suitable for a person going on a hike.

1. Suggest suitable fibres that would be used for outwear.

2. Suggest suitable fibres for a long-sleeved top that needs to keep the wearer warm, yet not make them feel clammy or sweaty. Give reasons for your choice.

3. Design your hiker's walking garments, giving reasons for your choice of fibres and clothes. **[15 marks]**

Activities

1. Examine your school uniform. What fibre is each piece of your uniform made from? Suggest three reasons for the choice of fibre.
2. Choose five items of your favourite clothing and identify the fibres that each item is made from. Suggest three reasons for the choice of fibre. Could alternative fibres be used? Explain your answer.
3. Choose a new fibre and create a presentation about its ecological impact on textiles and clothing. **[15 marks]**

Resources

British Wool Marketing Board: www.britishwool.org.uk

Cotton Incorporated: www.cottoninc.com

Tencel: www.tencel.at

Lyocell: www.fibersource.com and click on the link to Lyocell

Ingeo: www.natureworksllc.com

Tactel: www.tactel.com

4.2 Properties and characteristics 2

Learning objectives

By the end of this section, you should have a key understanding of:

- woven fabrics (plain, twill, satin)
- knitted fabrics (warp, weft)
- non-woven fabrics
- microfibres
- modern and smart materials
- technological advances (encapsulation, laminated)
- wider uses of textiles in society
- methods of construction.

Key points

- Analytical skills
- Communication skills
- Innovative ideas
- Creative ideas
- Linking technology and design
- Values

Introduction

Fabrics are all around us, and are used not only for clothing but also for other diverse products, from building to extreme sports, from geo-textiles for roads to clothing for astronauts. It is essential for a designer to understand how fabrics are created and the process for developing fabrics from fibres and yarns to finished fabrics. Fabrics are also given finishes to enable them to meet demanding end uses, as well as laundering and cleaning processes.

Weaving

Weaving as a process of fabric production has a long history. The advent of the Industrial Revolution in the mid-1700s brought new powered methods of weaving fabrics. This enabled manufacturers to produce fabrics on an industrial scale. Today, weaving can be done on small or large, industrial scales.

How are woven fabrics made?

Weaving is a method of making fabric on a piece of equipment called a weaving loom. The fabric is constructed by interlacing two yarns at right angles to each other. The yarns that go horizontally in direction across the loom are called **weft yarns** and the threads that lie in a vertical direction in the loom are called **warp yarns**.

The yarns that overlap at each side of the loom creating a neatened edge are called the **selvedge**. A diagonal direction across the fabric is known as the **bias**. The vertical length of the fabric is called the **straight grain**.

Key terms

Warp – the yarns that lie in a vertical direction in the loom.

Warp knitting – the process of constructing fabric, using a series of loops formed along the fabric.

Weft – the yarns that go across a woven fabric wicking the ability of the fibre to transfer moisture along its surface.

Weft knitting – the process of constructing knitted fabrics using a series of interlacing loops that run the length of the fabric.

Woven fabrics – constructed by weaving weft yarns in and out of warp yarns placed on a loom.

The type of loom used will depend on what type of fabric is being made. A shuttle loom may be used for creating a simple plain weave, whereas

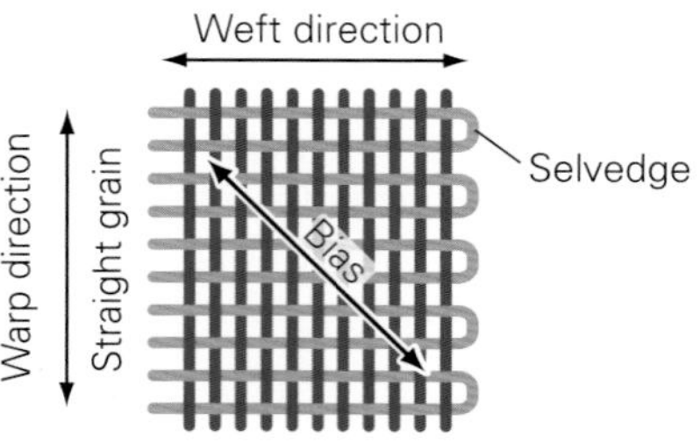

△ **Figure 4.15** Woven fabric construction

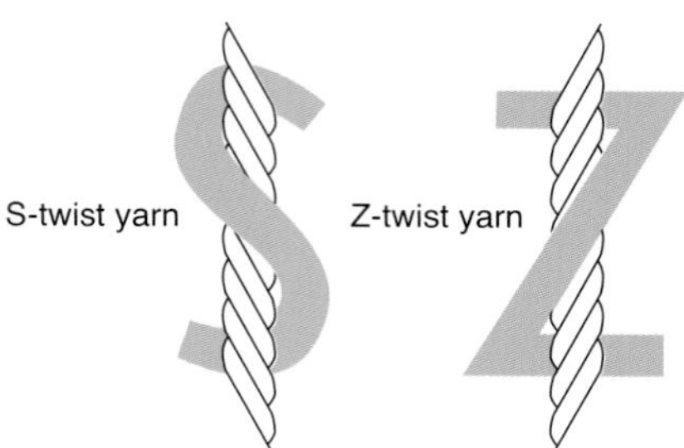

△ **Figure 4.16** 'S' twist and 'Z' twist

a Jacquard loom is used to create heavier, complex-patterned fabrics.

From fibre to weave

Woven fabrics are made in the following way:

- Fibres are twisted and spun to the required count (thickness). This is measured and recorded as tex or decitex.
- The fibres are then spun into yarn. This can be given an 'S' or 'Z' twist. When the yarn is woven, the direction of the twist gives different optical effects and reactions to light.
- The yarn is then wound onto large bobbins or cones to be used for weaving the weft threads. The warp threads are placed on a huge beam. The addition of a sizing (starch solution) makes the yarns smoother and stronger.
- Drawing is the process by which the yarn is drawn through the heddles using the technical (lifting) plan.
- The fabric can now be woven, as the weft yarn is placed in its shuttle or holder, ready for the weaving to begin.

Key term

S-twist – the direction of twist (S) added to a yarn during spinning.

Z-twist – the direction of twist (Z) added to a yarn during spinning.

Types of weaving

The main types of woven fabrics are outlined in Table 4.3.

Type of weave	Key characteristics	What does it look like?
Plain weave	The simplest to construct and gives the tightest method of weaving fabrics. Fabrics such as muslin, taffeta and voile are all plain-weave fabrics. It looks the same on both sides and is the cheapest weave to produce.	△ **Figure 4.17**
Twill weave	The twill weave is easily recognisable by its diagonal stripe. The fabrics produced using this method are soft and durable. Fabrics made using this method are denim, tweed and gabardine.	△ **Figure 4.18**

△ **Table 4.3** Main types of weaving

Cont.

Type of weave	Key characteristics	What does it look like?
Jacquard	This is the name given to a fabric that is created on a special loom. It is created by the lifting of each of the individual warp threads to create complex patterns. The fabric was first created by the Frenchman J.M. Jacquard in the eighteenth century. Fabrics created using this method are used for furnishings and formal wear. The fabrics are heavy and hard-wearing.	△ **Figure 4.19**
Pile weaves	Velvet is an example of a pile weave. It is created by weaving fibres together over rods or wires, so they interlock. When the weaving is finished, the rods are removed, then the fabric is run through the centre of the woven fabric, splitting the fabric in half to reveal the raised velvet finish. A variation of this process is the manufacture of corduroy fabrics. These are recognised by the ridges that run horizontally down the fabric. The ridges are known as wales; the more wales, the finer the corduroy. The fabrics made using this method tend to be hard-wearing and have a surface that can absorb moisture. Originally corduroy fabrics were made from cotton fibre. Other cord fabrics are Bedford cord, which has finer or pin-cord ridges and can be made from cotton or wool.	Warp section Tufts Ground warp △ **Figure 4.20**

△ **Table 4.3** Main types of weaving

Cont.

Type of weave	Key characteristics	What does it look like?
Satin or sateen weaves	These weaves are created by a uniform layout of either the warp or the weft yarns. This layout of the yarns gives the finished fabric a shiny finish and a soft handle (feel), as well as good drape properties. A key disadvantage, however, is that the fabric snags easily due to the long warp or weft thread, which lies on the surface of the fabric. Examples of fabrics produced from these weaves are satin, atlas and sateen. Satin fabrics have longer warp threads on the right side (face of fabric). Sateen fabrics have longer weft threads on the right side (face of fabric).	△ **Figure 4.21**

△ **Table 4.3** Main types of weaving *continued*

Key terms

Twill weave – a weave pattern using interlacing yarns that have a diagonal pattern (e.g. denim).

Jacquard – a decorative fabric woven on a Jacquard loom. Because it is so complex, it is normally woven using a computer system.

Satin weave – a woven fabric with an even surface known for its lustre. However, the long floating yarns on the surface mean it is easy to snag. It is therefore only suitable for products such as evening dresses and fine lingerie.

Pile – extra yarns woven into fabric and left as loops or cut to form a raised surface.

Velvet – a warp file woven fabric that has a soft, tactile surface. It can be made from silk or polyester.

Corduroy – a cut weft pile fabric, which is characterised with cords or ribs running vertically down the warp.

The main weaves already mentioned are the ones that you need to remember. Other woven fabrics that you may use in your controlled assessment (design and make practice) or see on textiles or fashion products that you own are as follows:

- **Honeycomb weave** – these are sometimes called waffle fabrics. It is a heavy-textured fabric, which is created by shortening and lengthening the warp and weft threads, and is used for clothing such as jackets and also for furnishings.
- **Corduroy** – this weave is produced where the warp threads are thicker than the weft, leaving a textured surface. It is used for trousers and jackets.
- **Tartan** – based on the twill weave, tartan is a Scottish-based fabric. It is created by overlaying parts of the warp and weft threads to create a coloured, checked pattern.

Weaving and other cultures

Ikat weaving

This type of weaving can be easily identified due to the variegated colours that are applied to the warp and weft yarns. Before weaving begins, colour is printed onto the warp yarns using either a resist or a tie-dye method. In single Ikat fabrics, only the warp is printed; in double Ikat fabrics, the warp and the weft are printed. The most complex and precise types of Ikat are Oshima and Kasuri from Japan. Ikat weaving is thought to have originated in Far East Asia, in countries such as Malaysia, but evidence of Ikat weaving can be found in Central and South America.

Properties of woven fabrics

Woven fabrics have the following properties and characteristics:

- They are firm.
- They are stable.
- They are dense (closely woven or thick).
- They are low-stretch.
- If cut, the edges will fray.
- The fabric is strongest along the grain of the fabric (warp yarns). The warp yarns are also stronger than the weft yarns as they come under more load and strain.
- They are available in different weights.
- They can be used for a variety of purposes, from clothing to industrial uses.
- They can be made using a range of fibres, from natural to new smart materials.
- They can be developed in a variety of strengths, depending on end use.
- Different types of yarns or fibres can be used in the warp or weft threads depending on the end use.

How are woven fabrics used?

Woven fabrics have a number of end uses, such as clothing, furnishings, sailcloth, architecture and laminated fabrics.

Impact of CAD/CAM and new technologies in weaving

In both the design and the manufacturing of the cloth, CAD and CAM have had an impact on the way in which woven fabrics are produced. When designing woven fabrics, designers can use CAD software to do the following:

- Create a weave simulation to check a design for colour. This can be printed onto paper or card or digitally printed onto fabric.
- Create weave from scratch using a specialised weaving program – that is, scan in a design and then transform the design from a picture to a woven fabric. A specific part of the programme can then be used to create the weaving plan and point chart, and lifting plan, as this will show the technical details for weaving.
- The finished fabric can be 'virtually' woven, to ensure that the design works, before it is transferred to the loom.
- The designer can create different colourways for fabrics, which can be printed onto paper.
- At the loom, the designs or colourways can be changed using the computer keyboard as the weaving takes place.
- Setting up a loom for weaving can be time-consuming and expensive. CAD/CAM offers the designer the opportunity to create weaves on a small scale and show clients virtual possibilities.

Key term

CAD/CAM systems – computer-aided design and computer-aided manufacture. Computer-aided designs are designs created using a computer. Computer-aided manufacture is where computers are used in the manufacturing process.

Weaving summary

- Woven fabrics are created using two interlacing threads, running horizontally and vertically down the length of the fabric.
- More complex fabrics can be created using weaving methods such as Jacquard.
- The computer makes the design of woven fabrics easier and quicker, at both the design and the manufacturing stages.

Exam practice questions

1. What are the names for the horizontal and vertical threads used on a loom to create woven fabrics? **[2 marks]**
2. Name three woven fabrics and draw their woven structure. **[6 marks]**
3. Why is twist added to a yarn, and what are the advantages of this once the fabric is woven? **[4 marks]**
4. What is the difference between a satin and a sateen weave? What are they key properties of these types of fabrics? **[4 marks]**

Activity

You have been asked to create a new range of woven fabrics for a high-end fashion chain, to be showcased inside their coats and on their bags. Using a range of CAD skills and also historical research, create a presentation board highlighting the new fashion range. Present your findings in a Microsoft® PowerPoint® presentation. **[15 marks]**

Knitting

What is knitting?

Knitting is an age-old activity that has been undertaken by men and women. Although knitted fragments have been found that date to around 250BC, knitting in Europe became well known around 1000AD.

Knitted fabrics are made up of a range of interlocking loops. The loops run up the length (vertical) of the fabric and hold the fabric together; if any of the loops are broken, the fabric will come apart or ladder. The loops or columns of stitches running the vertical length of the fabric are called the **wales**; the rows of stitches running horizontally across the width of the fabric are called **courses** or **rows**. Knitted fabrics can be created by hand-knitting or by machine knitting.

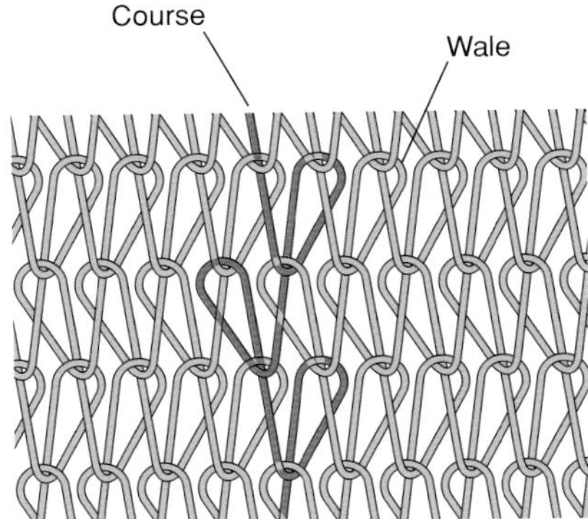

△ **Figure 4.22** Warp-knitted fabric

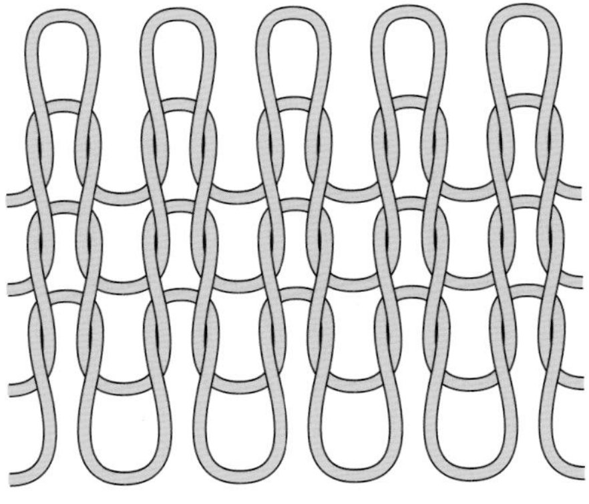

△ **Figure 4.23** Weft-knitted fabric

Types of knitted fabric

After yarns are spun and twisted, they can be used on knitting machines to make fabric. There are three types of knitted fabrics:

1. **Warp knit**: this is done using a knitting machine. The yarn is fed to each individual needle and the fabric is created by making interlocking loops that all travel in the same direction along the length of the fabric. The machines used for warp knitting are called Raschel machines.
2. **Weft knit**: the rows of knitting in weft-knitted fabric interlock with each other during the knitting process. In weft knitting, the loops that run horizontally are called courses, and the threads that run vertically down the knitted fabrics are called wales. Weft-knitted fabrics can be created on flatbed machines or circular knitting machines. Circular knitting machines can be small or large, depending on the product being knitted. The fabrics are knitted in a tube, which can be slit to give a wider fabric.
3. **Hand knitting**: this is a manual form of weft knitting, usually using two needles, and is used to make garments, socks and scarves.

The key features of warp knitting are as follows:

- The loop yarns are fed in the direction of the fabric.
- Hard to unravel, so less likely to ladder.
- Faster to produce than weft knitting.
- Works best with long filament fibres than short fibres.
- Like all knitted fabrics, it has elasticity, but is able to keep its shape.
- The right and wrong sides of the fabric look very similar.

The key features of weft knitting are as follows:

- It unravels easily.
- It ladders if the fabric is cut or pulled.
- It has high elasticity and stretch.
- It loses its shape very easily.
- It is easy to tell which is the wrong side and the right side.

There are several types of weft-knitted fabrics for clothing. Knitted fabrics for other uses can also incorporate these techniques.

Types of weft-knitted fabrics include:

- single jersey – used for t-shirts, sweaters
- rib fabric – underwear and socks
- purl fabric – baby romper suits, cardigans
- interlock – sportswear, leisurewear
- Jacquard – fashion jumpers and waistcoats
- fake fur – fur coats, winter clothes, trimmings, shoes
- pique – sport shirts and leisurewear
- terry or plush – terry fabrics are knitted with loops on the surface of the fabric and are used for towels, bedding. Plush fabrics are created the same way as knitted terry fabrics, except the knitted loops are then cut to produce a velvet-like surface. Used for products such as tracksuits and sweatshirts.

There are four main types of warp-knitted fabrics:

- lock-knit, also known as terry – used for furnishing fabrics, bed sheets, babywear
- warp knit velour – used for beachwear, leisurewear and sportswear
- Raschel net – used mainly for bridalwear fabrics
- Raschel lace – used for trimmings, underwear, bridalwear.

Other uses of knitted fabrics include:

- tyres of cars
- vascular veins (for heart surgery)
- car seat coverings
- furnishing fabrics
- hoodies
- geotextiles
- architecture.

Key terms

Geotextiles – textile products that are used in the ground.

Elasticity – to retain shape after being stretched.

Key properties of knitted fabrics

Knitted fabrics have the following properties and characteristics:

- They can be used for a variety of products, such as clothing and furnishings.
- They can be stretched.
- They have good elasticity.
- They are mouldable.
- They can be laminated with other materials.
- They can also be used in technical textiles.

Creating knitted products

Knitted products are created in one of four ways:

1. They are knitted and shaped on a knitting machine and then sewn together. This is called fully fashioned knitting. Where only part of the garment panel is shaped, this is called partly fashioned knitting.
2. Knitted lengths of fabric are laid on a cutting table and the pattern pieces are cut out. The knitted pieces created using this process are called piece goods.
3. They are created using seamless integrated knitting – garments or products are knitted totally on the machine to create one integrated piece. These all-in-one garments need little or no finishing.
4. Virtual knitting is now a supported technology. It enables the technician or designer to check that the product will knit correctly before proceeding with an order. A video simulation of the knitting process can be viewed to check both design and technical details.

Knitting and new technologies

The use of the computer in the design-and-make process has become very important. The designer is able to design using simulated stitches on the computer screen.

Virtual 3D models of the product can be knitted via a simulation on screen and any faults can be rectified on screen and adapted.

With the use of computer-controlled machines, the knitter or technician is able to make changes and adaptations to the knitted product, as needed, via a computer keyboard. The designer can also design knitted fabrics on screen.

Knitting is used today for products other than clothing (e.g. medical products). In the medical industry, finely knitted fabrics are used to create knitted heart tube valves, which can be implanted into the body.

Further advances in knitting technology mean that, through the use of seamless integrated knitting, garments can be knitted 'whole', without seams, used especially for ski wear.

Fashion designer Issey Miyake designed the A-POC knitwear range in response to the growing interest in sustainable and eco designs. The A-POC range was developed so the individual could create their own knitted garment from the minimum amount of fabric.

Interior designer Karina Thomas of Salt, a UK-based textile design company, is showing what can be done by creating blinds made from knitted fabric and modern materials.

Knitting fashion and technologies

Knitting as a process has incorporated a range of technologies and has been a part of our culture for more than 400 years.

The invention of the powered stocking knitting machine in 1589 by William Lee gave knitting a new status, taking it from the home to mass industry.

Knitting became very popular during the First and Second World Wars, when women were encouraged to knit hats and gloves for soldiers. In the 1920s, designers such as Chanel made the knitted jersey very popular, and, by the late 1930s, Pringle of Scotland had started manufacturing jumpers.

The 'sweater' became a real fashion item in the 1940s and 1950s, and specialised knitting such as Fair Isle and Arran became popular forms of knitting. The Argyle jumpers favoured by golfers also became very popular.

In the 1960s, the 'skinny rib' jumper was the fashionable item of clothing, and, in the 1970s, haute couture knitwear designer Missoni created 'funky' knitted clothing.

Benetton became the leading knitting manufacturer of the 1980s and established itself as a company that specialised in creating plain, bright-coloured jumpers. Hand-knitting designer Kaffe Fassett is renowned for her colourful interpretations of flowers and patterns in hand knitwear.

In the early 1990s, designers such as Azzedine Alaia specialised in stretch-knit fabrics that were figure-hugging. In the late 1990s, companies such as Fake London, headed by designer Desiree Mejers, specialised in creating high-end fashion knitwear recycled from vintage cashmere sweaters. Drawing our attention to the materials that we dispose of, they developed unique products from waste textiles materials.

Today, modern designers such as Nora Fok create artwork and jewellery made from knitted monofilament yarn.

Since 2005, knitting as a pastime has become more popular, with the rise of knitting clubs in unusual places.

△ **Figure 4.24** Knitted jumper

Knitting summary

- Knitted fabrics can be created by machine or by hand.
- They have elastic properties and are used for a wide range of garments and textile products.
- Today's knitted fabrics can be created and seen in 'virtual mode'.

Exam practice questions

1. Name three advantages and three disadvantages of knitted fabric. **[3 marks]**
2. Name four different types of knitted fabrics. **[4 marks]**
3. Name three different products that can be knitted. **[3 marks]**

Activities

1. Using information in this chapter, choose one method of knitting and describe how it is done.
2. Create a mood board, showing your chosen method of knitting as a fashion product for young teenagers. **[15 marks]**

Non-woven fabrics

Non-woven or bonded fabrics are made only with fibres. One of the disadvantages of non-woven fabrics is that they have little strength. To make them usable, production methods have been developed to strengthen non-wovens.

The two methods of making non-woven fabrics are as follows:

1. Felting – felted fabrics can be produced using mechanical methods – for example, needle felt or using high-pressure water jets.

2. Bonded fabrics – glue is applied in layers between the fibres using melting, stitching or a combination of methods. Once the glue is dry, the fabrics can be used for anything.

Non-woven fabrics can be divided into the following categories:

- Felts
  - Wool felt
  - Needle felt
- Bonded webs
  - Dry-laid
  - Wet-laid
  - Direct-spun

Key terms

Non-woven – a fabric made up of layers of fibres, which are strengthened by being bonded together using heat or adhesive, or by mechanical or chemical means.

Bonded – the term given to fabrics that have been joined using heat or glue.

Needle felt – non-woven fabric made by passing barbed needles through a web of fibres.

Wool felt – woollen fibre that has been matted together (using heat, water or steam) to form felt fabric.

Production methods for non-woven fabrics

Mechanical felts

A wool felt is created by layering fibres on top of each other. The fibres are then submerged into a mixture of chemicals and heated water. This is combined with beating (mechanical action) and pressure to make the felt fabric.

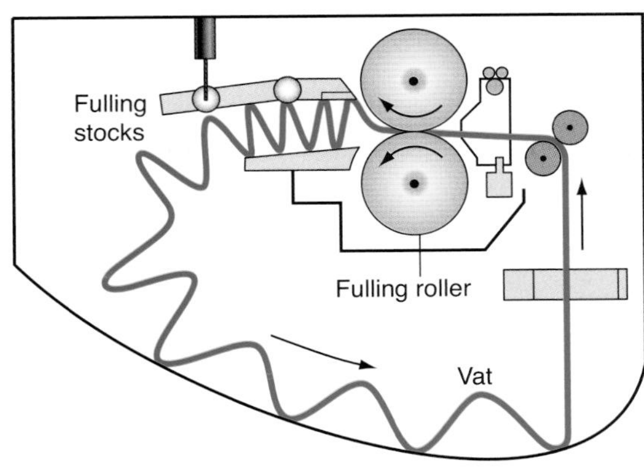

△ **Figure 4.25** Mechanical felting process

Needle felts

Needle felts are created by layering fibres. Once several layers of fibres have been created, the fibre layer is passed through a needle-felting machine. Felt is created using barbed needles that punch in and out of the layered felt, causing the fibres to join together to form the felt. It is a very quick process.

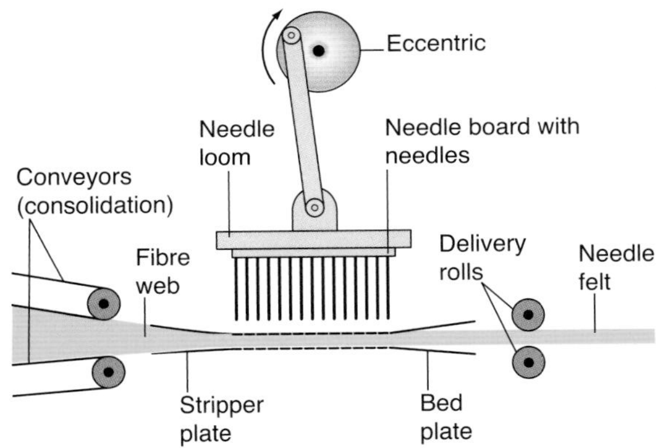

△ **Figure 4.26** Needle-felting process

Bonded webs

There are three methods of constructing bonded web fabrics:

- dry-laid
- wet-laid
- direct-spun.

In the dry-laid method, a web of fibres is laid onto a drum and air is pulled through the drum, which holds the fibres together.

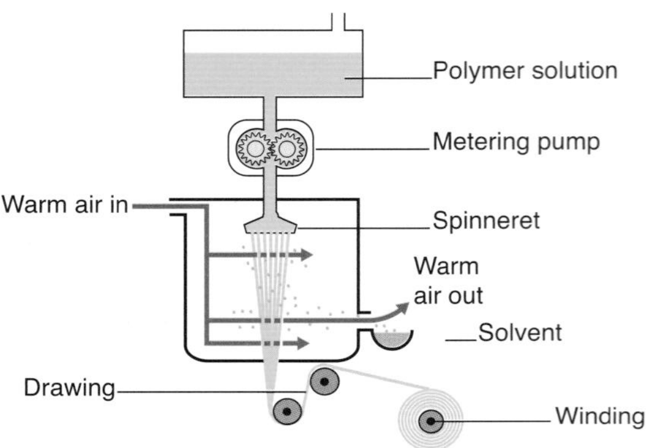

△ **Figure 4.27** Dry-laid method

The wet-laid method uses the same process as paper-making. The fibres are mixed with a liquid, which is then filtered through a giant sieve and laid flat to dry.

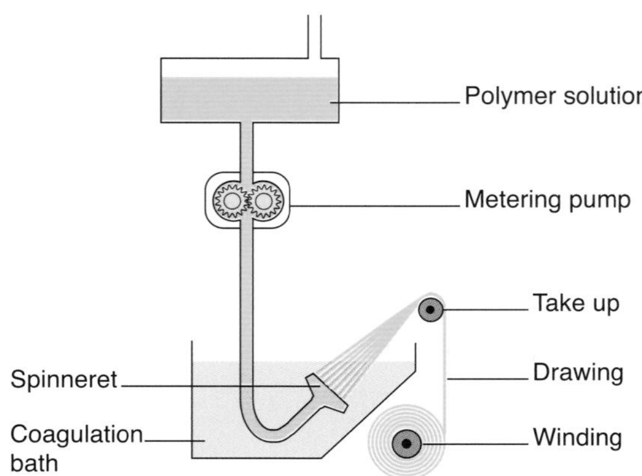

△ **Figure 4.28** Wet-laid method

In the direct-spun method, the fibres are spun directly onto a conveyor belt in either a random or an oriented way (criss-crossing over each other). A glue is then applied to each layer to hold it together.

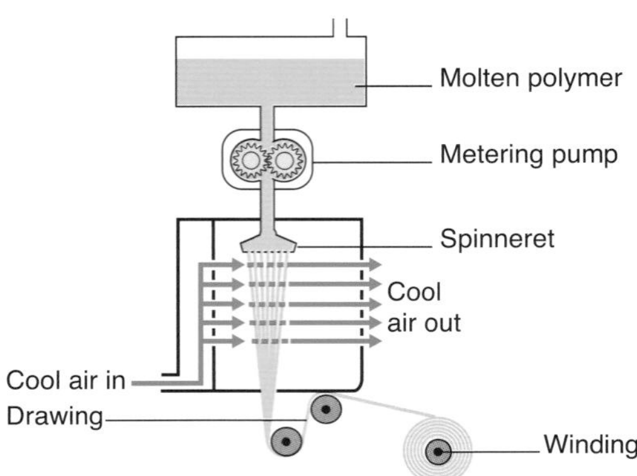

△ **Figure 4.29** Direct spun method

Key issues related to non-wovens

All bonded fibres have low strength. Strength is added using the following methods:

1. Adhesive (glue) is added to the fibre web by either spraying or dipping. The web is then pressed.
2. Solvents are used to soften the fibres. This releases a sticky substance, which glues the fibres together where they touch.
3. Webs made of synthetic fibres are softened using heat, then pressed together, either all as one fabric or at certain points along the fabric.
4. A form of stitching can be used to hold the fibres in place. Fabrics with added stitching are called stitch-bonded fabrics.
5. Using modern technology, new non-wovens and also knitted interfacings can now be produced.

Key properties of non-woven fibres

Felts are:

- good insulators
- strong.

Bonded webs are:

- breathable
- stable
- crease-resistant
- easy to work with.

In addition, knitted bonded fibres stretch with the garment/product.

Use of non-woven fibres

Felts are used in hats, furnishings, billiard cloths and roller coverings. Needle felts are used in floor coverings, wadding, mattress covers and filters.

Bonded web fabrics are used as follows:

- Fusible interlinings/interfacings are used for cleaning cloths (e.g. Vilene® and J-Cloths®) and car seat coverings.
- Knitted interfacings are used with knitted garments so that the fabric is more flexible.

Stabiliser fabrics and interfacings are key fabrics used in the construction of a range of garments and textile products.

Key term

Stabilisers – fabrics that can be added as backings to add additional support to certain areas of garments, or used to support areas of products that are embroidered.

The types of stabilisers/interfacings are:

- non-woven
- woven
- knitted
- iron-on – an interfacing that is printed with glue that reacts to heat at temperatures between 120 and 180 degrees; when applied to fabric with heat, it bonds/fuses to the fabric, making it more stable
- wadding – used in quilting
- paper-backed fusible (such as Bondaweb)
- water-soluble – dissolve by washing in either hot or cold water
- heat-soluble – these are dissolvable using dry heat (e.g. irons)
- self-adhesive stabilisers – these have a sticky backing that can be peeled away; used as a temporary stabiliser for machine embroidery; can also be used to create temporary stencils for stencil printing.

During your practical work, you may use interfacing or stabilisers in the following ways:

- stabilisers for embroidery work
- soluble stabilisers where you can embroider then wash/iron away the stabiliser, leaving a lacy fabric
- interfacing put into garments such as collars on shirts to help keep the shape of the garment
- Bondaweb when developing an appliqué design.

Non-woven fabrics summary

- Non-woven fabrics are made using only fibres.
- They can be strengthened using a range of mechanical and non-mechanical means.
- They are used for a variety of products to add strength or structure.

Exam practice questions

1. What are the two types of non-woven fabrics? **[2 marks]**
2. Name four examples of non-woven fabrics that are all around us. **[2 marks]**
3. Where would you expect to use stabilisers or interfacings in the work that you do in textiles? **[6 marks]**

Activity

Design an outfit for the future that combines both technical and smart materials. Include design sketches with annotation. Your finished outfit should have the following information:

(a) Age group the outfit is aimed at
(b) Whether it is for a boy or girl
(c) End use
(d) Type of technical materials used
(e) Type of smart materials included

[15 marks]

Microfibres

Microfibres are tiny fibres that are woven densely together – they prevent moisture from penetrating but still allow the skin to breathe when worn, so you do not become cold.

Key term

Microfibres – very thin, hair-like synthetic fibres; a type of modern fibre.

Microfibres have the following key properties, making them suitable for a wide range of products:

- lightweight
- very strong
- water-repellent
- insulating
- excellent handle (touch)
- breathable
- excellent drape
- once woven or knitted, surface textures can be added, such as brushing or velvet effects
- very absorbent.

Examples of products that can be made using microfibres include:

- underwear – used for underwear because of their absorbency, breathability, softness and lightness
- socks and tights (hosiery) – when used for these products, they give added lustre and softness, and produce lightweight products
- sportswear – because they are lighter than cotton, microfibres provide protection from the weather, but are also lightweight, not bulky and absorb moisture very well
- outdoor wear (e.g. rainwear) – microfibres are water-repellent and breathable, both of which help keep body temperature constant.

There is a range of microfibre products on the market, such as Meryl® Micro, which is used for active sportswear, and Tactel® Micro, which is used for underwear and sportswear.

Knowledge link

You can see more information on microfibres on pages 84–85.

Technical textiles and materials

Laminated fabrics

Laminated fabrics are manufactured fabrics where two or more woven or knitted fabrics are combined using either a liquid resin rubber or foam-based fabrics. A resin or glue is used to hold them together – this is called a laminated membrane.

This laminated membrane is then applied to various products, such as clothes, shoes and sportswear. Additional properties can be added to these laminated fabrics, such as a waterproof finish and temperature control.

The most well-known laminated fabrics are Gore-Tex® and Sympatex®.

Laminated fabrics are sometimes referred to as technical fabrics. Technical fabrics can be used in conjunction with smart materials to give added functionality to products.

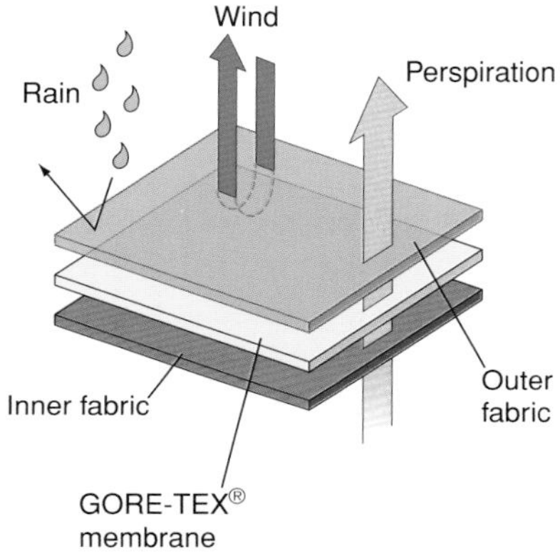

△ **Figure 4.30** How a laminated fabric works

Encapsulated fibres/fabrics

Micro-encapsulation is the process of adding nano-sized particles to fibres or fabrics. These nano-sized particles are stored in the fibre structure. They are activated when the fibre or fabric is rubbed or moves against the body. This action breaks the tiny capsules and releases the capsules' contents. The types of products or agents being added to fibres are:

- moisturising agents – these can help hydrate the skin
- antibacterial agents – these can release odour-reducing particles
- medicinal agents – for example, medicines or insect repellents.

The limitations of the technology mean that for some products the effect of the micro-encapsulation will end after a number of washes.

However, consumers in the future will be able to 'reload' or add more finishes to the product, using a washing technique, foam or spray.

This technology is being applied to products such as clothing, luggage and upholstery.

Geotextiles

Geotextile products are used in road and building construction.

Geotextiles for the soil are available in different types of materials. In areas where the ground is waterlogged or has a high amount of water seepage, fabrics like this are used. They serve two purposes: first, they keep the topsoil in place and limit soil erosion, and second, they only allow water through the fabric one way.

Geotextiles used in road building help maintain the stability of the road – for example, geotextiles can be used in a layer of the road structure and mimic movement in the road surface, which will prevent the top layer from cracking.

Geotextiles are also used in building and construction in such areas as insulation and cladding. They are also used widely in architecture on roofs – for example, the Millennium Dome (O2) and Hong Kong airport.

△ **Figure 4.31** Different uses for geotextiles

Knowledge link

For more information on technical textiles, see pages 140–146.

Fibres	Properties
Acrylic combined with phase-change materials	Helps to maintain body temperature, absorbs body heat, and then releases it when needed
Merino wool and Thermolite® or Coolmax®	A lightweight, warm fabric that can be machine-washed
Cocona	Polyester fibres are embedded with carbon from coconut shells. Fabrics made from this fibre can aid evaporation and control body odour
Repreve	A fabric that is made from 100 per cent post-consumer recycled material (PET)
TYR	This fabric is used in swimwear for competitive swimming and is made from two lightweight fabrics: one is made from 70 per cent nylon and the other from 30 per cent elastane, which can be stretched in two directions. The fabric is coated with Teflon® on one side to repel water and with polyurethane on the other for buoyancy. The swimwear is made a size smaller than the user would normally wear. This has the effect of compressing the wearer's body and reducing drag when swimming, allowing them to swim faster.

△ **Table 4.4** New fibres and fabrics that combine technical features, modern technologies and natural fibre properties

Key terms

Encapsulation – the process of adding nano-sized particles to fibres or fabrics.

Laminated/laminating – joining two or more fabrics together using adhesive.

Smart fabrics/smart materials – materials that can sense, read and adjust themselves to changes in the environment.

Smart materials and smart textiles

Smart textiles can be divided into the following areas:

- wearable technology – utilising conductive threads and materials
- power-assisted textiles – combined with power sources such as solar panels
- medical textiles – utilising wearable technology, and flexible textiles and micro-encapsulation
- communication textiles – textiles incorporating GPS and other communications technology
- soft interfaces – the development of textiles with other soft technologies, such as thermochromic paints and dyes.

Knowledge link

For more information on smart materials and textiles, see pages 140–43.

Summary

- There are now ranges of fibres and fabrics on the market that fulfil a range of needs for different end users.
- Today's fabrics are given special finishes to enable them to be used for a range of activities or conditions.
- Technical textiles is one of the fastest-growing areas of development in the textiles industry.
- Textiles products can now be used in buildings and road construction.
- Smart materials can be combined with technical textiles to give users additional benefits.

4.3 Product maintenance, suitability and fitness for purpose

Learning objectives

By the end of this section, you should have a key understanding of:

- product maintenance and design for the maintenance needs of a product
- suitability and fitness for purpose of products
- textile labelling
- product properties.

Key points

- Analytical skills
- Communication skills
- Innovative ideas
- Creative ideas
- Linking technology and design
- Values

Introduction

Before any product can be sold, it needs to meet key safety requirements for the end user. Designers, manufacturers and testing companies, as well as consumer legislation, ensure that all the textile products that we use meet exacting standards.

Design for maintenance needs of product

All textiles products need care and attention. Once they start being used, they will need constant cleaning and repairs where necessary.

The need to maintain a textile or fashion product starts in the design specification. As soon as the types of fabrics to be used for the garments are confirmed, the fabrics will be checked for their suitability. Companies will test all aspects of a textile or fashion product before they are placed on the market.

Key terms

Maintenance – the process of looking after a textile product during its lifespan – for example, laundering and repairing.

Testing – ensuring that standards are met.

It is essential that a product is designed for its end use. In order to understand in what conditions the product might be used, tests may be carried out by the intended user or in the laboratory. The design, production and testing teams will work together to ensure that the fabric or product that is being produced is suitable for its end use.

Note: when developing your product, you will need to refer back to your product specification and also to client feedback to identify the key maintenance issues related to your product.

Textile labelling

All textiles products must be clearly labelled with the correct aftercare processes. This is usually displayed on a care label. In the UK, it is a legal requirement that all garments or textiles and fashion products must be clearly labelled.

What is on the label?

Labelling is controlled by UK regulations, EU regulations and international regulations. Table 4.5 outlines where labels may be found on a textiles product.

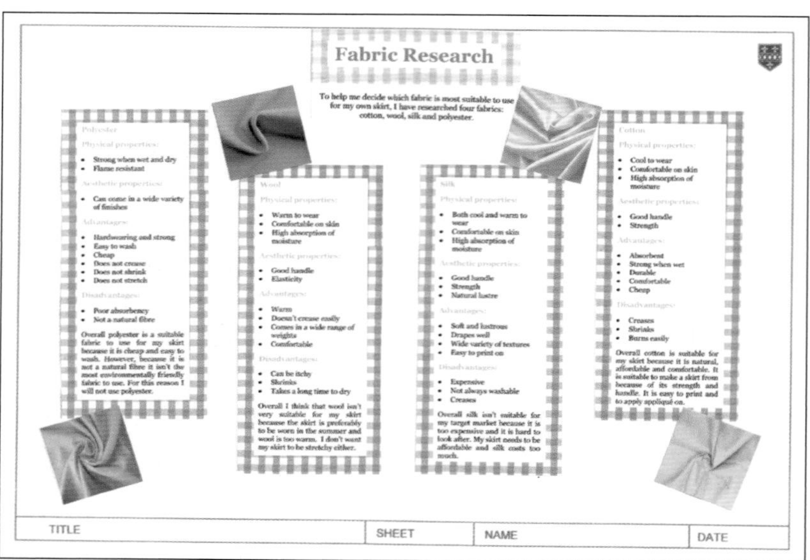

△ **Figure 4.32** Student page to show understanding of the use of certain/suitable fabrics

Type of label	Where is it found?
Permanent label	This is stitched into the garment on the neckline, side seam or waistband.
Gummed label	This is usually found on the outside of a product or on packaging.
Swing ticket	This is usually attached to the product.
Pure fibre label	100 per cent cotton or 100 per cent wool products can show special symbols on their labels that show they are pure fibres.

△ **Table 4.5** Different types of labels

Table 4.6 shows what information labels can show.

Type of label	What does the label look like?
Quality or safety	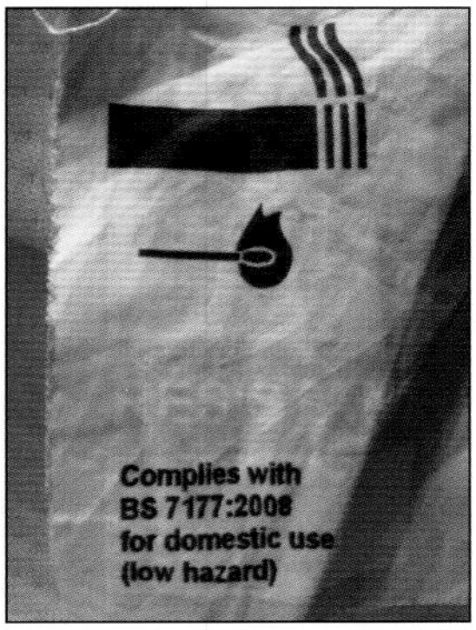 △ **Figure 4.33**
Advice	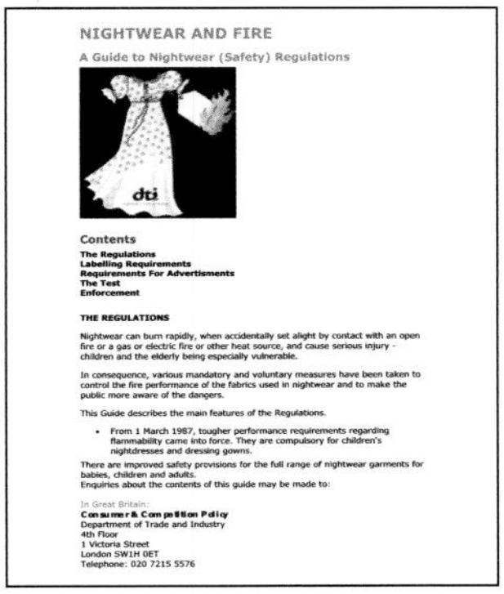 NIGHTWEAR AND FIRE A Guide to Nightwear (Safety) Regulations Contents **The Regulations** **Labelling Requirements** **Requirements For Advertisments** **The Test** **Enforcement** **THE REGULATIONS** Nightwear can burn rapidly, when accidentally set alight by contact with an open fire or a gas or electric fire or other heat source, and cause serious injury - children and the elderly being especially vulnerable. In consequence, various mandatory and voluntary measures have been taken to control the fire performance of the fabrics used in nightwear and to make the public more aware of the dangers. This Guide describes the main features of the Regulations. • From 1 March 1987, tougher performance requirements regarding flammability came into force. They are compulsory for children's nightdresses and dressing gowns. There are improved safety provisions for the full range of nightwear garments for babies, children and adults. Enquiries about the contents of this guide may be made to: In Great Britain: **Consumer & Competition Policy** Department of Trade and Industry 4th Floor 1 Victoria Street London SW1H 0ET Telephone: 020 7215 5576 △ **Figure 4.34**
Compulsory care labelling	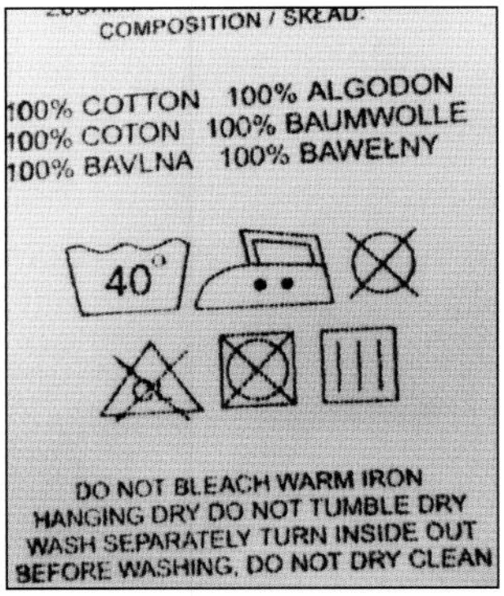 △ **Figure 4.35**
Bar codes	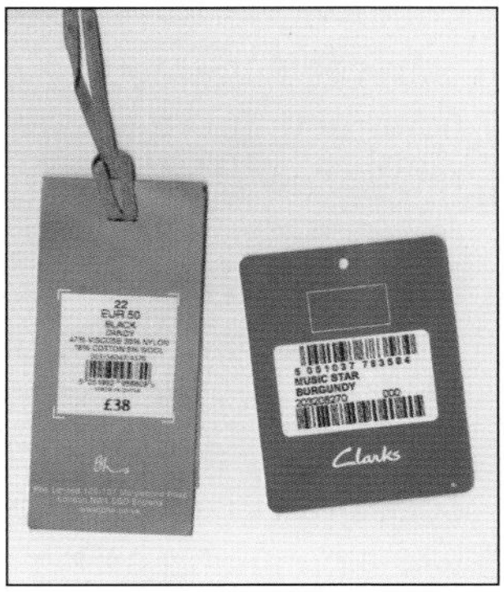 △ **Figure 4.36**
Trade associations	WOOLMARK △ **Figure 4.37**
Green labels	EU Ecolabel www.ecolabel.eu △ **Figure 4.38**

△ **Table 4.6** Information on labels

Cont.

Labels

Care labels need to include the following information:

- country of origin – where the product comes from
- fibre content – starting with the main fibre/fibres and then the subsidiary fibres
- retailer's symbol/logo or trademark
- retailer's store and product number
- bar code – a special code made up of stripes and numbers which is used by the retailer to track the product from production through to delivery to the store. Companies also use bar codes linked to EPOS systems to track how well a product is selling and if they will sell out
- product details – the type, size, style and colour of garment
- proper chemical name of the fibre/fabric (not just a trade name).

All care labels on products are overseen by the Home Laundering Consultative Council (HLCC). The HLCC also provides further information about textile products and how to care for them, especially for products that are going to be used in other areas of Europe.

Key terms

Aftercare – instructions on how to care for fabrics and other textiles products.

HLCC – the Home Laundering Consultative Council, which oversees the meaning and application of the symbols on care labels on clothing and textiles.

Labelling – the adding of an identification to a product.

Statutory legislation – laws and regulations that are controlled by the legal process.

Wash care labels

Wash care labels are placed on garments to inform the user how to care for and clean the textile product. This is sometimes referred to as product maintenance or aftercare. The main ways of cleaning textile products are:

- hand-washing
- machine-washing
- dry-cleaning
- ironing or pressing.

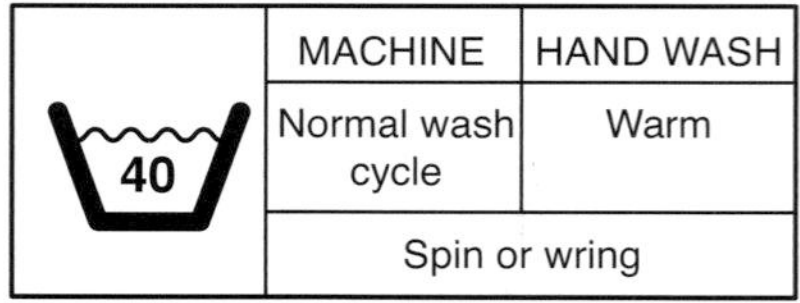

40	MACHINE	HAND WASH
	Normal wash cycle	Warm
	Spin or wring	

△ **Figure 4.40** Wash care labels

For hand-washing, machine-washing and ironing (pressing) of textiles products, standard symbols are used. This means that the consumer can care for the products in their own home.

Where dry-cleaning symbols are used, products need to be cleaned by a specialist outlet called a dry-cleaner. Dry-cleaners use special products to clean certain fabrics, such as leather, suede, silk and cashmere.

The symbols that you find on clothes are also mirrored on the labels found on washing products, such as soap powders and liquid washing solutions. These help the consumer to identify the best product to care for their clothes and textile products.

Aftercare of textiles and the environment

New government guidelines mean that washing machine manufacturers need to be energy-efficient. Many washing machines now specify that textile products can be washed in temperatures as low as 15 °C.

Cleaning products and the environment

To clean textile products, we use washing powders and fabric softeners. Cleaners and softeners, and the containers they are purchased in, are not always easily recyclable. Many manufacturers of these products are now making environmentally friendly substitutes, with reduced packaging, small tablets, high-concentration products and new solutions that can clean clothes at lower temperatures.

If a product is made from 100 per cent of a certain fibre or has a high content of a particular fibre, the manufacturer is allowed to use certain labels to let the buyer know that the product has been made using that particular fibre and is of a certain quality.

Consumer law and labels

Consumer awareness of the laws related to looking after textile products is essential. Trading standards and consumer protection agencies are able to advise the public on their rights. Some of the key laws and regulations are outlined in Table 4.7.

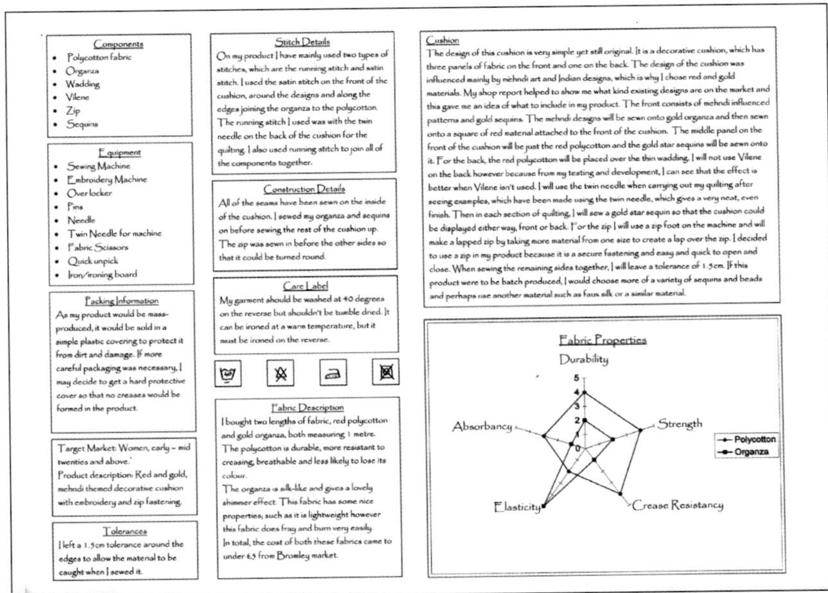

△ **Figure 4.41** Student work showing an understanding of care labelling and the maintenance of the textile product

Law	What it says
The Trade Descriptions Act 1968	States that goods must not be falsely described
The Sale of Goods Act 1979	States that goods must correspond with their description, be of a satisfactory quality and be fit to use
The Weights and Measures Act 1985	States that you have to be given goods that are of the correct weight or quantity – for example, if you ask a shop to give you 3 metres of fabric, they must not serve you with 2.5 metres
The Textile Products (Indication of Fibre Content) Regulations 1986	Companies must state the composition of fabric/fibre on a textile product; this includes knitted and woven fabrics, as well as those used for upholstery

△ **Table 4.7** Key laws for consumer protection

Special labelling for protection

All textile products must carry labelling that states if the product is dangerous under certain conditions. Here we look at a common label found on goods such as nightwear or furnishings: flammability.

Flammability

Key terms

Flammability – the ability of a fibre to catch fire.

Flame resistance – will prevent fabric from burning, inhibit burning or end burning when the product is placed in an open flame.

It is illegal to mark textile fabrics or goods as being either 'non-flammable' or 'flame-resistant'. The fabrics made for these products have to meet a set standard called 'low flammability'. This standard is one that has been worked out by the British Standards Institution and follows very strict guidelines.

For upholstered furniture, there are special labelling rules. Since July 1983, all upholstered furniture has had to carry a fire label of some sort. It should either say 'resistant', if it is made from a flame-proofed material, or it should carry a warning label about the dangers of fire from cigarettes.

Nightwear for children must be made from low-flammable material, materials that have had a flame-resistant chemical finish added, or fabrics treated with a fire-resistant finish. It must carry notifications such as 'keep away from fire'. This is covered by the Nightwear Safety Regulations1985 and 1987.

Note the difference between 'flammability' and 'flame resistance' (see Key terms box).

Other key consumer and safety acts for textiles are as follows:

- **Sale of goods:**
  - Consumer Protection Act 1987 (Commencement No.1) Order 1987
  - Sale of Goods Act 1979, amended 1994 and 1995
  - Supply of Goods and Services Act 1982
  - Sale and Supply of Goods Act 1994

- **Safety:**
  - Children's Clothing (Hood Cords) Regulations 1976
  - Nightwear (Safety) Regulations 1985, 1987
- **Other textiles regulations:**
  - Furniture and Furnishings (Fire Safety) Regulations 1988, amended 1989 and 1993
  - Toys (Safety) Regulations 1995
  - Textile Products (Indication of Fibre Content) Regulations 1986, amended 1982, 1988, 1994 and 1998.

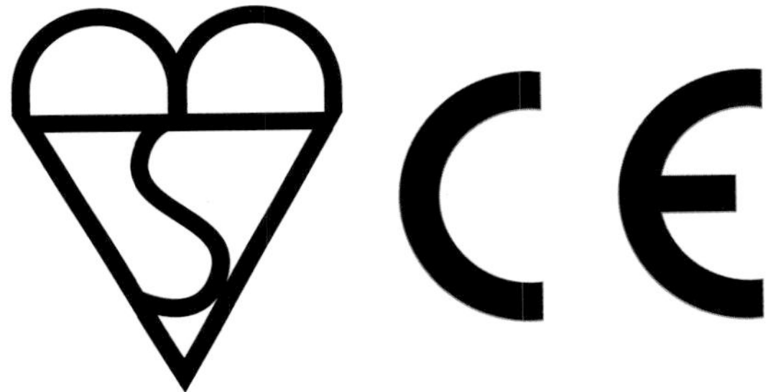

△ **Figure 4.42** Safety care labels

Labels and smart technologies

Smart labels

These new labels use special ink that is placed on electronics and can be used to track where you shop and what you buy. They also have a second function in that they can be used by manufacturers and retailers to prevent goods being stolen. They can also be used at special points in a store to tell you what other sizes and colours are available. In countries such as Japan and South Korea, special computer terminals can show you what other products you might also be interested in.

RFID tags

RFID (radio frequency identification) tags are new, special tags that retailers can apply to products to track them more precisely. They can also be used with current computer technology to supply the consumer with what they require.

△ **Figure 4.43** RFID tag

Augmented reality and QR codes

This is a new type of label that uses smartphone technology. It allows companies to give added information about a product. An augmented reality label can be added to the swing ticket on a product. Using your smartphone still or video camera, you can capture the augmented reality label, which will then activate a website, a link, an image or even a video that tells you more about the product. These labels are often used for promotions. QR codes are another form of barcode and are used on everyday products, they can be seen in newspapers and magazines, and direct the user to a promotional website or product page. They can be used with a webcam or mobile phone with a camera.

△ **Figure 4.44** QR code

Fitness for purpose

Fitness for purpose is an important aspect of all clothing and textile products – it is essential that products are fit for their end use.

Key term

Fitness for purpose – a product is made of a good enough or satisfactory quality and must be what is stated on the label attached to the product – for example, on a garment this would be a care label.

Properties needed for textile products	What does this mean?	How is it measured?	Fitness for purpose would be:
Warmth	The product should be at a specific standard to provide warmth.	For example, the warmth of a duvet is measured by its 'fill property'; the warmth of a sleeping bag is measured by EN 13547 using a mannequin. Heat retention can be measured by using a heat camera.	The duvet meets the relevant standards.
Wearability	The product meets the needs of the user – that is, it does not start to fall apart after one wear.	For example, stitching that may come undone when worn	The stitching stays intact after several weeks of wear.
Comfort	The product does not pinch, restrict movement or hurt when worn.	The ability to reduce sweat in shoes; use of a walking simulator	The use of artificial feet to measure water vapour escape to ensure that shoes are adequate for purpose; sweaty feet can lead to infections
Absorbency	The product will be able to absorb a certain amount of moisture – for example, babies' nappies or extreme sportswear.	Testing how long it takes for a fabric to absorb moisture	What happens to the product after exposure to moisture

△ **Table 4.8** Fitness for purpose

Cont.

Properties needed for textile products	What does this mean?	How is it measured?	Fitness for purpose would be:
Durability	The strength of a product, and its ability to withstand long-term use	For example, a car seat has to undergo a simulated test related to 50,000 rubs to ensure it meets the equivalent of five years of use.	That seams do not come apart, or that the fabric does not wear out
Safety	The product is safe to use for its intended purpose.	It will have passed the CE or Kitemark tests.	The toy does not fall apart and there are clear warnings on it for the age range for which it is intended.
Flammability	The product withstands current legislation related to flammability.	Using the relevant BSI standards test	For fabrics to be used in clothing, the correct labels are attached.
Flame resistance	The product is flame-resistant as stated in legislation.	Can be tested in a laboratory setting to see how long the product takes to combust	The use of appropriate labels and finishes
Stain resistance	Stains can be removed.	The product might be washed at a particular temperature to ensure total removal.	For example, men's ties and children's schoolwear has added Teflon coating to reduce stain impression.
Aftercare	Laundry and aftercare is appropriate and fits with the product end use.	The product did not shrink or change drastically from its original form when washed.	The correct care label has been added.

△ **Table 4.8** Fitness for purpose *continued*

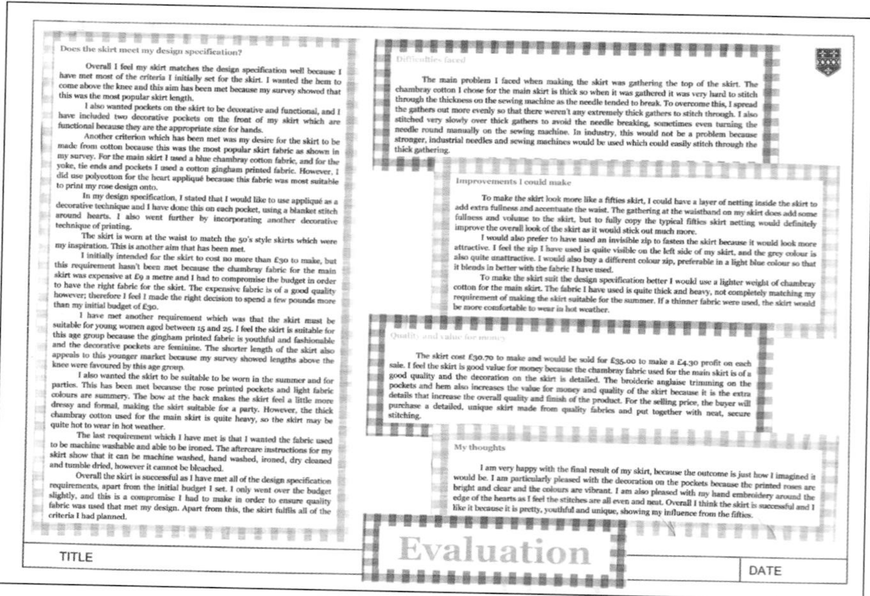

Does the skirt meet my design specification?

Overall I feel my skirt matches the design specification well because I have met most of the criteria I initially set for the skirt. I wanted the hem to come above the knee and this aim has been met because my survey showed that this was the most popular skirt length.

I also wanted pockets on the skirt to be decorative and functional, and I have included two decorative pockets on the front of my skirt which are functional because they are the appropriate size for hands.

Another criterion which has been met was my desire for the skirt to be made from cotton because this was the most popular skirt fabric as shown in my survey. For the main skirt I used a blue chambray cotton fabric, and for the yoke, tie ends and pockets I used a cotton gingham printed fabric. However, I did use polycotton for the heart appliqué because this fabric was most suitable to print my rose design onto.

In my design specification, I stated that I would like to use appliqué as a decorative technique and I have done this on each pocket, using a blanket stitch around hearts. I also went further by incorporating another decorative technique of printing.

The skirt is worn at the waist to match the 50's style skirts which were my inspiration. This is another aim that has been met.

I initially intended for the skirt to cost no more than £30 to make, but this requirement hasn't been met because the chambray fabric for the main skirt was expensive at £9 a metre and I had to compromise the budget in order to have the right fabric for the skirt. The expensive fabric is of a good quality however; therefore I feel I made the right decision to spend a few pounds more than my initial budget of £30.

I have met another requirement which was that the skirt must be suitable for young women aged between 15 and 25. I feel the skirt is suitable for this age group because the gingham printed fabric is youthful and fashionable and the decorative pockets are feminine. The shorter length of the skirt also appeals to this younger market because my survey showed lengths above the knee were favoured by this age group.

I also wanted the skirt to be suitable to be worn in the summer and for parties. This has been met because the rose printed pockets and light fabric colours are summery. The bow at the back makes the skirt feel a little more dressy and formal, making the skirt suitable for a party. However, the thick chambray cotton used for the main skirt is quite heavy, so the skirt may be quite hot to wear in hot weather.

The last requirement which I have met is that I wanted the fabric used to be machine washable and able to be ironed. The aftercare instructions for my skirt show that it can be machine washed, hand washed, ironed, dry cleaned and tumble dried, however it cannot be bleached.

Overall the skirt is successful as I have met all of the design specification requirements, apart from the initial budget I set. I only went over the budget slightly, and this is a compromise I had to make in order to ensure quality fabric was used that met my design. Apart from this, the skirt fulfils all of the criteria I had planned.

Difficulties faced

The main problem I faced when making the skirt was gathering the top of the skirt. The chambray cotton I chose for the main skirt is thick so when it was gathered it was very hard to stitch through the thickness on the sewing machine as the needle tended to break. To overcome this, I spread the gathers out more evenly so that there weren't any extremely thick gathers to stitch through. I also stitched very slowly over thick gathers to avoid the needle breaking, sometimes even turning the needle round manually on the sewing machine. In industry, this would not be a problem because stronger, industrial needles and sewing machines would be used which could easily stitch through the thick gathering.

Improvements I could make

To make the skirt look more like a fifties skirt, I could have a layer of netting inside the skirt to add extra fullness and accentuate the waist. The gathering at the waistband on my skirt does add some fullness and volume to the skirt, but to fully copy the typical fifties skirt netting would definitely improve the overall look of the skirt as it would stick out much more.

I would also prefer to have used an invisible zip to fasten the skirt because it would look more attractive. I feel the zip I have used is quite visible on the left side of my skirt, and the grey colour is also quite unattractive. I would also buy a different colour zip, preferable in a light blue colour so that it blends in better with the fabric I have used.

To make the skirt suit the design specification better I would use a lighter weight of chambray cotton for the main skirt. The fabric I have used is quite thick and heavy, not completely matching my requirement of making the skirt suitable for the summer. If a thinner fabric were used, the skirt would be more comfortable to wear in hot weather.

Quality and value for money

The skirt cost £30.70 to make and would be sold for £35.00 to make a £4.30 profit on each sale. I feel the skirt is good value for money because the chambray fabric used for the main skirt is of a good quality and the decoration on the skirt is detailed. The broiderie anglaise trimming on the pockets and hem also increases the value for money and quality of the skirt because it is the extra details that increase the overall quality and finish of the product. For the selling price, the buyer will purchase a detailed, unique skirt made from quality fabrics and put together with neat, secure stitching.

My thoughts

I am very happy with the final result of my skirt, because the outcome is just how I imagined it would be. I am particularly pleased with the decoration on the pockets because the printed roses are bright and clear and the colours are vibrant. I am also pleased with my hand embroidery around the edge of the hearts as I feel the stitches are all even and neat. Overall I think the skirt is successful and I like it because it is pretty, youthful and unique, showing my influence from the fifties.

TITLE

Evaluation

DATE

△ **Figure 4.45** Student example of fitness for purpose, including consideration of specific qualities of the product

Key terms

Absorbency – the ability to soak up moisture.

Comfort – how a product feels when it is being worn or being used.

Durability – how hard-wearing something is.

Flammability – the ability of a fibre to catch fire.

Safety – the process of designing something that prevents injury or damage

Stain resistance – the process of adding a finish to fabrics that repels dirt and stains.

Warmth – the ability of a fabric to retain heat and keep you warm.

Wearability – the process of testing how much wear and tear a product can take.

Summary

- Care labelling of products is essential to tell consumers what fibres their products are composed of and how to care for them.
- Care labels are a legal requirement.
- Special labels need to be applied to products that react to fire.
- All textile products must be fit for purpose.

Exam practice questions

1. Why are care labels added to textile products? **[2 marks]**
2. What important legal information has to be added to care labels? **[3 marks]**
3. What do the following terms mean?
   (a) flammable
   (b) flammability. **[2 marks]**
4. How does caring for textiles products affect the environment? **[4 marks]**
5. What steps are washing machine and soap powder manufacturers taking to reduce the impact on the environment? **[6 marks]**

Stretch yourself

1. Explore your wardrobe and other textile products that you have at home.

(a) Use a table to record the temperatures at which all your products have to be washed or dry-cleaned. **[6 marks]**

(b) What do your results show? Give three reasons for your choice. **[6 marks]**

2 Detail some ways in which you can reduce energy, cleaning costs and your carbon footprint in the aftercare of your products. **[6 marks]**

Resources

Home Laundering Consultative Council:
www.care-labelling.co.uk

chapter 5 Finishing processes

5.1 Dyeing and printing

Learning objectives

By the end of this section, you should have a key understanding of:

- the application of dyes to fabrics
- how different printing and dyeing methods are used
- the environmental issues related to dyeing and printing
- the health and safety issues related to dyeing and printing.

Key points

- Innovative ideas
- Creative ideas
- Linking technology and design
- Values

Introduction

In the fashion and textiles industry, the use of colour is of vital importance in both presentation and sale of products. Trend forecasters predict colours for the next season. Designers are also faced with the methods or processes of applying colour to products, and must be aware of the methods that apply not only to fabrics and garments, but to other product types such as homeware. They must also have a good understanding of fibres and their properties. This is important as different printing and dyeing techniques work differently on different fibre types. Technological advances in colour and printing applications are also changing techniques and methods used for applying colour. Sustainable issues are also key, as the dyeing and printing industry must reduce its impact on the environment and also review its water usage and wastage.

Colour and textiles

Colour is an important component in textiles and is a key marketing tool in any promotion of textile products. The process of adding colour to textile products is complex, and it means that today's designers need to understand clearly the properties of different fibres and fabrics.

Knowledge link

For more information on colour, see page 224.

Colours are dictated by trends and also by personal likes and dislikes. In different countries, colours have different cultural meanings, and designers need to consider this when developing design ranges.

All aspects in the production of a fashion and textile product are dictated by the application of colour. In many companies, a specialist called a colourist is employed to oversee how colours are chosen and applied to textile products across the supply-and-make chain. They work with the design and production teams to ensure that products have been correctly dyed and prints applied, and they follow the correct tests for their end use. The problems that can occur as a result of bad dyeing or printing are:

- shade variation
- fading
- bleeding
- colour staining
- streaking.

The multifibre strip allows companies to test the take-up of dye across different fibres. It consists of a woven strip made up of several fibres, both synthetic and natural. The multifibre strip can be placed in a sample dye bath to see how the colours will react to different fibres. This is important as garments and other products are made of different fibres, and it is important that all components in a product will be the same colour.

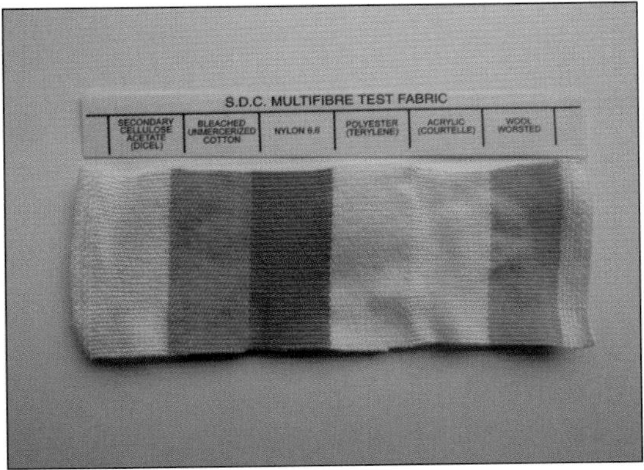

△ **Figure 5.1** Multifibre strip before and after dyeing

Computers and dyeing

Sophisticated computer systems are now used in the dyeing of products. These are called shade or colour management systems. The use of computer systems in the dyeing process gives the following advantages:

- reduced faults
- increased accuracy and consistency
- reduced costs
- saves time
- can create dye formulations for small- or large-scale printing.

What is dyeing?

Dyeing is the process of adding colour to fibres, yarns, fabrics or garments, using water and dyestuffs, also called colourants and mordants, which are added to ensure that the dye particles stick to the product being dyed.

Key terms

Colourant – a chemical agent added to the dye bath to produce colour.

Cross staining – where one colour stains another when both are being washed at the same time. This can make both products unwearable.

Dyeing – the process of applying colour to a textile product, which is soaked in a coloured solution.

Mordants – used to control the uptake or colour fastness – for example, in fabrics – and to control colour-fastness.

Multifibre strip – a woven strip of fabric that is made of several different types of fibres. It can be used to test fabrics for cross staining and dye take up.

Synthetic, natural and mixed or blended fibres and fabrics can all be dyed. Dyes can be made from synthetic chemicals or from natural substances.

Many companies will combine dyes with special finishes to give garments a different look. This is especially true of the denim fashion industry, where dye techniques are used to add key details to garments.

Dyed products must be fit for purpose and so must provide the following to the user:

- fastness to light
- fastness to perspiration
- fastness to washing and laundering
- fastness to dry-cleaning
- fastness to chlorine (e.g. swimwear)
- fastness to rubbing.

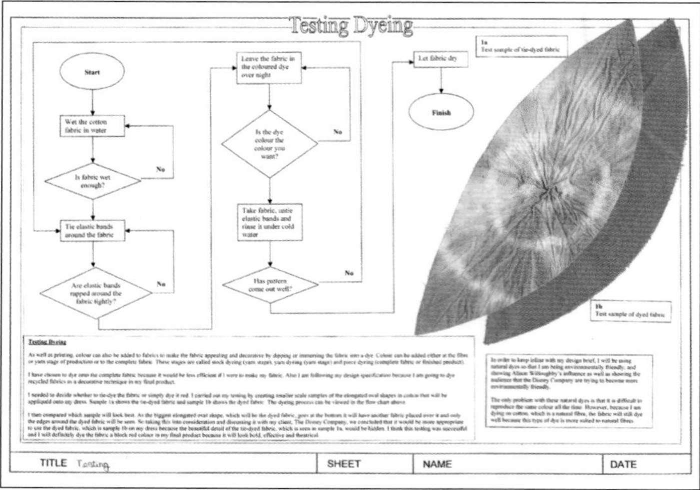

△ **Figure 5.2** Dyeing/printing techniques

The process of dyeing

Dyeing is normally carried out in three stages:

1. Cleaning of fibre/fabrics to remove oils or other products that might stop the dye from being applied to the product: this is done to ensure that the dyes work well on the products and no faults will occur.
2. The dyeing process: the textiles and the dye liquid are put together. This might be for a few minutes or hours, depending on the fibre type being dyed.
3. The finishing process: the excess dye is removed from the product and scoured with soaps and detergents. This is an important part of the process in dyeing fabrics because, if insufficient dye is removed, the product can develop faults, such as streaking or losing colour quickly when washed.

Dye type	Uses	Key issues
Acid	Used on protein fibres, such as wool and silk, and synthetic fibres, acrylic and nylon	Can produce bright colours; good fastness to light and perspiration, with excellent fastness to dry-cleaning; excellent for dyeing silk
Direct	Used mostly on cellulosics (e.g. cotton and linen)	Poor washing fastness; fastness to light is variable; excellent fastness for perspiration and dry-cleaning
Disperse	Used mostly on nylon, acetate, modacrylic, polyester and olefin fibres	Wash fastness varies depending on the fibre the dye is applied to; it offers excellent fastness to perspiration, but light fastness is variable
Reactive	Mostly used on cellulosic fibres	Gives very bright shades and provides excellent fastness to light
Pigments	Can be used on all fibres	Not a dye as such, and is applied to a resin or binder base; can stiffen fabric; gives good fastness to light and hand-washing

△ **Table 5.1** Key types of dyes used for textile products

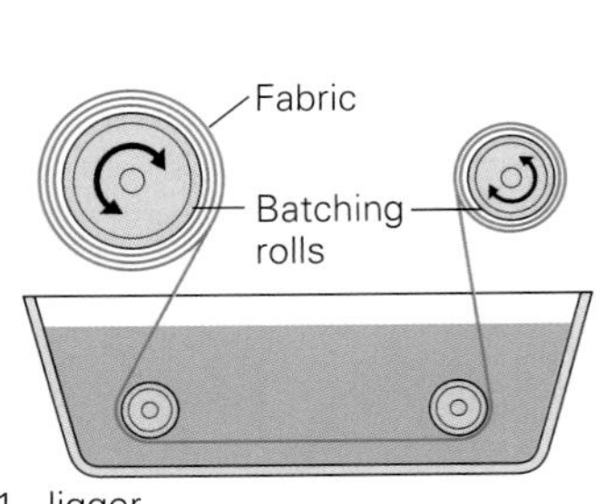

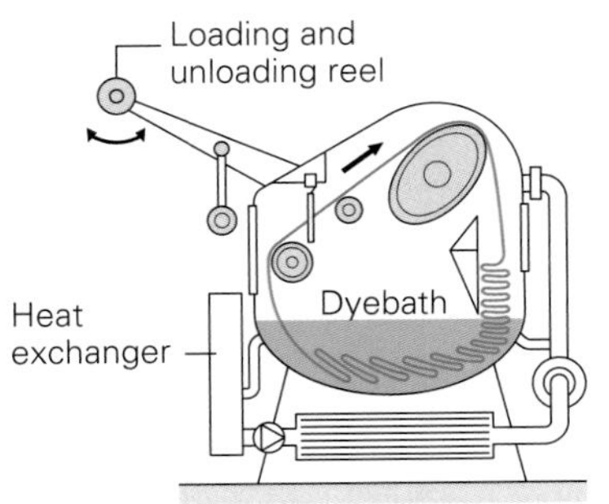

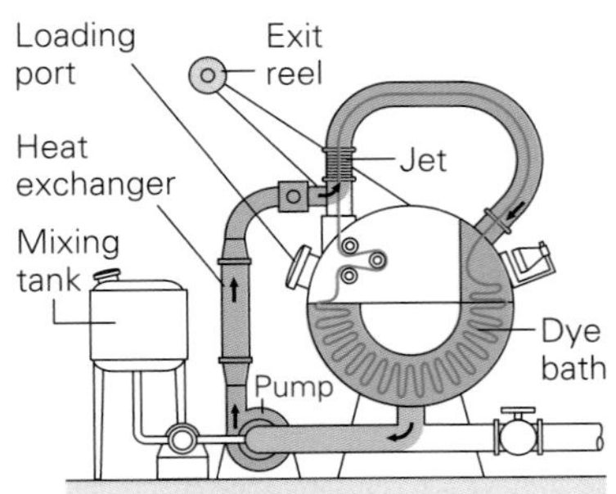

△ **Figure 5.3** Batch dyeing methods

Methods of dyeing fabrics

In the fashion and textiles industry, the dyeing of fabrics is done on a large, industrial scale. The dyeing process has to be accurate to ensure that the same colours can be produced again and again. The type of dyeing process used is dependent on the following:

- type of fabric
- the fibres it contains.

Textiles and fashion products can be dyed using the following production methods:

- stock dyeing
- batch dyeing
- continuous dyeing
- yarn dyeing
- garment dyeing (also known as product dyeing).

Method of dyeing	How is it done?
Stock dyeing	This is the dyeing of fibres before being spun into yarn. This is the most costly of all the dyeing processes.
Yarn dyeing	After the yarn is spun, it can be dyed. It is used mostly for those fabrics where stripes, patterns or multicoloured effects are needed. It can also be done by hand and is used a lot by those who spin their own yarn.
Batch dyeing	A fabric of a set weight is dyed. Each dyed lot is then given a batch number. This allows companies to match batches prior to manufacturing garments. Differences in batches that are dyed can occur.
Continuous dyeing (also known as pad dyeing)	Lengths of fabrics pass through a special pad and container of dye. After the fabric passes through the container, it is squeezed to remove excess dye.
Garment dyeing	Used to bulk-dye garments that are simple in shape. This method produces the least waste.

△ **Table 5.2** Main dyeing processes

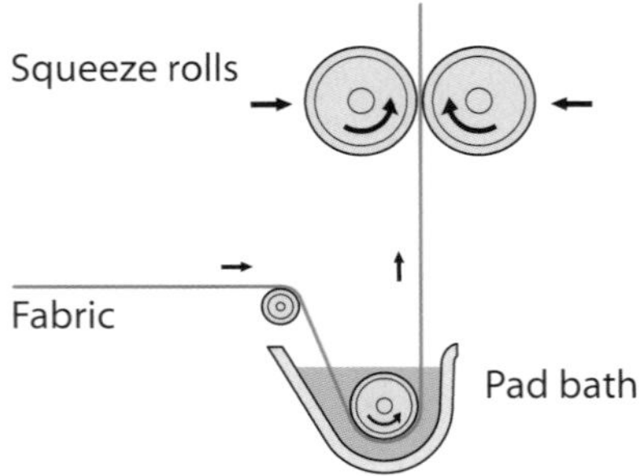

△ **Figure 5.4** Continuous dyeing

Other methods of dyeing fabrics

Resist method

The resist method of dyeing fabrics involves applying dyes to certain parts of a fabric.

The dye is restricted from moving up the fabric using a tie. The tie can be a thread, string or rubber band. Once the tie is removed, the pattern is revealed.

△ **Figure 5.5** Tie-dye

Name of resist method	How is it done?
Tie-dye	The fabric or product can be tied, folded or wrapped. It is then placed in a dye bath for a certain amount of time, depending on the effect required. It is then removed and rinsed. Once dried, the ties/folds/wraps are undone and the pattern is revealed. Multicoloured patterns can be achieved by refolding/tying/wrapping the fabric and putting it back in the dye bath with another colour. It works well on natural fabrics.
Batik	A pattern is applied to the fabric using a paste, which can be rice-, flour- or wax-based. This can be done by hand or using special blocks. The fabric is then dyed and the pattern is removed. This is a popular method of applying colour to fabric. Complex designs can be created. Works well on natural fabrics. Although this process originates from Indonesia, you will also find similar processes in Malaysia and India, as well as Nigeria.
Tritik	Fine, running stitches are applied to fabrics, and then pulled tightly. The fabric is then placed in the dye bath. Once removed, the stitching is removed, revealing the pattern. Intricate designs can be achieved using this method. Best results can be achieved using natural fabrics.
Shibori	This method originates from Japan. It is a method of folding or tying fabrics and then using a combination of heat and dyes, or chemicals. The fabric is then dried and the ties removed. Works on all types of fibres and fabrics. Issey Miyake refined this process and made it famous with his 'Pleats Please' range of designs.

△ **Table 5.3** Different resist methods

What is printing?

Printing is the process of applying a pattern or text to fabrics or products. Prints can be applied by hand or by machine. Printing is widely used in the textiles industry as one of the primary methods of adding colour to fabrics. This process is known as adding surface pattern.

Key terms

Printing – the process by which colour, type or pattern can be transferred to a textile or other substrate.

Commercial methods – production processes on a large scale, using machinery.

Hand methods – using hand tools to manufacture products on a small scale or producing a small quantity.

Printing method	How is it done?
Direct printing	A printing paste is applied directly to the fabric. A stencil may be used to create the pattern.
Discharge printing	A method of applying a design to a pre-printed fabric using a special paste that removes the colour, revealing the design.
Resist printing	A method of applying a wax, paste or chemical resist to a fabric. The fabric is then dyed, and the resist removed by washing or heat.
Flock printing	A process of applying a glue to certain areas on a fabric, then applying fine fibres, which stick to the glue. The resulting print gives the fabric a velvet-like surface.
Pigment printing	This method of printing uses pigments mixed with a binder. This can then be applied to fabrics.
Hand block printing	The process of adding colour to a block, which is then used to transfer a design to fabric. It is done by hand and is one of the oldest methods of printing.
Roller printing	One of the oldest methods of printing by mechanical means. The key advantage of using this process is the sharp image that can be achieved. It is an expensive process. Designs are carved onto copper rollers. One is needed for each colour in the design. Printing paste is placed in containers that the roller sits in, and as the fabric passes between the rollers the pattern is applied.
Screen printing 1 – flat screen printing	A design is first applied to a flat, meshed screen, either using a stencil or a photo-based screen. This is then transferred to fabrics by pushing the dye through the screen using a squeegee. A screen is required for each colour that is to be applied to the design. Can be used on any type of fabric.
Screen printing 2 – rotary printing	A design is first applied to a cylinder meshed screen, then transferred to fabrics by pushing the dye through the screen cylinder using a squeegee as it rolls over the fabric. This is the fastest form of printing fabric. Can be used on any type of fabric.

△ **Table 5.4** Methods of printing

Cont.

Printing method	How is it done?
Digital printing	The process of printing directly onto fabrics that have been coated with a special chemical wash. The fabric is steamed to set the dye and then rinsed to remove any finishes before being used. Can be used on natural fabrics.
Transfer or direct printing	This process involves applying designs directly to a paper. The designs are then transferred to fabric using either heated rollers for mass-produced designs, or a heat press for small-scale designs. This process works best on synthetic or synthetic blend fabrics.

△ **Table 5.4** Methods of printing *continued*

Printing onto fabrics can be combined with other techniques of adding patterns to fabrics, such as:

- hand embroidery
- machine embroidery (e.g. free machining or computerised embroidery)
- embellishments (e.g. beading and sequins)
- manipulating fabrics using heat or steam
- combining hand techniques and digital techniques.

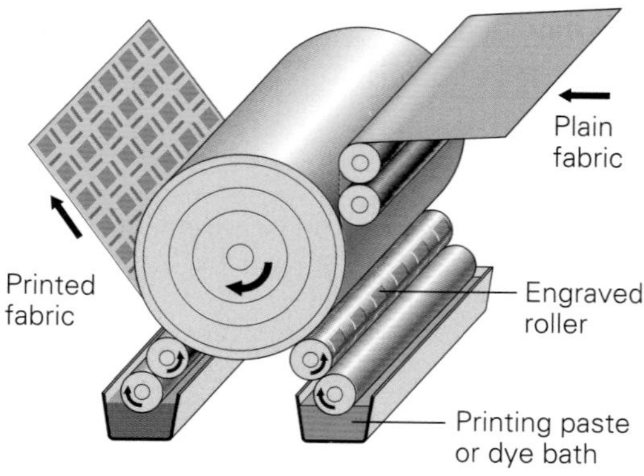

△ **Figure 5.6** Roller printing

Finishing prints

After dyeing or printing, textiles products have to pass through a finishing process to remove excess dyes or print paste, as well as to set the dyes into the fabrics, so that they do not run when washed. This finishing process also involves removing oils or other substances that gather on the fabric as it is being produced.

△ **Figure 5.7** Digital printing

The four key finishing processes that fabrics may go through either before or after printing are:

- **fixation** – fixing dyes and colours to fabric so they do not stain or run
- **washing** – cleaning fabrics prior to printing and dyeing
- **drying** – removing excess moisture from fabrics, which is important because fabrics need to be dry, ready for use
- **heat setting** – used mainly for synthetic fabrics, but most fabrics will undergo some sort of setting process to ensure that they are as they should be in appearance and stability.

Dyeing, printing and the environment

Dyes can be dangerous to the environment. Companies must now follow strict rules with regard to reducing waste from the dyeing process and developing more ecologically friendly dyes that can be applied to textile products.

Processes such as screen and rotary printing use a lot of water in the cleaning process, so companies are developing methods to reduce water use. New EU regulations mean that companies must adhere to strict rules when disposing of waste so it does not affect the environment.

Many companies are now developing new dyes and printing materials that are organic, or water-based, so they do not need chemicals to clean equipment.

The use of digital printing is beginning to make an impact on the textile printing industry. It provides a key way of making printing localised and reduces the need for lots of natural resources.

Knowledge link

For more information on digital printing, see pages 268–69.

Dyes, printing and safety

As most textiles products will come into contact with the skin, all dyes used on garments or textile products must follow strict health and safety guidelines.

Dyes are also dangerous if inhaled, so it is important that when using dyes you wear the appropriate protective equipment, including gloves, and follow the safety guidelines. You may also be required to wear safety goggles.

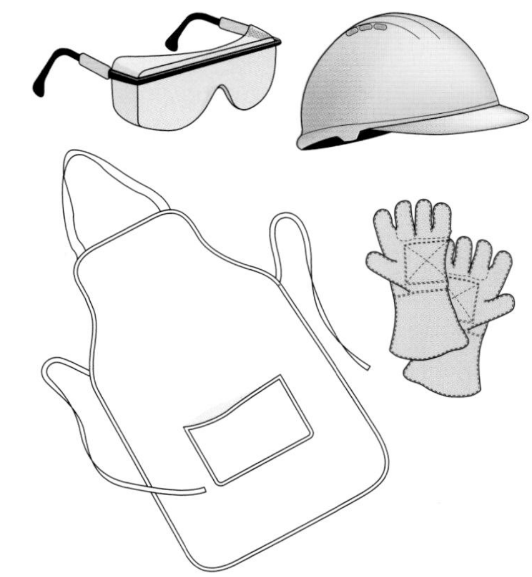

△ **Figure 5.8** Safety equipment for dyeing and printing

Knowledge link

For more information on safety guidelines in textiles, see Chapter 8, pages 200–15. You can also see more information on how students have used health and safety in their controlled assessment (coursework).

Summary

- Dyeing and printing are the key methods of applying colour to textile products.
- The colour of textiles is used as a key marketing tool by companies to promote their products.
- The dying and printing process uses a lot of water and companies are looking at ways of reducing this.
- As dyes and print pastes contain chemicals, they have to be disposed of very carefully. Many companies are now developing new dyes and printing materials that are organic, or water-based, so they do not need chemicals to clean equipment.

Activities

1. Choose one method of applying colour to fabric, whether dyeing or printing.

(a) Compile a report on the process.

(b) Collect images of designs created using your chosen method of applying colour.

(c) How can this method of applying colour be made more environmentally friendly? **[15 marks]**

2. Designers such as Orla Keily and Donna Wilson, and design companies such as Marrimekko, IKEA and Missoni, create distinctive designs using a range of dyeing and printing techniques.

(a) Compile a design report about one of these companies or another of your choice.

(b) Choose one of the companies and create a design or designs that you feel will fit in with their range, giving reasons for your choice. **[15 marks]**

Exam practice questions

1. What is a dye, and what is the process of applying dyes to textile products? **[2 marks]**
2. Why are computer systems used in managing colour application to textiles? **[2 marks]**
3. What are some of the environmental issues that need to be considered when printing or dyeing textile and fashion products? **[4 marks]**
4. What are the key methods of printing on fabric? **[5 marks]**

Stretch yourself

Using a multi-fibre strip experiment with different dyes, explain how different dyes react to different fibre types. Show your results on an experiment sheet with the headings given below:

1. Experiment heading

2. Dye type

3. Multi-fibre strip

4. Expected results

5. Actual outcome

Note: a multi-fibre strip is a woven length of fabric that has several different fibres woven next to each other. The dyeing industry uses this to test how dyes react to different fibre types. This is important as many products are made up of more than one fibre/fabric type, and different dyes react differently to different fibre types. **[15 marks]**

Resources

The Society of Dyers and Colourists: www.sdc.org.uk

The Colour Experience: www.colour-experience.org

Multi-fibre strip-dyeing kit: www.sdc.org.uk

5.2 Decoration and enhancement

Learning objectives

By the end of this section, you should have a key understanding of:

- surface decoration techniques
- applying chosen and relevant techniques to your coursework.

Key points

- Communication skills
- Innovative ideas
- Creative ideas
- Linking technology and design
- Values

Introduction

Surface decoration is a method of applying stitching and creating patterns with the addition of beading or the use of other decorative processes. Surface decoration enhances the surface of a fabric and can also add value. In the haute couture industry, specialist workers called *ateliers* use their expertise to apply designs to expensive garments. These garments require hundreds of hours of labour and sell for thousands of pounds.

△ **Figure 5.9** Different types of surface decoration

Key terms

Surface decoration – a method of applying stitching and creating patterns with the addition of beading or other decorative processes.

Patchwork

Patchwork is a method of applying colour and uses small pieces of fabric that are joined together to create a pattern. This method of applying colour means that you can use small pieces of fabric. Patchwork is known as one of the earliest methods of recycling fabrics.

Embroidery

Hand techniques

Embroidery can be done by hand or by sewing machine. There is a wide variety of threads that can used, as well as needles. There is a series of decorative hand stitches that can be used as well. The most popular are shown in Figure 5.11.

Machine techniques

Using sewing machine stitches

A standard sewing machine has a limited range of stitches that can be used to create a range of different, patterned fabrics. You can apply patterns to ribbons and fabric strips, which can then be applied to other products.

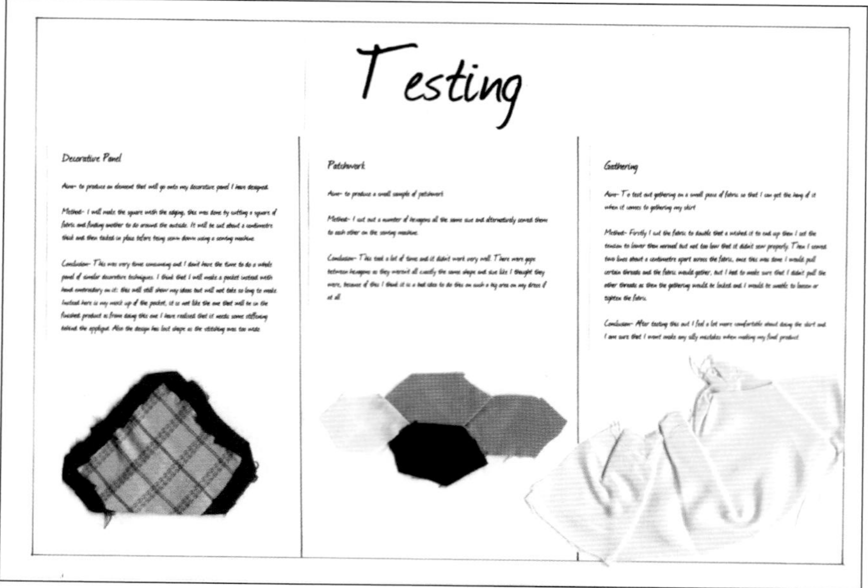

△ **Figure 5.10** Student example of surface decoration

Free-machine techniques

Free-machine embroidery is a technique where the dog feed is lowered, enabling the user to create patterns on any aspect of the fabric. For free-machining embroidery techniques, you can use:

- existing stitches on the sewing machine
- computerised stitches that you make up yourself
- satin stitch or straight stitch.

Free-form embroidery allows you to decide in which direction the stitching will go and how it will look. You can overlay stitches and colours. You can develop your design by painting or adding dyes to the fabric before stitching begins.

Embroidery using CAD

Computerised embroidery is done using a specific type of computerised sewing machine. Designs created using this type of machine can be done in one of two ways:

- The design can be done on the machine itself, using the machine's built-in memory and design aids.
- The design can be created on the sewing machine's software on a computer. The design can then be exported to the embroidery machine using a special card or using a direct link between the computer and the sewing machine's memory.

Key terms

Embroidery – a pattern being sewn into fabric using either hand or machine stitches.

Hand embroidery – the method of adding surface decoration to fabrics by hand. Intricate stitches are used to create designs.

Machine embroidery – the method of adding surface decoration to fabrics using a sewing machine. There are two main methods of creating designs – freehand or using computer digitizing software.

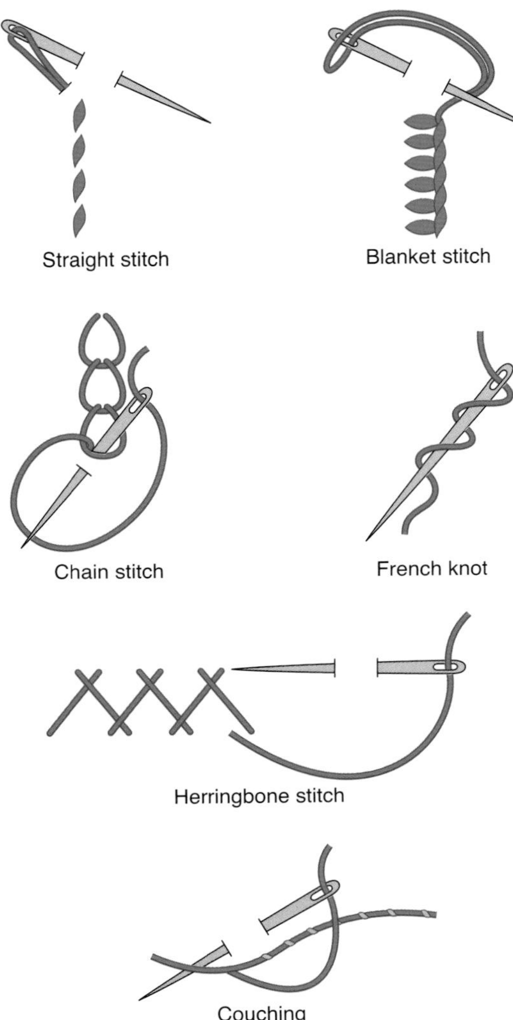

△ **Figure 5.11** Stitches

There is a wide range of domestic sewing machines available that are able to create computerised designs. In industry, the machines use multi-heads (can stitch more than one colour). These machines are very fast and can sew hundreds of products of the same design at any one time. They are controlled by a central computer.

Embroidery using CAD/CAM – picture stitching

Picture-stitching embroidery utilizes the CAD/CAM embroidery machine's ability to multi-stitch. Picture stitching can be used to create textile images that could be displayed on a wall or an open area. They look impressive when seen from far away.

You can also use picture stitching to create small images that can be developed and made into larger pictures or used as a decorative technique.

This process is also suitable for costumes and theatre images or backdrops.

Appliqué

This is the process of layering shapes of one fabric onto the surface or background of another fabric. It is a popular way of adding surface decoration. The pattern pieces that make up the appliqué are usually backed with interfacing or interlining to give them strength and stability. Designs are applied to the fabric using a fine zigzag or satin stitch, which overlaps the fabric, neatening the edge.

Key term

Appliqué – a surface decoration technique, where a design is created by cutting out shapes and then stitching them to a backing fabric to create a design.

△ **Figure 5.12** Finished appliqué

Appliqué and modern CAD/CAM machines

New, computerised machines can also be used to create appliqué designs. Designs for the appliqué can be created in the embroidery design software and you can then use the machine to help you create a step-by-step appliqué. The use of computerised embroidery machines means that designs are more accurately placed and the finishing is of a high quality.

Industrial processes and practices for appliqué

To ensure that accuracy and consistency are maintained, the appliqué shapes are cut out using special die-cutting equipment. This speeds up the manufacturing process.

Embellishment

Embellishment is also known as surface decoration. This is the process of applying textured decoration onto fabrics. The designer may apply several techniques. Processes where beading, sequins or textured stitches are applied to add decoration are known as embellishment.

A popular embellishment technique is called shisha work. Small mirrors are embroidered onto fabrics to reflect other materials and catch the light. This is a popular form of decoration on Indian costume.

△ **Figure 5.13** Examples of shisha work

Other stitch and dye or print techniques can be combined with shisha work.

Other methods of embellishment, such as traditional Mola work from South America, found in countries such as Peru and Panama, are also popular. Mola work is sometimes referred to as reversed appliqué.

Ethical textiles and decoration techniques

Many ethical textiles companies now work in countries such as Malaysia, India and Africa. They work with locals to maintain traditional textile techniques and to keep them alive for the next generation. Companies such as Bristol-based company Bishopton Trading work with the people of the K.V. Kuppam village in southern India. A knitting company called Wool and the Gang works with women in Peru to create a limited edition selection of their seasonal pieces, which are hand-knitted by women who live locally close to Lake Titicaca in the Andean Highlands. Others like People Tree work with local partners such as Sasha Handicrafts, which is based in Kolkata, India. They create beautiful embroidered dresses.

The techniques are applied to fashion goods sold in Western countries. Many of these products have special swing tags attached that tell the story of the techniques and explain how the proceeds from the sale of the goods will be used to benefit the community.

Many of the textiles techniques used have never been written down and are usually passed on from mother to daughter or father to son. With such techniques, companies are recording the processes and placing them online through video-sharing websites such as YouTube or as podcasts on iTunes.

Knowledge link

You can see more about ethical issues in design in Chapter 8, pages 183–193.

Fabric manipulation

Fabrics can be manipulated using a range of techniques. For fashion garments, this manipulation can be in the form of darts. Darts are placed at certain parts of a garment or product to produce shape and form in the product. They can be used as decoration or design features.

Knowledge link

You can read more about darts in Chapter 9 on page 221.

Gathers can also be used to reduce fullness or to add decoration. The process can be done by hand or machine, by placing running stitches along the length of the fabric and then pulling the stitches to gather them together.

Fabric properties can be manipulated or changed using heat or chemicals. Shibori, a technique that originated from Japan, explores the manipulation of fabrics in this way.

The fabrics can be tied, as in tie-dye, or sandwiched between a card or metal template, and then subjected to high steam before the coloured is added. Once the fabrics are dried, they are released from their template.

This process works particularly well on synthetic fabrics because of their thermoplastic properties, which allow the fabric to retain its shape once heated at a high temperature. To remove the shape from synthetic fabric, it has to be heated at a higher temperature.

Distressed effects

Distressed effects are popular on products such as denim jeans. They are applied commercially using processes such as stonewashing or sandblasting. These commercial processes, although popular, are linked to environmental concerns about their use. Other distressed effects that can be tried in the classroom are shredding, fraying or even using sandpaper.

Quilting

This is a very traditional old method of applying texture and colour by stitching through layers of fabrics. There are many methods of quilting from all over the world. The surface texture in the fabric is achieved by layers of fabric combined with layers of wadding or stuffing. This process gives interesting 3D surface textures.

Quilting can be combined with other techniques of surface decoration to give unusual effects. Quilting can be done by both men and women. It is also used by many to recycle fabrics, and elaborate quilts are often handed down as heirlooms.

△ **Figure 5.14** Quilting

Summary

- A wide variety of decorative effects can be used on garments or textile products.
- Designers are increasingly using computers in developing designs and techniques.
- It is important to trial or model the techniques to understand how they can be applied to your work, and note how they might take.

Activity

Choose one method of surface pattern manipulation or techniques and compile a design report about it. Your report should include information about designers for companies that incorporate these techniques in their work. You must use information from a range of resources. You can create your report using Microsoft® PowerPoint®. **[15 marks]**

Exam practice questions

1. What is the difference between patchwork and quilting? **[2 marks]**
2. a) Name three decorative hand stitches **[3 marks]**

   b) Describe how one decorative hand stitch is done **[3 marks]**
3. What are the advantages of using synthetic fibres when manipulating them using heat? Give reasons for your answer. **[4 marks]**

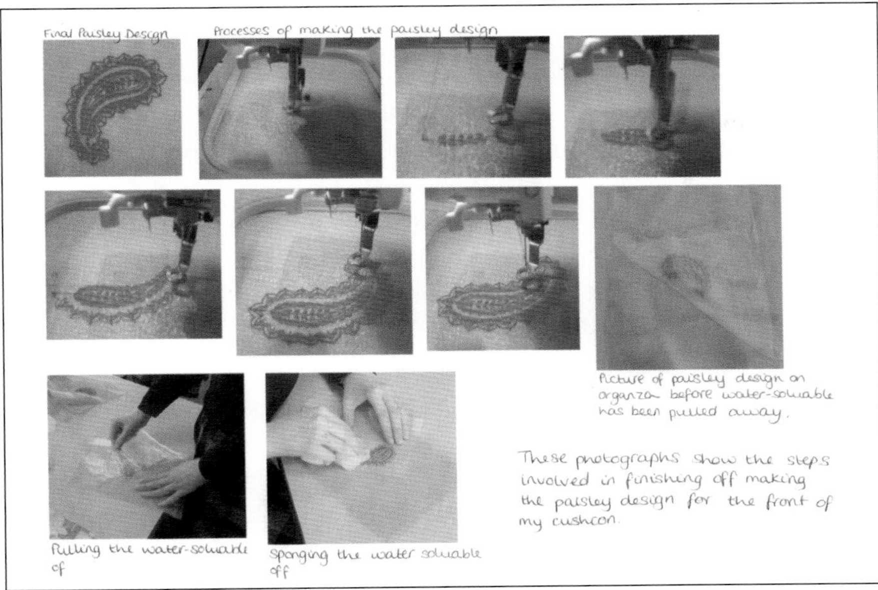

△ **Figure 5.15** A range of decorative techniques

Stretch yourself

Choose one of the following decades: 1920s, 1930s, 1960s, 1990s.

Choose either a fashion or a textile design from your chosen decade.

Choose a designer from that decade.

Choose a method of decoration made popular by the designer of your chosen period.

Create a Microsoft® PowerPoint® presentation detailing the design, designer and method of decoration.

[15 marks]

You can use websites such as those listed below to help you.

The V&A Museum: www.vam.ac.uk

The Design Museum: http://designmuseum.org

The Museum of London: www.museumoflondon.org.uk

The Whitworth Gallery, Manchester: www.whitworth.manchester.ac.uk

The Colour Experience, Bradford: www.colour-experience.org

The 24 Hour Museum: www.culture24.org.uk

5.3 Finishes

Learning objectives

By the end of this section, you should have a key understanding of:

- the key finishes that are applied to textiles and how they can enhance their properties
- how to choose the correct fabrics according to their properties and finishes
- smart materials and the application to textiles
- technical materials and their use in the wider society.

Key points

- Analytical skills
- Communication skills
- Innovative ideas
- Creative ideas
- Linking technology and design
- Values

Introduction

It is important when choosing fabrics for a particular end use that the correct fabrics are chosen. To do this, you need to understand the key properties of fibres and also fabric construction techniques.

In terms of textiles, each fabric or fibre has certain qualities or properties that make it good for a specific end use when manufacturing products. Some fibres have better qualities or properties than others. The properties of fabrics can be enhanced by mixing or blending them together.

Knowledge link

You can read more about the properties of fibres, and mixtures and blends in Chapter 4.

Fabric qualities are often further enhanced by the application of finishes. Finishes can be in the form of a chemical finish, a physical finish or a combination of both. Finishes can be added to fabrics to do the following:

- change the look of the fabric
- change the handle (feel or texture) of the fabric
- change the resilience or durability of the fabric
- improve the drape
- improve drying properties
- reduce shrinkage
- ensure colour-fastness.

When are finishes applied?

Finishes can be applied at various stages of the production process, such as spinning and dyeing. They can also be applied at the end of production. With the use of new technologies, finishes can be applied at the fibre stage using nanotechnology.

Key terms

Finishes – the process of applying a chemical or mechanical finish to a fabric that it does not possess naturally. These finishes can enhance the performance of the fabric.

Nanotechnology – the process of manipulating individual atoms in fibres to enhance the fibre properties. Nanotechnology allows fabrics to retain their natural handle, and other properties, such as water repellency, oil repellency and wrinkle resistance, can be added to cotton fibres.

Knowledge link
You can read more about nanotechnology on page 144.

Knowledge link
For more information on these properties, see Chapter 4.

Decisions will be made on what finish to apply and when to apply it very early on in the design and manufacturing process. Adding a finish adds to the overall cost of the fabric and companies will then often market a textile product as having 'added value' and increase the cost.

Types of finishes

The standard finishes that can be applied to all fabrics are:

- stain resistance
- water resistance
- flame resistance
- crease resistance.

Finishes are evaluated on their ability to improve:

- use
- comfort
- safety
- maintenance
- manufacturing costs
- retail price.

Finishes can be broken down into the following types:

- **Physical finishing** – this is done using a machine, which can change the surface of the fabric, such as by brushing it. Flannelette is an example of a fabric that has been brushed.
- **Biological finishing** – this process uses bacteria or enzymes. These are placed in a solution with the fabric and then attack the

Finish	Ties	Socks and hosiery	School uniforms	Underwear and lingerie
Teflon®	To prevent staining		To prevent loss of colour when washed; to reduce pilling on jumpers; crease-free finish so easy to iron	
Coolmax®		To prevent sweating		
Purista™		Antibacterial finish to prevent smells		
Chitosan				Anti-allergenic finish to prevent itching and reduce inflammation for those with medical skin conditions such as eczema

△ **Table 5.5** The types of finishes that can be added to textile products

cellulose fibre, removing the short fibres, resulting in a softening of the fabric. In biostoning, fabrics are often washed with pumice stone. Biostoning and biowashing are often used on denim fabrics.

- **Chemical finishing** – chemicals are applied to fabrics during or after processing. The chemicals will be used to soften the fabric or remove scales or the outer coating of fibres so they can be manipulated in a different way.

Name of finish	Fabrics it can be applied to	How is it done?	Possible applications
Physical finishes			
Brushing	Cotton, wool, polyester, polyamide	Fabrics are passed between a series of wire rollers, which brush the fabric, leaving it soft and fluffy.	Bedding, fleece garments
Calendaring	Cotton, wool	Fabrics are passed between two heated rollers, which iron and smooth the fabric, giving a high sheen.	Chintz fabric for furnishings
Laminating	Cotton, polyester	This is a layered fabric that is bonded together using heat or adhesive (e.g. Gore-Tex®).	Clothing, footwear and tents
Embossing	Synthetic fabrics	Fabrics are passed through pattern-engraved heated rollers, which leave the embossed pattern on the fabric.	Furnishing fabrics and some clothing
Laser	Cotton, synthetics, leather, wool	A pattern is drawn or burnt onto the surface of the fabric. The laser can cut through several layers. Synthetic fabrics can also be bonded using this process.	Decorative patterns on jeans, upholstery and other furnishing fabrics
Chemical finishes			
Mercerising	Cotton	Used primarily on cotton fabrics. The fabric is placed in a sodium hydroxide solution, which makes the cotton fibres swell. This solution is neutralised and rinsed out. This finish makes the cotton shinier, more absorbent and stronger.	Clothing
Waterproofing	All fabrics	Chemicals are used for this process and they are normally silicone-based. They are applied by spraying directly onto the fabric. This creates a protective barrier.	Clothing, tents
Flameproofing	Cotton, linen, rayon	For this finish, the chemicals used are applied at either yarn or fabric stage. The key aim of using this finish is to slow down the burning process of the textiles. It does not stop the textile from burning.	Interior fabrics, furnishings

△ **Table 5.6** Physical, chemical and biological finishes

Cont.

Name of finish	Fabrics it can be applied to	How is it done?	Possible applications
Stain resistance	All fabrics	This is a silicone-based finish and is used to stop the absorption of stains or dirt onto the fabric surface. This is a key area in the development of nanotechnologies.	Clothing, interior products
Antistatic	Synthetic fibres, acetate, silk	This chemically based finish stops the build-up of electrostatic charge that occurs naturally in fabric.	Underwear, carpets
Anti-felting	Wool	This finish helps to retain the warmth of wool but prevents the wool from felting. This is done by adding what is called an oxidative finishing treatment. The aim of the treatment is to soften the outer, scaly fibres of the wool. For alternative treatments, the wool fabric can be coated with a synthetic polymer film.	Clothing
Bleaching	Cotton, linen	This process is used to remove the natural colour of the fabric, such as cotton and linen, bleaching them white. This process can also weaken the fabric and add to its overall cost.	Clothing, bedding
Crease resistance	Cotton, linen, rayon	A liquid resin-based treatment is applied to the fabric. It is then passed through an oven to bake/seal the finish.	Clothing
Shrink resistance	Wool	A resin-based finish or chemical treatment using chlorine can be applied to wool. This stops the wool shrinking when washed under normal circumstances. Products labelled machine washable or Superwash Wool will have had this finish applied to them.	Clothing, such as jumpers
Biological finishes			
Biostoning	Cotton, Tencel®, lyocell	A process of subjecting the fibre to rubbing with a product such as pumice.	Clothing
Biopolishing	Cotton, Tencel®	A process of adding a sheen to the fabric using an enzyme.	Clothing

△ **Table 5.6** Physical, chemical and biological finishes *continued*

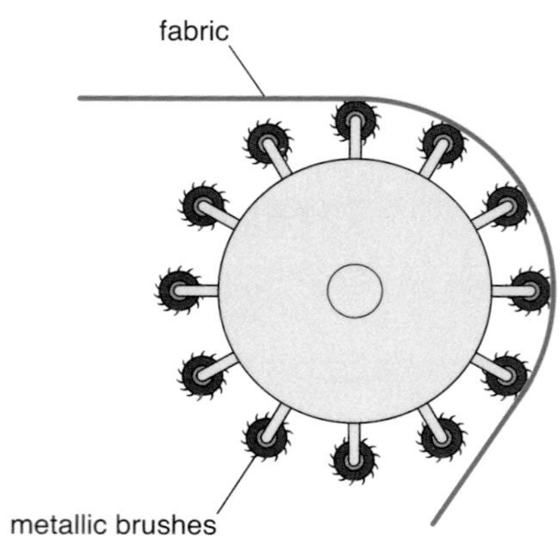

△ **Figure 5.16** Brushing

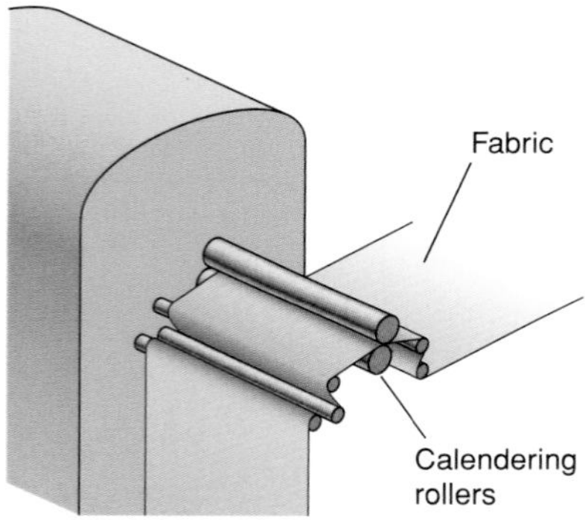

△ **Figure 5.17** Calendaring

Further fabric enhancements

Fabrics can also be given coatings – this involves the addition of a natural or chemical polymer on one side of the fabric. A good example of this is PVC (polyvinyl chloride). This finish is used on products such as raincoats and tablecloths for outdoor use. It adds waterproof protection to textile products.

Fabric finishes and the environment

Many fabric finishes have been known to affect both our health and the environment. With this in mind, many companies are researching ways to utilise less hazardous materials in the finishing process.

Knowledge link

You can read more about textiles and the environment in Chapter 8 on pages 183–199.

Smart, technical and nano-materials

Key terms

Smart fabrics/smart materials – materials that can sense, read and adjust themselves to changes in the environment.

Technical textiles – textile fabrics that are developed where the primary reason for development is focused on end use and not aesthetic issues. These might include combining several materials together.

Smart materials

Smart materials are made up of a range of materials that have been specifically developed to respond to a range of specific stimuli by reproducing responses which are, in some way, seen as special or intelligent. The terms 'intelligent materials' or 'intelligent textiles' are also often used to describe smart materials.

The main types of smart materials are:

- Conductive fibres and yarns
- Conductive polymers
- Shape-memory alloys
- Heat-storage material
- Optical fibres
- Piezoelectric materials
- Quantum tunnelling composites (QTC).

Smart materials	What are they?	Where you can find examples and more information
Conductive fibres and yarns	Can be used to provide connectivity with batteries or other electronic devices. These fabrics can be created to handle electrical power or signals. Synthetic fibres are made conductive either by coating them with copper sulphide or by embedding carbon into polyester fibres.	www.r-stat.com
Conductive polymers	Plastics are also known as polymers. They are now being used to replace metals in many applications. They are lightweight, do not corrode and can be formed into very complex shapes using moulding processes. Plastics are also good insulators of electricity. A plastic embedded with electrical conductivity could offer many possibilities in textile design.	www.panipol.com
Shape-memory alloys	Can be used in one of two ways: in response to external temperature or in response to physical stimuli. Shape-memory polymers have the potential to be combined into fabrics to provide responsiveness to heat.	www.dynalloy.com
Heat-storage material	Heat-storage materials can regulate the heat of products in response to changes in the external environment. Textiles applications include outdoor clothing, underwear, ski wear, blankets and gloves.	www.outlast.com
Optical fibres	Optical fibres project light using a process called internal reflection. They are made from either glass or plastic with a high level of optical clarity and purity. Light can travel in an optical fibre over long distances with very little reduction of brightness. Optical fibres can be used for passing signals in serial digital or analogue form, between places in a machine or from one machine to another, or when encased in textiles from one textile product to another.	www.gtwm.gatech.edu
Piezoelectric materials	A piezoelectric element acts as a sensor in response to a form of pressure or force which then produces an electrical voltage output in response to pressure. It is very compact, reliable and very durable.	www.emfit.com/en/sensors

△ **Table 5.7** Smart materials

Cont.

Smart materials	What are they?	Where you can find examples and more information
Quantum tunnelling composites (QTC)	Peratech makes quantum tunnelling composites (QTCs). These are substances that are extremely sensitive to pressure, heat, radiation and smells. When QTC is put into textiles, the textiles become sensitive to these inputs. QTC has been used as textiles switches and sensors for textiles products, and for uses as diverse as finger sensors for NASA robots and fabric control switches on astronauts' suits, as well as military and civilian (consumer) clothing, especially in the snowboarding and extreme sports area.	www.peratech.co.uk

△ **Table 5.7** Smart materials *continued*

Another area where smart materials are being used is wearable electronics and e-garments or e-textiles.

Wearable electronics and integrated electronics

Textiles and electronics should not really work together, but they do. Some examples of when textiles techniques and technologies are combined with textiles making skills are:

- designing electronic textiles products
- electronics and textiles
- electronic functionality in textiles garments and products.

Wearable electronics refers to clothing that ranges from fabrics and garments that can contain micro-electronic sensors, which can be used to monitor, gather and also transmit information on the wearer's health or physical state. It also refers to garments that enable portable communications and entertainment systems, such as MP3 players, to be incorporated and activated within the garment itself.

Key terms

e-fabrics – these fabrics will contain conductors or connectors such as silver. They may be used for wearable items or clothing, flexible keyboards or furnishings.

e-garments – these are garment items that are enhanced by the use of electronic devices, such as mobile phones, MP3 players and other small gadgets that have been adapted to be incorporated within garments. The garments incorporate interconnections and controls, such as buttons or embroidered patterns, which can be used to operate the products as well as support the electronic circuitry.

Resources

You can read more about this technology and how it is used on the following websites:

www.fibretronic.com

www.oneilleurope.com

Smart colouration materials

Thermochromic materials change colour in response to temperature change. Commonly used on garments, the garments change colour according to the user's body temperature. More recently, this technology has been applied not only to common products such as t-shirts, but also to babies' garments, so parents can monitor the baby's body temperature.

△ **Figure 5.18** Photochromism: military camouflage

Thermochromic materials

These are divided into two areas:

1. Thermochromic
2. Thermotropic.

Thermochromic materials are able to reversibly change their colour in response to light.

Thermotropic materials are able to reversibly change their optical properties – for example,their transparency – in response to temperature.

> **Resource**
> You can read more about smart colouration at www.chromazone.co.uk

Photochromic materials

Photochromism is a reversible process, usually triggered by light (commonly used in sunglasses that react to light). Other applications include fashion clothing for nightclubs where UV light is used; and military camouflage where colour change takes place to respond to the environment.

Photochromic inks/dyes react directly to sunlight.

Photochromism is a reversible transformation of colour using radiation. Photochromic dyes can be applied to threads and paints. These react to the sunlight and produce varying effects, depending on the UV or UVA light. They can be used on garments to reveal patterns or hidden messages. UV dyes are added to products so that when light is reflected they can glow or respond to a certain type of light. This technology is regularly used on products such as clubwear, but it is also being used on textiles, especially furnishing fabrics and areas where additional light might be needed where there is not natural light (for example, restaurants, galleries or other spaces).

Reflective materials

Retro-reflection: 3M™ Scotchlite™ Reflective Materials uses a technology known as retro-reflection.

Retro-reflection occurs when light rays are returned in the direction from which they came. You will find retro-reflective materials on protective wear as used by firemen, or on cyclewear, so you can be seen safely when the lights from vehicles reflect on your garment. Modern reflective materials mean that the wearer can be seen up to 30 metres from the light source.

> **Resource**
> You can read more about reflective materials at www.3m.com
> www.photochromics.co.uk/index.htm

Nano-materials

Nanotechnology is a new and emerging branch of technology. Nano is a term that denotes something that is a one-billionth in size. Therefore nano-materials refers to materials whose size is one-billionth of a metre.

Scientists have found that the properties of materials, when reduced to the nano size, have different properties than when they exist in their 'normal', larger sizes, and this discovery is what is now being used to develop new textiles products. Nanotechnology allows the creation of new materials by direct manipulation of individual molecules or atoms. This means that fabrics can be manipulated to contain the properties that are needed for a particular end use – for example, cotton fibres can be made both water and stain repellent; or new dyes can be developed that can be added to the fibres, just needing the addition of water to activate them, which could change the way fabrics are manufactured

However, there is much work that is being researched in this area and there are concerns that nano-materials may pose a health and/or environmental hazard.

The main types of fibres used in technical textiles

Technical textiles can be divided into **inorganic fibres** (such as synthetic polymers) and **organic fibres** (such as alginates, which come from brown seaweed; chitin, which is a natural polymer found in products such as fungi and crab shells; Chitosan, which comes from shrimp shells, and is used in products such as underwear, as it provides protection from irritation caused by illnesses such as eczema).

Medical technical textiles

Medical technical textiles are an excellent example of how far technical textiles are aiding advancements in tissue engineering. For example, a sample of cells can be taken and grown under the right conditions to form tissue around a technical textile scaffold. Medical embroidered textiles are also being developed, so instead of using traditional metal implants, embroidered implants are now being used which ensure that the broken bone grows around the new embroidered implant, eventually dissolving.

Textiles for agriculture and horticulture

- **Ropes and twines** – originally made from hemp or sisal, now made from polypropylene.
- **Agricultural bags** – originally made from jute or cotton, now made from high-tenacity polypropylene.
- **Non-woven agro textiles** – made from perforated/non-perforated polymeric film; their function is for climatic protection against the elements.
- **Nets/netting products** – mainly woven, Raschel knitted or extruded; Raschel-knitted nets are used for packing hay bales; non-woven nets are being used for crop protection against the elements and wildlife.

Other uses

- **Waterproofing and breathable materials** – PVC-coated rip-stop fabric is now being used as it enables air circulation, which prevents water vapour condensation, which is harmful to timber-frame roofs. Conductive textiles are being used in ceiling, wall and underfloor heating.
- **Protective functions** – woven and non-woven fabrics incorporating copper conductors or conductive fibres are used to provide electromagnetic and electrostatic screening of interior areas, which are essential in hospitals and other buildings housing special computers and sensitive electronic devices.
- **Communication** – woven and warp-knitted fabrics are incorporating optical fibres which illuminate panels, ideal for emergency exit signs. Textile structures can also be used for communication networks such as computer cables, telephone wires, electrical distribution wiring and transport vehicles.

- **Architectural textiles** – technical textiles are replacing traditional building materials. These textile structures are more weather-resistant, lighter in weight and far more economical to install than traditional materials. The Millennium Dome in London is a prime example of an architectural textile.

The following properties of a fibre are important for use with technical textiles:

- Structure
- Fibre density
- Tensile/rigidity
- Elastic recovery
- Thermal
- Chemical/biological/UV resistance
- Friction
- Moisture absorption and retention
- Electrical resistance/static electricity
- Optical.

High-performance fibres are a form of technical fabric and have properties beyond the normal performance of fibres or fabrics used in everyday products.

Examples of trademark technical textile fibres are:

- Kevlar: www.dupont.com
- PBO Zylon: www.toyobo.co.jp
- Peek: www.zyex.com
- Twaron: www.twaron.com
- Vectran: www.goodfellow.com
- PPS: www.rhodia.com
- Normex: www.dupont.com
- Dyneema: www.dsm.com
- Sulfar: www.testori.it
- PBI: www.pbiproducts.com
- Profilen: www.lenzing.com
- P84: www.lenzing.com

Other fibres that have changed textile uses

Elastanes

The best known of this type of fibre is Lycra, also called Spandex. As an elastane, one of its main properties is high stretch. It is added not only to sportswear and swimwear, but also to medical products such as stockings and men's and ladies' suits to prevent bagging. You will also see it used in everyday wear such as denim.

Biodegradable fibres

A new type of reusable and biodegradable material is that made from fibres that have been recycled from plastic water bottles, or PTFE or PET.

Textiles companies such as Malden Mills, who produce Polartec®, and Patagonia use these types of fibres to produce fleeces that are lightweight and breathable. They have also created systems that make it easy for the consumer to recycle their products.

Breathable fabrics

These fabrics use fibres that allow air out and in, but not moisture. An example of this is Gore-Tex®.

Microfibres

These are small, fine fibres, up to 60 times finer than human hair. They can now be made from any type of fibre.

Nomex®

A key synthetic fibre, Nomex® has been developed for use in garments and products used by firefighters and the military.

Kevlar®

This material is hard-wearing and extremely strong. It can be given soft characteristics, but on impact the fabric stiffens up. It is five times stronger than steel and is used for products such as protective jackets.

Biosteel

Biosteel is a genetically modified fibre that contains the casein protein from goats' milk and the protein silk from a spider's web. This combination gives added strength to fabrics. It is being developed for use by the military and is said to be biodegradable.

△ **Figure 5.19** Kevlar® bulletproof vest

Sympatex®

Sympatex® consists of a range of fibres that use what is known as a hydrophilic membrane, meaning that it can absorb or repel water or moisture. It is both breathable and waterproof. It can be used for a range of sporting products, but has found popularity in its use in extreme sports or extreme weather conditions.

Summary

- Finishes enhance the properties of fabrics.
- They can also raise the cost of the final product.
- Some finishes are harmful to the environment.
- Smart materials and technical textiles are changing the way in which designers work.
- Smart and technical textiles can be combined with different technologies for different uses.

Activities

You have been chosen to go on a weekend outdoor camping trip and need a range of clothing, sleeping products and tents.

1. Create a research report, identifying the following:
   (a) Products that keep you dry and wick moisture away from your skin **[15 marks]**
   (b) Products that can keep you warm.
2. Create your ideal kit for the weekend, using examples of products to illustrate your answer. **[15 marks]**

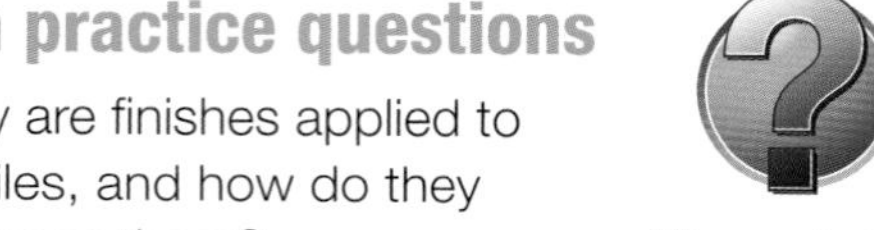

Exam practice questions

1. Why are finishes applied to textiles, and how do they enhance them? **[2 marks]**
2. What are the four different types of finishes that can be applied to textile products? **[4 marks]**
3. What impact have textile fibres like elastane had on textile products? **[4 marks]**
4. Many textile finishes can harm the environment. How do you think manufacturers can change this? **[4 marks]**

Stretch yourself

A skateboarding company is developing a range of trendy garments aimed at 14- to 16-year olds. They need a new collection that uses the latest finishes and combines smart and technical materials. Create a collection for the company. You can present your collection using Microsoft® PowerPoint® or a CAD package of your choice. **[15 marks]**

chapter 6 Components

6.1 Manufactured components

Learning objectives

By the end of this section, you should have a key understanding of:

- how to select, use and evaluate the function, suitability and safety of components
- the different types of components
- the key components used for textile and fashion products
- the technical advances in the design of components
- why components are added to garments and textile products
- the importance of adding the correct components.

Key points

- Analytical skills
- Innovative ideas
- Creative ideas
- Linking technology and design

Introduction

Components are products that are used to enhance or give additional functionality to textile products. Components can also be referred to as haberdashery. The standard components that are used in textiles products are known as pre-manufactured components.

Key term

Components – parts such as buttons and interfacing that are an integral part of a textile product.

In many countries, such as Hong Kong, there are specific districts or streets where you can view and purchase different components. Because of the global nature of the fashion and textiles trade, many designers visit areas such as these to see the latest trends and designs that are available for products.

What types of components are available?

Components can be divided into the following categories:

- threads (e.g. embroidery, sewing, overlocking)
- fastenings (e.g. buttons, snap fasteners, toggles, rivets, covered buttons)
- trimmings (e.g. lace, ribbon)
- tape (e.g. bias binding)
- cords (e.g. cording or cable)
- elastics (e.g. shirring elastic, tape elastic)
- interfacings/linings (e.g. iron-on, stitch and tear)
- pre-manufactured cuffs and collars
- support (e.g. bra cups, boning, shoulder pads)
- beads (e.g. sequins, beads)
- insulation (e.g. wadding)
- lights (e.g. LEDs to give a visual effect)
- patches (e.g. elbow or knee patches to give added protection or repair).

△ **Figure 6.1** Sample component cards

Key terms

Electronic components – electronically based products that can be added to textiles products. They normally need a power source, such as a battery, to operate.

Interfacings – can be made from a woven or non-woven material. They are placed in garments to give strength, structure or reinforcement. They can be ironed on (they have a low-tack adhesive) or stitched into place.

Threads – a thread is a flexible yarn that is made from fibres that have been spun into filaments. They can be made from natural or synthetic fibres. The threads are made by twisting two or more filaments together. There are threads that are made specifically for sewing by hand methods and sewing machines.

Trimmings – often referred to as braids and ribbons, they are added to garments or textile products as decoration.

Component name	Uses and functions
Threads	To add temporary or permanent joins to textile or fashion products. Threads can be made from different types of fibres and in different thicknesses. You can choose different types of threads for different jobs.
Fastenings	To hold a product closed temporarily
Trimmings	To add colour or decoration to a product

△ **Table 6.1** Components and their uses

Cont.

Component name	Uses and functions
Tape	Used to neaten or add strength to certain areas of a garment
Cords	Can be used for decoration or functionality for closing a hood or a bag
Elastics	Can be used to add decoration, such as shirring elastic, or to keep a garment in place or give support
Interfacings/ linings	To give added strength and support to garments; help to keep their shape; can be stitched or ironed onto the fabric
Pre-manufactured cuffs and collars	Can be used to replace worn collars and cuffs; pre-manufactured to reduce making times
Support	Bra pads, or products such as Rigilene; used to add support to undergarments; shoulder pads even out the appearance of garments when worn
Beads	To add decoration to garments
Insulation	Wadding; can be made from synthetic or natural sources. It can be used as insulating material or used in decorative 3D effects
Lights (LEDs)	Electronic components are added to garments for added decoration or function
Elbow or knee patches	Add extra protection at certain points on a garment

△ **Table 6.1** Components and their uses *continued*

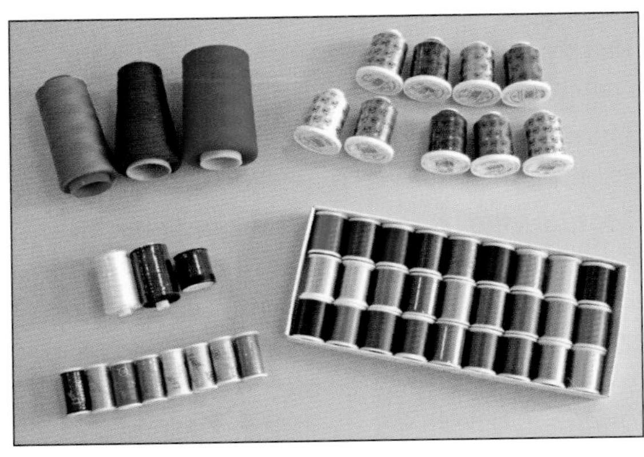

△ **Figure 6.2** Threads

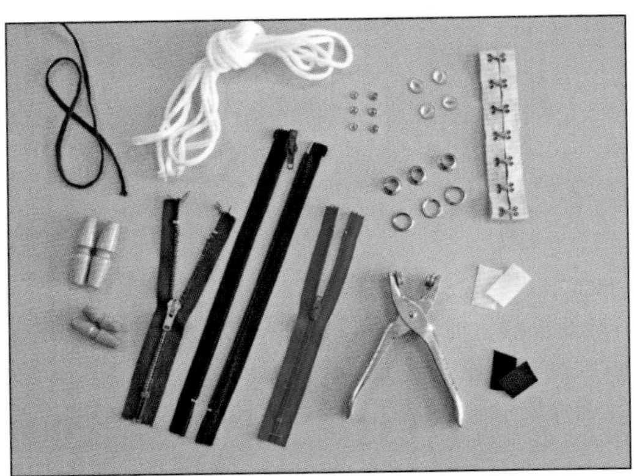

△ **Figure 6.3** Fastenings

△ **Figure 6.4** Trimmings

△ **Figure 6.5** Cords

Choosing the right components

Components are an essential part of any product and are used primarily to do the following:

- add shape
- insulate
- decorate
- mould a product
- give added protection
- aid repair or extend the life of product
- strengthen
- open or close a product temporarily or permanently
- add support.

It is essential that you choose the correct component for your fashion or textile product. The properties of the component should match or mirror that of the product it will be attached to. When choosing components, you should consider:

- the end use of the garment or textile product being made
- how often the product will need to be washed
- how the components are to be applied
- where the components will be applied
- how easily the components can be removed
- the weight of the components, which should complement the weight of the product they will be attached to
- what additional functions the components add to the end product
- the cost the components will add to the overall cost of the product
- whether the components will be decorative or functional
- whether the components could cause any skin reactions or allergies.

Key terms

Buttons – a three-dimensional form that is attached to a garment or other textile product. The button is usually passed through an opening called a buttonhole.

Care label – a set of instructions that explains the aftercare of a fabric or product.

Motifs – the name given to a small design, such as a picture or a flower, that might form part of a larger design.

Zip – a type of fastening that has interlocking teeth or coils. The teeth are brought together using a tab pull.

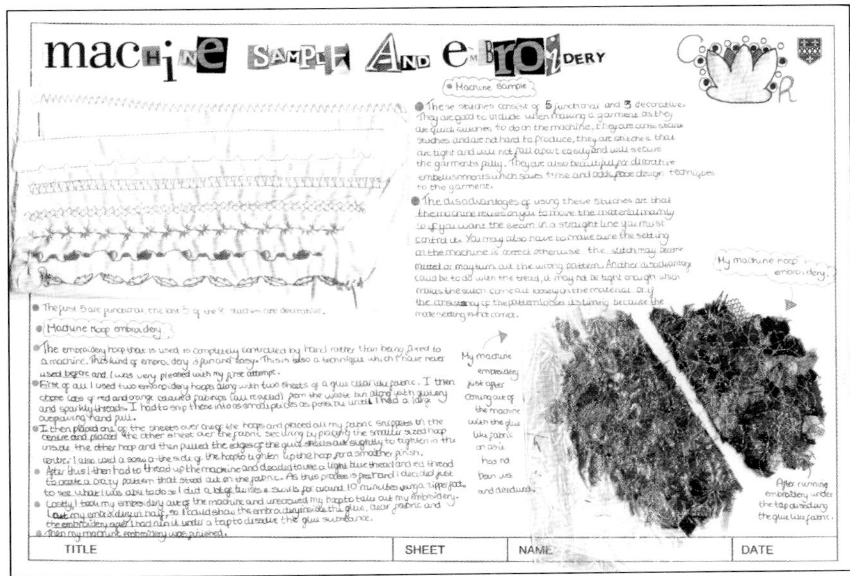

△ **Figure 6.6** Student using components

Components and design development

Just as there are trends in colours that are applied to fashion and textile products, there are trends in the use of different components. These trends will reflect the styling and the construction methods that are used for products.

The component industry is currently looking at methods to reduce waste and reuse components such as buttons, and reviewing the materials it uses to make components. When designing products, designers are now thinking about sustainable components and how they can be reused once the textile product comes to the end of its useful life. When designing products, designers will also review how and where components can be integrated into a product.

Figure 6.7 shows products for carrying objects. When analysing these products you must also consider the user, and how and where they might use the product.

Key features of a bag need that to be **designed** to meet the needs of the user:

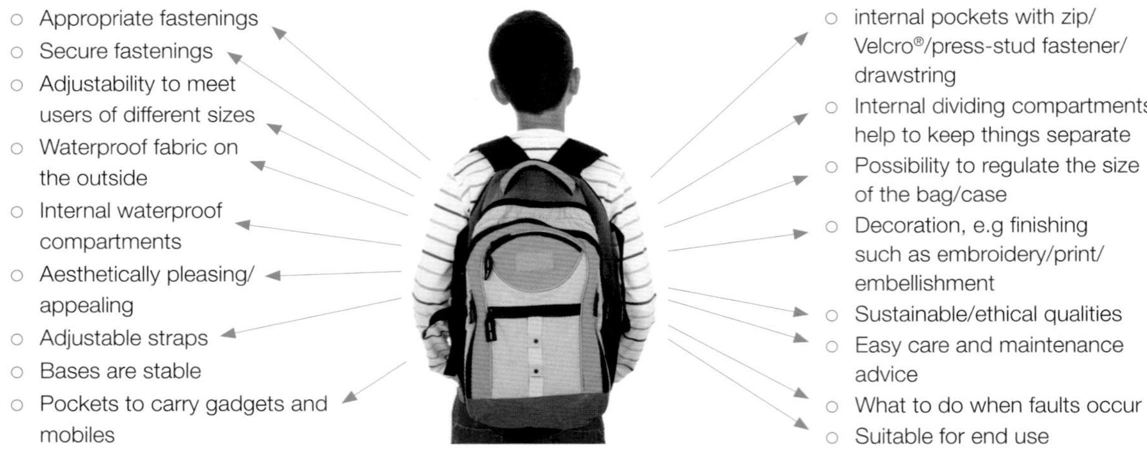

Key features of a bag need that to be **manufactured** to meet the needs of the user:

△ **Figure 6.7**

Safety and components

All components used on textile products have to pass health and safety standards. The components have to withstand wear and tear and washing or cleaning processes, and they should last as long as the product they will be attached to.

In the children's wear industry, there are particularly strict standards that have to be met with regard to components. If a product fails, it can be recalled instantly through consumer support services such as Trading Standards.

Many components also have to meet key regulations with regard to allergies or skin reactions. This is especially true of products that may come into contact with your skin, such as zips and rivets.

Knowledge link

For more information on health and safety standards, see Chapter 8.

Modern components and technology

Components are used in all aspects of different types of garments and products.

For military wear, the Velcro® (hook and loop) that is used has to support a lot of weight (up to 25 kg – this is industrial-strength) and, as such, needs to withstand a high amount of wear and tear.

Key term

Hook and loop (or Velcro®) – a fastening that comprises hooks and loops that close together.

In sports such as cycling, new technology in the manufacture of garments means that they can now be streamlined so cyclists can go faster. To do this, manufacturers do not use normal sewing machines and threads, as they can cause faults in the garment. Instead, they use special welding machines to join seams, keeping them flat, and add components such as zips to the garments. This gives the garments that streamlined effect.

△ **Figure 6.8** Garments can be streamlined for sports such as cycling and swimming

Components such as zips and fasteners are also used in other industries, such as architecture, as they give added flexibility.

Summary

- Your chosen component should match the product it is being applied to.
- The component must meet health and safety regulations.
- The quality of the components should be comparable to the quality of the product they will be attached to.
- Components can add both function and decoration to a garment or textile product.

Activities

1. Look at your school uniform and school bag. Sketch both your school uniform and bag and sketch the components used on these products. **[10 marks]**
2. Think of alternative fastenings that could be used for your products. Draw these fastenings. **[5 marks]**
3. Taking into account sustainable issues, how would you use your textiles skills to design new types of fastenings created from sustainable or renewable resources? **[10 marks]**

Exam practice questions

1. Choose three different products: an accessory, a garment and an interior textile product.
   (a) Identify and list the components that are used on these products. **[6 marks]**
   (b) Are the components for function or decoration? **[6 marks]**
   (c) What materials are the components made of? **[3 marks]**

Stretch yourself

A shop-bought pattern provides information about the components needed to make a product. Read the pattern shown in Figure 6.9 and list the components needed to complete the pattern. Using an online source or catalogue, compile a spreadsheet showing the cost of the components needed to make the product.

[15 marks]

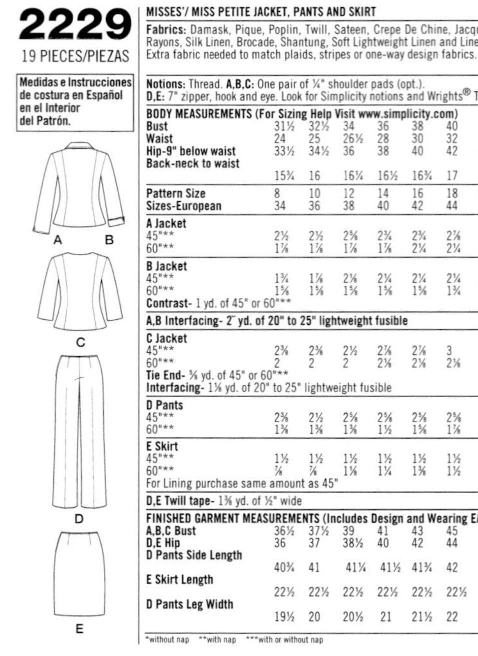

2229

19 PIECES/PIEZAS

Medidas e Instrucciones de costura en Español en el Interior del Patrón.

A B C D E

MISSES'/ MISS PETITE JACKET, PANTS AND SKIRT

Fabrics: Damask, Pique, Poplin, Twill, Sateen, Crepe De Chine, Jacquards, Laundered Silks-Rayons, Silk Linen, Brocade, Shantung, Soft Lightweight Linen and Linen Blends. Extra fabric needed to match plaids, stripes or one-way design fabrics.

Notions: Thread. **A,B,C:** One pair of ¼" shoulder pads (opt.). **D,E:** 7" zipper, hook and eye. Look for Simplicity notions and Wrights® Trims.

BODY MEASUREMENTS (For Sizing Help Visit www.simplicity.com)										
Bust	31½	32½	34	36	38	40	42	44	46	In
Waist	24	25	26½	28	30	32	34	37	39	"
Hip-9" below waist	33½	34½	36	38	40	42	44	46	48	"
Back-neck to waist	15¾	16	16¼	16½	16¾	17	17¼	17⅜	17½	"
Pattern Size	8	10	12	14	16	18	20	22	24	
Sizes-European	34	36	38	40	42	44	46	48	50	
A Jacket										
45"**	2½	2½	2⅝	2¾	2¾	2⅞	3	3	3⅛	Yd
60"**	1⅞	1⅞	1⅞	1⅞	2¼	2¼	2¼	2¼	2⅜	"
B Jacket										
45"**	1¾	1⅞	2⅛	2¼	2¼	2¼	2½	2½	2½	Yd
60"**	1⅝	1⅝	1⅝	1⅝	1⅝	1¾	1¾	1¾	1¾	"
Contrast- 1 yd. of 45" or 60"**										
A,B Interfacing- 2˘ yd. of 20" to 25" lightweight fusible										
C Jacket										
45"**	2⅜	2⅜	2½	2⅞	2⅞	3	3	3	3⅛	Yd
60"**	2	2	2	2⅛	2⅛	2⅛	2⅛	2⅜	2⅜	"
Tie End- ⅝ yd. of 45" or 60"**										
Interfacing- 1⅛ yd. of 20" to 25" lightweight fusible										
D Pants										
45"**	2⅜	2½	2⅝	2⅝	2⅝	2⅝	2⅝	2⅝	2⅝	Yd
60"**	1⅜	1⅜	1⅜	1½	1⅝	1⅞	2¼	2⅜	2⅝	"
E Skirt										
45"**	1½	1½	1½	1½	1½	1½	1½	1½	1½	Yd
60"**	⅞	⅞	1⅛	1¼	1⅜	1½	1½	1½	1½	"
For Lining purchase same amount as 45"										
D,E Twill tape- 1⅜ yd. of ½" wide										
FINISHED GARMENT MEASUREMENTS (Includes Design and Wearing EASE)										
A,B,C Bust	36½	37½	39	41	43	45	47	49	51	In
D,E Hip	36	37	38½	40	42	44	46	49	51	"
D Pants Side Length	40¾	41	41¼	41½	41¾	42	42¼	42½	42¾	"
E Skirt Length	22½	22½	22½	22½	22½	22½	22½	22½	22½	"
D Pants Leg Width	19½	20	20½	21	21½	22	22½	23	23½	"

*without nap **with nap ***with or without nap

JEUNE FEMME / PETITE JEUNE FEMME: VESTE PANTALON ET JUPE

Tissus: Damas, Piqué, Popeline fine, Twill, Satinette, Crêpe de Chine, Soie damassée, Soies/Rayonnes prélavées, Mélange Soie et Lin, Brocard, Shantung, Lin et Mélanges de Lin souples et fins. Prévoyez davantage de tissu pour raccorder les écossais, les rayures ou les motifs unidirectionnels.

Mercerie: Fil. **A,B,C:** Une paire d'épaulettes de 6mm (facult.). **D,E:** Une glissière de 18cm, une agrafe. Demandez la mercerie de Simplicity et les garnitures de Wrights® Trims.

MESURES NORMALISEES										
Poitrine	80	83	87	92	97	102	107	112	117	cm
Taille	61	64	67	71	76	81	87	94	99	"
Hanches (23cm au-dessous de la taille)	85	88	92	97	102	107	112	117	122	cm
Dos (encolure à taille)	40	40.5	41.5	42	42.5	43	44	44	44.5	cm
Tailles	8	10	12	14	16	18	20	22	24	
Tailles-Fr.	36	38	40	42	44	46	48	50	52	
A Veste										
115cm**	2.30	2.30	2.40	2.50	2.50	2.60	2.70	2.70	2.80	m
150cm**	1.70	1.70	1.70	1.70	2.00	2.00	2.10	2.10	2.10	"
B Veste										
115cm**	1.60	1.70	2.00	2.00	2.00	2.00	2.30	2.30	2.30	m
150cm**	1.40	1.40	1.50	1.50	1.50	1.50	1.60	1.60	1.60	"
Parties Contrastantes - 0.90m de 115cm ou 150cm**										
A,B Entoilage - 2.30m de 51cm à 64cm, léger, thermocollant										
C Veste										
115cm**	2.20	2.20	2.20	2.60	2.70	2.70	2.70	2.80	2.80	m
150cm**	1.80	1.90	1.90	1.90	1.90	1.90	1.90	2.10	2.20	"
Lien- 0.50m de 115cm ou 150cm**										
Entoilage - 1.00m de 51cm à 64cm, léger, thermocollant										
D Pantalon										
115cm**	2.10	2.30	2.40	2.40	2.40	2.40	2.40	2.40	2.40	m
150cm**	1.20	1.20	1.30	1.40	1.50	1.70	2.10	2.20	2.30	"
E Jupe										
115cm**	1.40	1.40	1.40	1.40	1.40	1.40	1.40	1.40	1.40	m
150cm**	0.80	0.80	1.00	1.20	1.30	1.30	1.30	1.40	1.40	"
Pour la doublure, achetez la même quantité que pour le tissu en 115cm										
D,E Talonnette de coton - 1.20m de 1.3cm de large										
MESURES DES VÊTEMENTS FINIS										
A,B,C Poitrine	92.5	95	99	104	110	115	120	125	130	cm
D,E Hanches	91.5	94	98	102	107	112	117	125	130	"
D Longueur côté du Pantalon	104	104	105	106	106	107	107	108	109	"
E Longueur de la Jupe	57	57	57	57	57	57	57	57	57	"
D Largeur de Jambe du Pantalon	49.5	51	52	53.5	54.5	56	57	58.5	59.5	"

*sans sens **avec sens ***avec ou sans sens

△ **Figure 6.9** Pattern

Resources

Simplicity Patterns: www.simplicitynewlook.com

London Fashion Week: www.londonfashionweek.co.uk

Maculloch and Wallis (specialist components, consumer): www.macculloch-wallis.co.uk

Eastman Staples (specialist components, industry): www.eastman.co.uk

chapter 7 Product analysis

7.1 Textiles and fashion product design

Learning objectives

By the end of this section, you should have a key understanding of:

- how to generate design ideas
- how to analyse textile products and processes
- the place of trends in the design-and-make process
- the importance of health and safety
- trend forecasting and analysing past and present textile design
- how to use trend research to generate new designs.

Key points

- Analytical skills
- Communication skills
- Innovative ideas
- Creative ideas
- Linking technology and design
- Values

Introduction

To generate original designs is an extremely demanding activity, which means that the designer has to use a range of skills and processes. These will include planning, research, modelling, evaluation and analytical skills. Designers are influenced by many things – for example, by products that are around them, or by books, paintings, fabrics and nature. The skills used to gather information are then used to sort out and analyse the information, to create a range of designs for a specific client or market.

Analysing design – analysing products

Designing new products offers designers the opportunity to look at products, from the past as well as existing products, and to explore design inspirations from a range of ideas – for example, from nature. This process is known as product analysis or design research. This is one of the key processes used in secondary research.

Key term

Analyse – to examine or explore an issue from different angles or perspectives.

Knowledge link

For more information on secondary research, see pages 165–68.

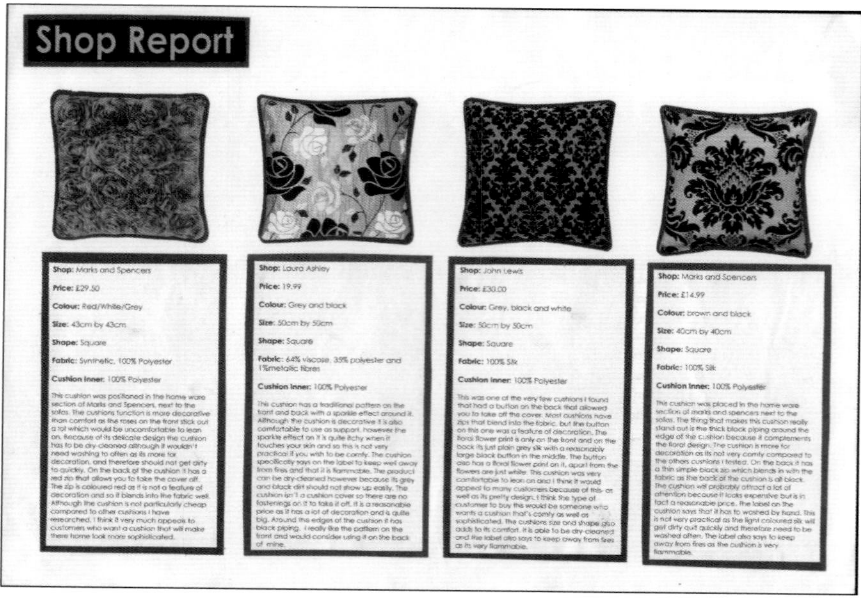

△ **Figure 7.1** Student example of product analysis/design

In your own coursework (controlled assessment, also called design and make practice), you will be asked to analyse products when developing your own design ideas. Whether they are designing garments, accessories or fabrics, designers use product analysis as a way of understanding how the product works or how a fabric is made or constructed. This leads to a greater understanding of what skills, materials and components might be needed to develop their own work.

For example, in developing new fabric designs based on florals, a textile designer might review the work of the following contemporary designers:

- Celia Birtwell – 1960s, and 2007 onwards
- Laura Ashley – 1970s
- Cath Kidston – 1980s onwards
- Orla Kiely – 1990s onwards
- Donna Wilson – 2003 onwards.

Each of these designers uses florals as a key design feature in their products, focusing on use of scale and colour. Each applies them in a different way.

△ **Figure 7.2** Use of florals in design: Donna Wilson

Understanding product analysis

Here are some of the ways in which you can analyse textile products:

1. Research the design of products similar to the one you want to make. Look at colour, shape, application and style.
2. Evaluate existing products – this might mean taking them apart or looking at the fabrics under a microscope, so you can understand the number of components in a product.

3. Explore how the product could be modified or made better. Could it be made accessible to more users?
4. Increase your own knowledge and understanding about materials and the differences between them.
5. Understand how products operate under different conditions. What are the safety rules that apply to the product?
6. Choose to develop a feature of a particular fabric – for example, an aesthetic or technical feature, such as the heat-setting properties of a fabric.
7. Increase your knowledge of manufacturing techniques and create a skills portfolio, where you might explore different products and techniques – for example, cuffs, or using darts in a particular way.

Displaying your analysis

You should display your initial ideas from the analysis in the form of a mind map. This allows you to see links between different aspects of your work. A mind map can take the form of:

- text and notes
- text, notes and visuals
- if using a computer, video or other types of multimedia.

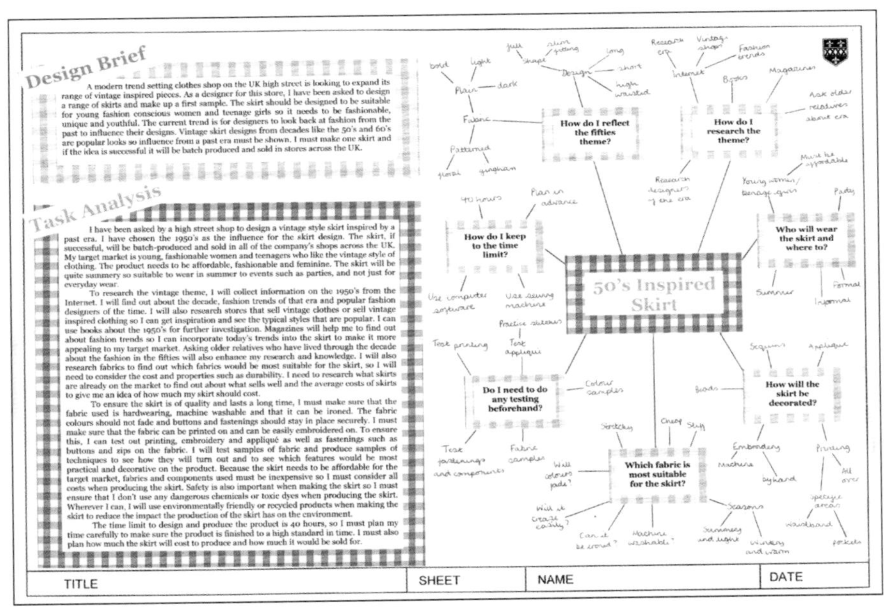

Design Brief

A modern trend setting clothes shop on the UK high street is looking to expand its range of vintage inspired pieces. As a designer for this store, I have been asked to design a range of skirts and make up a first sample. The skirt should be designed to be suitable for young fashion conscious women and teenage girls so it needs to be fashionable, unique and youthful. The current trend is for designers to look back at fashion from the past to influence their designs. Vintage skirt designs from decades like the 50's and 60's are popular looks so influence from a past era must be shown. I must make one skirt and if the idea is successful it will be batch produced and sold in stores across the UK.

Task Analysis

I have been asked by a high street shop to design a vintage style skirt inspired by a past era. I have chosen the 1950's as the influence for the skirt design. The skirt, if successful, will be batch-produced and sold in all of the company's shops across the UK. My target market is young, fashionable women and teenagers who like the vintage style of clothing. The product needs to be affordable, fashionable and feminine. The skirt will be quite summery so suitable to wear in summer to events such as parties, and not just for everyday wear.

To research the vintage theme, I will collect information on the 1950's from the Internet. I will find out about the decade, fashion trends of that era and popular fashion designers of the time. I will also research stores that sell vintage clothes or sell vintage inspired clothing so I can get inspiration and see the typical styles that are popular. I can use books about the 1950's for further investigation. Magazines will help me to find out about fashion trends so I can incorporate today's trends into the skirt to make it more appealing to my target market. Asking older relatives who have lived through the decade about the fashion in the fifties will also enhance my research and knowledge. I will also research fabrics to find out which fabrics would be most suitable for the skirt, so I will need to consider the cost and properties such as durability. I need to research what skirts are already on the market to find out about what sells well and the average costs of skirts to give me an idea of how much my skirt should cost.

To ensure the skirt is of quality and lasts a long time, I must make sure that the fabric used is hardwearing, machine washable and that it can be ironed. The fabric colours should not fade and buttons and fastenings should stay in place securely. I must make sure that the fabric can be printed on and can be easily embroidered on. To ensure this, I can test out printing, embroidery and appliqué as well as fastenings such as buttons and zips on the fabric. I will test samples of fabric and produce samples of techniques to see how they will turn out and to see which features would be most practical and decorative on the product. Because the skirt needs to be affordable for the target market, fabrics and components used must be inexpensive so I must consider all costs when producing the skirt. Safety is also important when making the skirt so I must ensure that I don't use any dangerous chemicals or toxic dyes when producing the skirt. Wherever I can, I will use environmentally friendly or recycled products when making the skirt to reduce the impact the production of the skirt has on the environment.

The time limit to design and produce the product is 40 hours, so I must plan my time carefully to make sure the product is finished to a high standard in time. I must also plan how much the skirt will cost to produce and how much it would be sold for.

△ **Figure 7.3** Student work of the analysis stage

Using analysis to identify key issues

The analysis phase of a project can help you to identify the following:

- key issues highlighted in the design brief
- key client requirements
- relevant research and what you already know
- additional information you may need
- whether more market research is needed
- what colours could be used in your product (colour plays a large part in choosing textiles and fashion products).

In addition, designers in industry will use data gathered from retail sources to identify the following:

- which products were the bestsellers in the previous season
- what the range/product needs to include
- who the products will be aimed at and whether they are targeting the right market and age group
- whether they need to develop new fabrics or finishes for the product
- feedback of ideas.

How to analyse a fashion product

1. From a photograph.

Key details to look at in a photograph:

- colour
- end use
- designer/retailer
- price
- key design details.

2. Actual product

Key details to consider:

- fabric handle
- care label
- stitch details
- components
- possible method of adding colour
- weight of product
- retailer/designer
- price
- quality of manufacture
- end use/user
- laundering/aftercare.

How to analyse textile processes

1. From a photograph

Key details to look at in a photograph:

- colour
- end use
- designer/retailer
- price
- key design details.

2. Actual product

Key details to look at in a photograph:

- fabric handle
- care label
- stitch details
- components
- possible method of adding colour
- weight of product
- retailer/designer
- price
- quality of manufacture
- surface decoration
- end use
- laundering/aftercare.

Note: you can use fashion, interior magazines or websites to view examples of how products are discussed or analysed.

The importance of ergonomic and anthropometric data

The world of fashion uses data of all types, but anthropometric and ergonomic data are used to create both footwear and patterns for clothes. Without these data, we would not have well-fitting clothes.

Key terms

Anthropometric data – the science of body sizes that helps designers make products at the correct size for people to use – for example, the height of chairs.

Ergonomic data – a range of scientific data related to the design of objects for human use.

Anthropometric data

These are data used in the scientific study of human measurements as related to products. In textiles and fashion, these data are commonly used in the measurement of clothing.

Ergonomic data

This is a range of scientific data related to the design of objects for human use. The use of these data allows designers to create products that are easier for people to use. For example, in clothing, designers would consider whether or not a garment allowed enough movement and whether it was easy enough to put on or take off. In the case of shoes, ergonomic data would be used to create the right sizes.

The use of anthropometric and ergonomic data is also important in 'standardising' sizing. Standardised sizes allow companies to manufacture many products very fast. Haute couture or Saville Row suits use the measurements of the individual to create custom-made products.

Trend forecasting

Trend forecasting is the process of predicting key changes one, two or three years ahead. This involves looking at all types of data and information to try to identify the key things that we, as a society, might be using or wearing in the future.

Key term

Trends/trend forecasting – the direction in which something (for example, textiles design) tends to move over a period of time, and the effect that this has on other aspects, such as culture, society or business.

The people who tell us about trends are called trend forecasters, but are also known as futurologists.

There are also specific companies that support the textiles and fashion industry by supplying them with leading information related to all aspects of trends, which includes the following:

- fashion styling
- fabrics

△ **Figure 7.4** Cool Hunting

- components
- accessories
- new technologies
- new fibres and finishes
- key fabrics for a season.

Designers also use new technologies to keep aware of trends, such as:

- social networking media, like Facebook
- Twitter
- video blogs, such as YouTube
- blogs
- smartphone apps
- podcasting/vodcasting.

Designers also use trend books, which contain key fabrics and styling information, as well as links to technical colour information and themes, to help them build their own collection.

Displaying trend information

Trend boards are a way of displaying key information. The textiles industry uses trend boards to reflect concepts and ideas that are forward-looking and that could be developed for products needed in shops in two years' time.

In the textiles and fashion industry, designers work far in advance of when products need to be in the shops. They can react more quickly to online shops, so special companies produce a range of information, including on colour, lifestyle, and new fibres and fabrics, which aid designers in the development of their products.

△ **Figure 7.5** Trend books

The influence of trend forecasts

By analysing past and present textile designs and products, designers can form a better picture of what should be included in new products, including:

- shape
- style
- aesthetics
- choice of materials
- components
- construction techniques
- decorative techniques
- fitness for purpose
- potential marketability.

Designers draw not just on design, but also on social data. Analysis also helps designers to understand better the place of sustainable design and product recycling.

Using trend research to generate new designs

Trend research is the process of looking all around you, reading a range of different publications and analysing both the visual and written information. Once you have analysed the information that you have found, you will need to show both in written and visual format how that trend has emerged and developed, and where it will lead to. Trends will be presented as Microsoft® PowerPoint® presentations, a series of trend boards or in trend books. Many fashion and textiles companies will also pay a lot of money for this trend information, as they will use the information for planning their own product ranges or developing new products.

Trend forecasters are professional people who do this for a living. Many forecasters will try to predict changes for up to five years ahead; this is referred to as future thinking.

In your own work, you can review trends related to your chosen project, to do the following:

- explore the issues
- use a good range of secondary research
- find out what the new technologies are in your area of research and what impact they have on your design
- work out which people are the key influences
- examine how the colour ideas have developed for this area
- discover the motifs that are appearing for print design
- explore the new shapes in clothing.

Mood boards

Mood boards consist of a range of visual research information based on a particular theme, which is presented on either a board or a presentation page.

The images usually reflect the 'here and now', focusing on a specific theme. Mood boards may contain the following:

- words and text
- pictures/photographs/images
- fabrics and trimmings
- colours
- collage.

Knowledge link

You can see how mood boards can be used in your coursework (controlled assessment) by looking on pages 7–8.

△ **Figure 7.6** A student's mood board

The mood board can also be used as a starting point for developing concepts and ideas. It can be used to clarify ideas and visualise information to the client, for feedback, which is an important part of the design development process. Designers may use one or several mood boards to tell the design story.

Mood boards, therefore, can be used in the following ways:

- to act as a focus for developing new design ideas and concepts
- to focus on research ideas and modelling techniques
- to reflect on research and model ideas, concepts, colours, and so on.
- to clarify market and target information
- to inform the client about your ideas, and what you see as the way forward in developing designs.

Key terms

Health and safety – the process of ensuring that you are working in a safe environment and that the equipment and/or materials that you are working with meet safety requirements and are safe to use.

Mood boards – a collection of visual imagery that can be used to summarise design or visual thinking. It can act as a starting point in developing new design ideas.

Trend board – a display of ideas that predicts designs for the future.

Health and safety

In the analysis stage of your design work, you will need to identify key areas for development. It is essential, therefore, that even at this stage you are aware of the potential health and safety issues related to your design work.

For example, in developing designs for a children's wear collection, you would need to know the key issues related to safety in children's wear. If you were developing designs for furnishings, you would need to understand the difference between flame resistance and flame retardance. You also need to know the potential risks of the equipment or modelling techniques you might use in relation to your own design work and the finished product.

Knowledge link

For more information about health and safety, see pages 200–10.

Summary

- Design analysis is an important part of the design process. It allows you to identify the key factors in developing your design project and keeps you focused.
- Analyses can be displayed as mind maps.
- Analysis helps to define the project and identify good and bad points.
- Trend and mood boards are part of the analysis process and help to identify visuals and other colour data that could be relevant.

Activity

You have been asked to compile a trend report based on printed fabrics. Choose the product area, of fashion, accessories or interior products, and create a written and visual report. In your findings show the following:

- developing trends for the last two years
- new colours
- fabrics that are being developed
- shapes of products
- other influences – for example, designers, gallery shows, materials and architecture.

[15 marks]

Exam practice questions

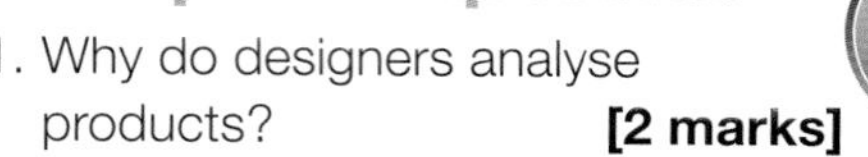

1. Why do designers analyse products? **[2 marks]**
2. How does analysing a product help the design process? **[4 marks]**
3. What is the difference between a trend board and a mood board? **[4 marks]**
4. Why is health and safety important at the analysis stage? **[4 marks]**

7.2 Evaluation techniques

Learning objectives

By the end of this section, you should have a key understanding of:

- design proposal versus design criteria
- design criteria influences – how designers get ideas
- design brief
- design specifications
- design for disassembly
- the use of disassembly to make critical judgements about design, manufacture and performance of existing products
- how to review current products critically
- how to evaluate and improve designs
- quality assurance
- how the end user influences product development (third-party influence).

Key points

- Analytical skills
- Communication skills
- Innovative ideas
- Creative ideas
- Linking technology and design
- Values

Introduction

Understanding how to relate design research to design proposals is key for developing design projects. It is important to be able to explore and analyse information and then use that information to make informed decisions about what you will do next to develop your designs. Using design criteria allows you to identify the key things needed to take the design forward. The design proposal is then used to formulate your wider thinking and interact with the client or user that the product is for.

Design criteria versus design proposal

The design of all products is guided by a set of rules or criteria. These criteria become an essential tool for mapping the way in which initial design ideas are developed. For example, before a children's wear designer starts working on a design project, they may already have incorporated the following rules into their design criteria:

1. No cords.
2. No use of zips on garments for boys under five.
3. No buttons that look like food.

The designer will then incorporate the design criteria into the final design proposal, which sets out the key information about their design.

Key terms

Design criteria – a list of key/important points needed for a design.

Design proposals/design solution – initial ideas that are further developed and explored.

Where do the design ideas come from?

Design ideas are developed from different viewpoints. The designer can be guided by the client, who may have proposed an idea, by the design team of a large company that has collated information from trips overseas, by another artist, or even by the world around them. All the information collected must be reviewed and put into some sort of order or visual layout before concrete ideas can be developed.

The designer or design team will develop the design brief to focus ideas using a range of methods and processes. This is called research.

There are two key types of research:

- primary research
- secondary research.

Primary research

This type of research is original – that is, it has not been done before. Using this type of research provides you with key information that might be difficult to get from other sources. Information gained from primary research is analysed and the results can be displayed using data charts (e.g. pie charts, bar graphs). This helps you to see where things are similar or different in your research and apply the findings to your project.

Where does primary research come from?

You can use some of the methods listed in Table 7.1 below to gather primary research. The best kind of primary research combines several methods of data collection.

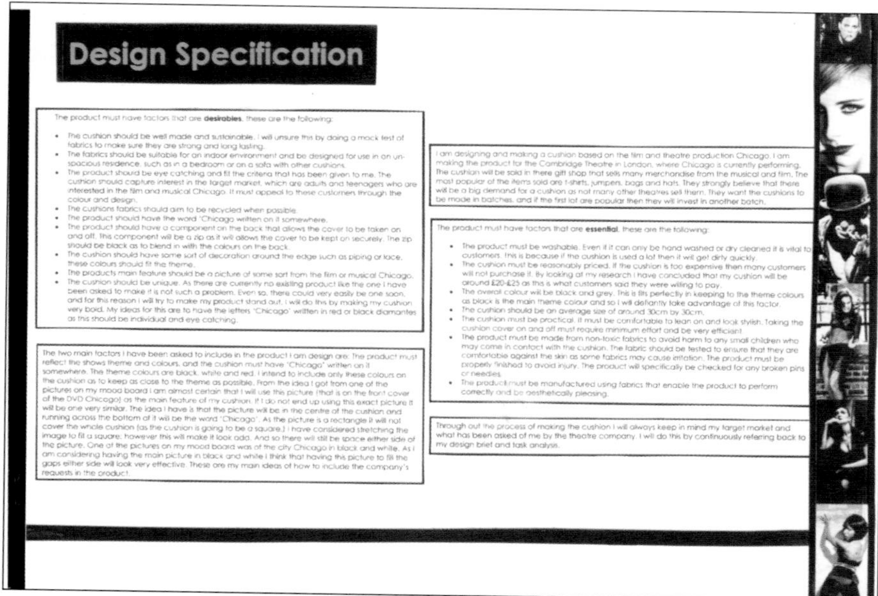

Design Specification

The product must have factors that are **desirables**, these are the following:

- The cushion should be well made and sustainable. I will unsure this by doing a mock test of fabrics to make sure they are strong and long lasting.
- The fabrics should be suitable for an indoor environment and be designed for use in an un-spacious residence, such as in a bedroom or on a sofa with other cushions.
- The product should be eye catching and fit the criteria that has been given to me. The cushion should capture interest in the target market, which are adults and teenagers who are interested in the film and musical Chicago. It must appeal to these customers through the colour and design.
- The cushions fabrics should aim to be recycled when possible.
- The product should have the word 'Chicago written on it somewhere.
- The product should have a component on the back that allows the cover to be taken on and off. This component will be a zip as it will allows the cover to be kept on securely. The zip should be black as to blend in with the colours on the back.
- The cushion should have some sort of decoration around the edge such as piping or lace, these colours should fit the theme.
- The products main feature should be a picture of some sort from the film or musical Chicago.
- The cushion should be unique. As there are currently no existing product like the one I have been asked to make it is not such a problem. Even so, there could very easily be one soon, and for this reason I will try to make my product stand out. I will do this by making my cushion very bold. My ideas for this are to have the letters 'Chicago' written in red or black diamantes as this should be individual and eye catching.

The two main factors I have been asked to include in the product I am design are: The product must reflect the shows theme and colours, and the cushion must have 'Chicago' written on it somewhere. The theme colours are black, white and red. I intend to include only these colours on the cushion as to keep as close to the theme as possible. From the idea I got from one of the pictures on my mood board I am almost certain that I will use this picture (that is on the front cover of the DVD Chicago) as the main feature of my cushion. If I do not end up using this exact picture it will be one very similar. The idea I have is that the picture will be in the centre of the cushion and running across the bottom of it will be the word 'Chicago'. As the picture is a rectangle it will not cover the whole cushion (as the cushion is going to be a square.) I have considered stretching the image to fill a square; however this will make it look odd. And so there will still be space either side of the picture. One of the pictures on my mood board was of the city Chicago in black and white. As I am considering having the main picture in black and white I think that having this picture to fill the gaps either side will look very effective. These are my main ideas of how to include the company's requests in the product.

I am designing and making a cushion based on the film and theatre production Chicago. I am making the product for the Cambridge Theatre in London, where Chicago is currently performing. The cushion will be sold in there gift shop that sells many merchandise from the musical and film. The most popular of the items sold are t-shirts, jumpers, bags and hats. They strongly believe that there will be a big demand for a cushion as not many other theatres sell them. They want the cushions to be made in batches, and if the first lot are popular then they will invest in another batch.

The product must have factors that are **essential**, these are the following:

- The product must be washable. Even if it can only be hand washed or dry cleaned it is vital to customers. This is because if the cushion is used a lot then it will get dirty quickly.
- The cushion must be reasonably priced. If the cushion is too expensive then many customers will not purchase it. By looking at my research I have concluded that my cushion will be around £20-£25 as this is what customers said they were willing to pay.
- The overall colour will be black and grey. This is fits perfectly in keeping to the theme colours as black is the main theme colour and so I will defiantly take advantage of this factor.
- The cushion should be an average size of around 30cm by 30cm.
- The cushion must be practical. It must be comfortable to lean on and look stylish. Taking the cushion cover on and off must require minimum effort and be very efficient.
- The product must be made from non-toxic fabrics to avoid harm to any small children who may come in contact with the cushion. The fabric should be tested to ensure that they are comfortable against the skin as some fabrics may cause irritation. The product must be properly finished to avoid injury. The product will specifically be checked for any broken pins or needles.
- The product must be manufactured using fabrics that enable the product to perform correctly and be aesthetically pleasing.

Through out the process of making the cushion I will always keep in mind my target market and what has been asked of me by the theatre company. I will do this by continuously referring back to my design brief and task analysis.

△ **Figure 7.7** Student's design specification

Type of primary research	Examples
Questionnaires	These are usually made up of a range of questions that are given to either individuals or a group. The questions are analysed and then presented in the form of charts or graphs. This type of information helps the designer to understand key aspects of the design criteria or to get key information about a particular aspect of the product being designed.
Specific trade exhibitions	Premiere Vision in France, for example, focuses on new fabric designs.
Speaking to focus groups	Focus groups are people that are to be the key customers. By speaking to these groups, you can find out how they might use a product.
Surveys	Aimed at specific target groups to get an understanding of the key issues, such as places that they go in design circles. This is also called intelligence gathering.
Shop reports	Going to the types of shops that your potential customer may use. A shop report can involve going to one particular shop or several shops and comparing similar products. This process of going to several shops and comparing similar products is called comparative shopping.
Product analysis	Analysing past products or analysing existing and current products. From this, you can get a clear understanding of product manufacture and construction.
Modelling and making	Creating models from fabrics or experimenting with colour on fabrics or even making sample toiles can be considered a form of primary research. Designers source fabrics and components from different trade shows and create sample ideas that could be developed further.
Photographs	Original photographs that act as a starting point are also considered primary research.

△ **Table 7.1** Types of primary research

Secondary research

This type of research is also called desk research, as you can work from a desk to carry it out. Secondary research is information that already exists in the public domain – for example, in libraries, newspapers, magazines and the internet (e.g. on Wikipedia or blogs). Examples of secondary research are listed in Table 7.2.

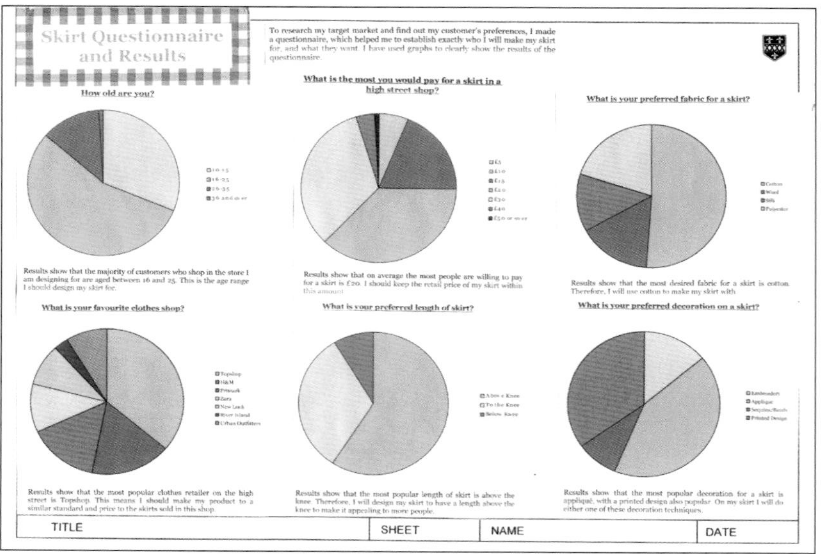

△ **Figure 7.8** Primary research

Types of secondary research	Examples
Statistics	These are data provided as figures or numbers and then converted into visual information, such as graphs.
Market reports	These are very specialised and focused reports, created by specialised writers or companies about specific product types or markets.
Trade information	This is information from trade journals or specialist websites.
Books	These are any types of books related to the subject or research.
CD/DVD-ROMs	This might be a visual CD or a database.
Specific trade or e-fashion websites	Websites such as Cotton Incorporated and Fashion Capital provide key information related to all aspects of the fashion and textiles trade.
Magazines	These are specific trade magazines that are related to textiles and fashion, or other general design magazines.
Technical websites	There is a range of websites/blogs and Twitter feeds that you can use to get specific technical information.
Visual information	This could be visuals of past designs and information about designers or their work. This information can come from books or the internet. You must always check that you can use visuals in your work and be aware of copyright infringement (using others' work without permission).

△ **Table 7.2** Types of secondary research

Cont.

Types of secondary research	Examples
Internet (e.g. blogs, wikis, tweets)	The internet can provide a rich source of information, but there is so much information out there that you need to think carefully about what to include. You must also double-check the information for its accuracy – this can be done by cross-referencing it with other published information.

△ **Table 7.2** Types of secondary research *continued*

Key terms

Comparative shopping – comparing like-for-like products from different retailers and analysing them in terms of price and quality.

Focus group – a specifically selected group of people who can act as representatives of the general public. Their opinions are used as a form of market research.

Intelligence gathering – the process or gathering a range of specific information and the ability to link key concepts or facts from that information.

Primary research – original research that has not been done before and is originated by the user.

Secondary research – also called desk research, secondary research is information that already exists in what is known as the public domain – for example, at libraries, or in newspapers or magazines, or on the internet.

Target group/target markets – a range of people at whom a product is aimed.

△ **Figure 7.9** Secondary research

The list in Table 7.2 is not exhaustive, and designers and design companies will use a wide range of secondary research to support design ideas. Although primary research and secondary research are necessary, the designer will still need to develop ideas that will help them to develop the designs. These ideas can come from a range of sources – this is called design inspiration.

Design criteria influences – how designers get ideas

Designers use visual information to develop design ideas. These ideas can come from:

- books and magazines
- graphics and photographs
- materials, fabrics or components
- the cinema (the latest films)
- art and crafts
- travel
- architecture
- nature
- music and theatre
- product design.

Designers also need to be aware of design aesthetics (how the design looks), which includes line, pattern, texture, form and colour. The designer will use this information to create a visual summary of the content collected.

However, ultimately, how the design is developed is linked directly to the design brief that is specified by the client. Using the client's specification, the designer or design team will create a range of visual presentation materials developed from their research. This is collated (collected together) and then displayed as either trend boards or mood boards.

Mood boards and trend boards

Designers will summarise the visual design information or research gathered in different ways. Initial ideas may be collated in a sketchbook or a folder. The final summary of the research may then be presented using either a mood board for initial ideas and developments or a trend board for products that are to be developed for the future.

△ **Figure 7.10** Design criteria

Mood boards

A mood board is a visual summary of the design theme, using a combination of images, key words, colours, fabrics and other textured materials. Designers may create one or several boards in order to tell the design story. The client will be able to give feedback to the designer or design team on the mood board and designers will use this feedback to refine the design criteria.

Trend boards

Trend boards are similar to mood boards, but they are targeted for specific areas – for example, colour, theme or fabrics – and will be used by designers to help them to understand key future market directions or trends in a specific design or product area. They are developed using a range of design, social and economic data. It is a very specialised market. With modern technologies, trend information can be accessed online for a fee or purchased from specialised companies, such as WGSN, TrendStop, Global Mix or Cool Hunting, or it can be seen in specialised magazines, such as *View*, or specialised websites such as Pantone, where the focus is on colour, or Cotton Incorporated, where the focus is on the ways that cotton is used across a variety of markets.

Controlled assessment link

For more information on mood boards and trend boards, see pages 7–8.

What is a design specification?

The design specification is a document that contains a list of the criteria that the client wishes the designer to follow in the final design of the product.

The specification can consist of the following:

- essential criteria – the key elements or factors that the product must have
- desirable criteria – desirable, but not essential, elements of the product.

△ **Figure 7.11** Student examples of mood boards

Key terms

Design specification – the specific design details that a product has to match.

Desirable criteria – desirable, but not essential, elements of the product.

Before finalising the design specification, designers also need to consider the information in Table 7.3, also known as profiles.

Essential criteria – the key elements needed to make a product.

What is a design brief and why is it important?

A design brief is a key document that is used by the client to guide the designer with their initial research in the development of a product. A design brief can have a specific theme or the client can give the designer a range of guidelines to follow. A design brief can be described as being either an open brief or a closed brief.

- An open brief has no specific theme, but the designer will be given an indication by the client as to what should be included. However, it is left to the designer to develop the design theme. The designer will then present to the client a range of alternatives that can be further developed. The final design solution is not specified, giving the designer the opportunity to develop a range of unique products.
- In a closed brief, the client gives the designer specific guidelines to follow and lists the types of things that must be included in the design, in terms of product, colour, theme, target market and costs. Here the final design solution is specified. The designer must fulfil the brief and give the client what they have specified.

Key terms

Design brief – a short statement explaining what is going to be designed and made.

Inspiration – a source for ideas or thinking.

What is in the design brief?

A design brief is a clear set of instructions and guidelines that will be used to by the designer to develop a product. In the design industry, the key things to be included are as follows:

1. The current market overview or an analysis of their current products – who buys their product and where do they sell the most?

Profiles	Details
Price	This will include the price that the product will be made for, as well as the price it will be sold for. Is it the correct price based on the market for which it is intended?
Aesthetics or design	Are the key aesthetic and design features (colours, etc.) correct for the product and the intended market?
Cultural	Does the intended product match the market that it is intended for culturally?
Social	Does the product match consumer requirements or company requirements in terms of ethical, environmental and other social issues?
Technical	What technology needs to be used to create the product and will the technology that will be used to create the product need special machinery or processes?
Performance	Does the product stand up to tests? Is it safe?

△ **Table 7.3** Profiles

2. Their main competitors – who are the main competitors of similar products? This may include comparative shop reports.
3. What products the client wants the designer to design.
4. The design budget – the overall cost of using a designer as part of the process, and also the budget for selling the product.
5. The completion date for the project – when the project starts and when it ends. They might use a Gantt chart or a simple flow chart to help plan the time it will take. Usually, the longer the time taken to complete the project, the more expensive it will be. Also, where something takes longer than planned, it could affect the type of production method that can be used.
6. Key colours to include or not to include in the final design, logos or company (corporate) colours, plus any cultural changes to be considered.
7. What are the things that can be changed about the existing product to make it more appealing and to take it forward?
8. Price range of the products to be designed – this needs to include all information needed to make the products, including costs of materials, decoration, components and production.
9. Manufacturing outlet – where will the product be manufactured (e.g. UK, the Far East or Eastern Europe)? Where the product is manufactured will have an effect on the overall cost of the product.
10. Sustainable issues to be considered.

Note: you might want to use this list to check your own design brief and specification.

When working to your own design or clients' briefs, you should consider all factors, but the important thing is that you understand the design brief and what is to be expected. That is why initial presentations of ideas is important, as it gives both the designer and the client the opportunity to discuss key ideas and how the product can be developed.

Design for disassembly

Design for disassembly is a process used in product design to assess the following:

- the number and types of components/parts/materials contained in a product
- the possible reassembly process
- the manufacturing process
- how to reduce waste
- how to minimise material usage
- how to adjust the ways in which a product is joined together.

Within the fashion and textiles industry, the disassembly process is used to do the following:

- review the make-up of a product
- assess the material construction (e.g. knitted, woven or non-woven)
- link back to quality control and quality assurance
- assess if the product has been made to the required specification
- research the process of applying pattern or decoration
- assess how to use the pieces of a disassembled garment as the base for a new pattern or to adapt a pattern
- make critical judgements about design, manufacture and performance of existing products
- gain a critical insight into design development and materials
- build up knowledge and skills
- provide a base from which to evaluate a product
- provide a starting point for how to improve a product
- enable the designer to critically review a product from different points of view
- give the designer the opportunity to review the product specification and criteria for a given product

- review the aftercare (laundry) instructions for example, could a fibre or fabric be used that requires less washing and/or ironing, so reducing energy usage?
- assess packaging requirements
- review life cycle and waste disposal
- review the product's sustainable footprint.

Key terms

Critical review – taking an analytical view of a process or product and its potential impact.

Design for disassembly – the process of taking a product apart and then analysing the making process and the materials used. The information can then be used to develop new processes, to change the making process or to review materials use.

Disassembly – taking products apart.

In your own work, you may use disassembly to:

- create a new pattern
- gain understanding about the number of components in a product
- review the types of materials used
- see how the product or components can be recycled.

How the end user influences product development

The end user, also known as the third-party influence or the consumer, can dictate or specify what they like or dislike about a product through a review or user testing process. This review process might take place through a questionnaire, a trial use of a product or a review of images of the product for its aesthetic qualities.

Key term

Third-party influence – the view of a third party or other person that is not initially included in the design brief.

The end user can also let the manufacturer know if there are faults in the product. If a product has developed a major fault, then the manufacturer might do a recall or alert Trading Standards.

Knowledge link

For more about consumer influences on product development, see Chapter 8.

Summary

- Design criteria are an essential part of the mapping process for developing design proposals.
- Design specifications give the designer the key things that should be part of the design. They give clear parameters about the product and the key details that the client requires.
- The design brief is used by the client to give the designer a clear guide for design inspiration.
- By disassembling a product, much can be learnt about the product and its component parts. It allows for the critical review of current products and allows the designer to develop ongoing evaluation and improvement. It can also be used to ensure that the correct quality control and quality assurance processes are in place.

Activities

1. Choose two similar textile products and take a digital picture of each product.
2. Compare and contrast the features of each product. What are the similarities or differences?
3. Design a new product utilising the key features you think are important. Annotate your answers with sketches and notes. **[15 marks]**

Exam practice questions

1. What is the difference between a design proposal and design criteria? **[2 marks]**
2. Why would designers need to use design for disassembly in developing their design work? **[4 marks]**
3. What is the difference between an open brief and a closed brief? **[2 marks]**
4. What is a design specification, and why do we use them in the design process? **[2 marks]**

Resources

Trading Standards:
www.tradingstandards.gov.uk

7.3 Evaluation of quality of own product compared with market alternatives

Learning objectives

By the end of this section, you should have a key understanding of:

- using design specifications
- the importance of understanding and testing existing products
- disassembly as a process of understanding the design of textile products
- how to test and evaluate products
- the importance of user and client feedback in the design-and-make process.

Key points

- Analytical skills
- Communication skills
- Innovative ideas
- Creative ideas
- Linking technology and design
- Values

Introduction

At each stage of the design process, you will have made decisions that impact on your product. Once you have completed your controlled assessment, you will need to critically review each stage of the process of design and making, and the effectiveness of the product you have designed and created. Ideally, you will have made modifications throughout your research and design-and-make phase, which means that you have

made decisions and changes to the different aspects of your work.

The design specification

Your design specification plays a crucial part in the development of your work and, as such, it is important that you evaluate how effective it was in helping you succeed in the making of your product. The types of specifications you might have encountered in your work are as follows:

1. **Fibre properties and specification** – the type of fibre that your fabric contains will have an impact on the effectiveness and end use of your product.
2. **Fabric specifications** – the key characteristics that you require for your fabric (e.g. soft handle, antimicrobial, or high technical finish).
3. **Design specification** – this identifies the key functions of your design, who it is for, its market, sustainable and environmental considerations, and design sketches.
4. **Product specification** – this details all the elements of your product, such as the working drawing, the technical specification sheet, all your component costings and size.
5. **Manufacturing specification** – these are the key details in relation to the making of the product. What are the stages involved and how long will each stage take to complete? You also need to understand that, in the working world, the manufacturing specification is often given to a third party – this may be the manufacturing or production plant – so you need to ensure that all the details are clear and that you have communicated effectively.

The review process

Critical evaluation of the processes you have followed will allow you to reflect on your own work, as well as review the following:

- appropriateness of the design focus
- effectiveness of planning
- relevance of the research
- how colour and design ideas were developed from the mood board
- suggestions for modifications to the design ideas
- the modelling processes undertaken
- the design specification and the criteria
- how to improve the manufacturing process, including the flow chart
- whether you included issues related to sustainability in your work
- how good your making skills were
- whether you understood how to care for your product
- effective use of equipment
- end user feedback
- what you have learnt overall
- what you would do differently
- what further modifications or amendments you would make to your work.

What does this review process do?

This review process allows you to step back and take a good look at the way in which you work and how you applied your thinking skills to the project. You need to remember that the controlled test is only one part of your assessment for the GCSE Textiles work; you will also need to take the information you have learnt during your controlled assessment and apply this to your written exam.

What does critical evaluation involve?

A critical evaluation involves gaining an overview of what you have learnt and how you can apply this to both your controlled assessment and the written examination.

In your own critical evaluation, you might want to consider the following:

1. How well have you proved the key points in your project?

2. How have you considered the impact of the data you collected on how your project developed?
3. Were you able to interpret the information that you gathered and create a suitable outcome?
4. How good were you at resolving any problems that arose?
5. How good were you at making clear, informed choices with regard to, for example, materials, the correct tools and equipment, or the correct decoration method?
6. Were you able to make judgements or evaluate specific processes to ensure the correct ones were chosen?
7. How did you test and check the validity of your ideas?
8. Are you able to assess your own knowledge base – what did you know before you started making your product and how have you added to your knowledge?
9. What did you know or not know about what you were designing and making?
10. How did you apply your knowledge?
11. How good were you at testing your results?
12. How effective were the key processes you used in making the product?
13. Did you develop a suitable end user questionnaire or survey?

Key terms

Test – a process to ensure that standards are met.

Evaluate – to consider the success of the product.

Suggesting modifications

Modifying something means changing or adapting it to make a better product. In your textiles work, you might decide how or when to add modifications by asking the following questions:

1. How can you improve the making process?
2. Did you gather enough information that was relevant to your product?
3. Is the product suitable for the end user?
4. How does your product compare to one that is already on the market?
5. Have you been able to predict your outcomes?
6. Are there any alternatives to your design decisions?
7. How could the materials, components and processes you have used be modified?
8. How have you performed in the task?
9. What were the key issues that slowed you down and how could they be resolved?
10. What are your alternative ideas?
11. What are your alternative solutions?
12. What modifications have you been able to make to your design?
13. What changes have there been in manufacturing?

Use of digital media to record your processes and thoughts

An important part of the development of your work will be the ability to integrate technology and digital media. In some schools, the use of a digital portfolio will allow you to integrate still and video images, even sound.

Digital cameras can be used to do the following:

- record the design collection process
- record aspects of modelling
- support the recording of the manufacturing process
- record the final product in use
- record various aspects that may be changed.

In addition, you can add audio directly to digital portfolios and also to Microsoft® PowerPoint® documents, enabling you to discuss key points about your controlled assessment.

Testing your results

Testing your results enables you to see what you could do differently next time and explore alternatives. Testing allows you to review the following:

- the method of data/research collection used
- the impact of the materials/processes or components used
- how effectively you collected, analysed and organised the information
- other methods and opportunities that may be available.

An important part of testing your product is the user trials. These ensure the following:

- that your product is made as specified
- that it meets health and safety standards and is fit for purpose
- that it represents good value for money (were your costings accurate?)
- that the materials and components used in manufacture are suitable
- that the techniques (e.g. decoration) have been applied correctly and will not fall off or wash off
- that your finished product is safe for the consumer to use.

An important part of testing is to get feedback from the end user about your product. This feedback might be in the form of:

- surveys
- questionnaires
- pictures
- videos
- blogs or wikis.

This research with the end user provides key information for future development.

Key term

Feedback – information that is passed from one section of the system to the other.

The importance of testing

In industry, products are tested at each stage of the design-and-make process, and feedback is given as to the accuracy of the testing to ensure that the product is suitable before being moved to the next stage. All textiles have to pass certain tests before they can be sold.

Knowledge link

See pages 50–58 for more information on product testing.

Equipment that you can use in school to carry out testing includes:

- digital cameras
- video cameras
- audio
- comparison of your product with one on the market (further research).

Evaluation of your manufacturing process

Just as you evaluate your written work, you must also evaluate the practical work you have done. Some of the key questions to ask at this stage are as follows:

1. How could you improve your manufacturing?
2. Was there enough development at the modelling stage?
3. Was there enough design and was it communicated well?
4. Did your plan allow for any potential problems?
5. At the pattern-making stage, did you make adaptations to reduce waste?
6. Did you know how to use all the equipment?
7. Was your flow diagram effective and accurate?
8. What were the problem areas?
9. What future improvements could you make to the process?

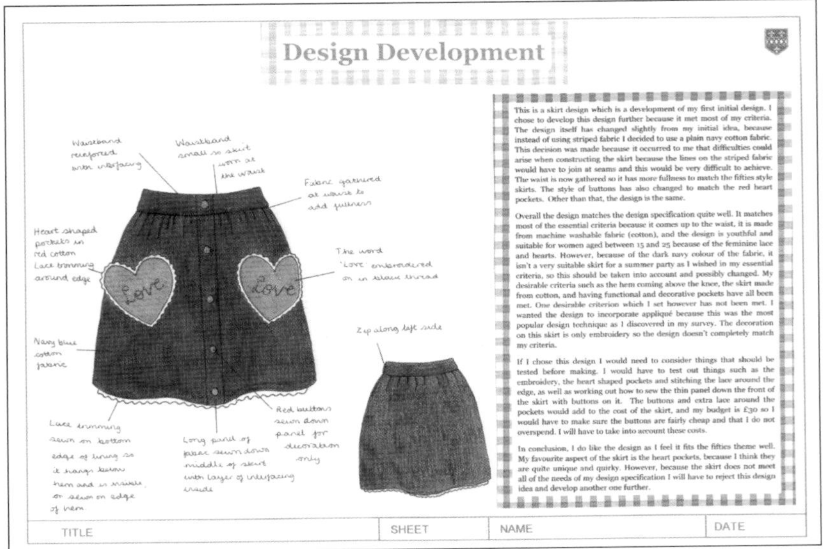

This is a skirt design which is a development of my first initial design. I chose to develop this design further because it met most of my criteria. The design itself has changed slightly from my initial idea, because instead of using striped fabric I decided to use a plain navy cotton fabric. This decision was made because it occurred to me that difficulties could arise when constructing the skirt because the lines on the striped fabric would have to join at seams and this would be very difficult to achieve. The waist is now gathered so it has more fullness to match the fifties style skirts. The style of buttons has also changed to match the red heart pockets. Other than that, the design is the same.

Overall the design matches the design specification quite well. It matches most of the essential criteria because it comes up to the waist, it is made from machine washable fabric (cotton), and the design is youthful and suitable for women aged between 15 and 25 because of the feminine lace and hearts. However, because of the dark navy colour of the fabric, it isn't a very suitable skirt for a summer party as I wished in my essential criteria, so this should be taken into account and possibly changed. My desirable criteria such as the hem coming above the knee, the skirt made from cotton, and having functional and decorative pockets have all been met. One desirable criterion which I set however has not been met. I wanted the design to incorporate appliqué because this was the most popular design technique as I discovered in my survey. The decoration on this skirt is only embroidery so the design doesn't completely match my criteria.

If I chose this design I would need to consider things that should be tested before making. I would have to test out things such as the embroidery, the heart shaped pockets and stitching the lace around the edge, as well as working out how to sew the thin panel down the front of the skirt with buttons on it. The buttons and extra lace around the pockets would add to the cost of the skirt, and my budget is £30 so I would have to make sure the buttons are fairly cheap and that I do not overspend. I will have to take into account these costs.

In conclusion, I do like the design as I feel it fits the fifties theme well. My favourite aspect of the skirt is the heart pockets, because I think they are quite unique and quirky. However, because the skirt does not meet all of the needs of my design specification I will have to reject this design idea and develop another one further.

△ **Figure 7.12** Student project pages exploring the different ways in which designs have been modified

10. What alternative production methods/ components could you have used?
11. Were your costings accurate?
12. Did you have the opportunity to develop additional remodelling ideas at the end of your controlled assessment?

Activity

Choose a textile product and, using the information on page 174 in this chapter about design specifications, create a design specification for your chosen product.

Summary

- Evaluation is a summative process – that is, it provides an overview.
- You need to think about the elements in your project that were a success as well as those that were not as successful.
- You can check to see if your product matches your original criteria by referring back to your initial specification, criteria and proposal. If it did not match, what changes were made to improve the product?

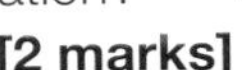

Exam practice questions

1. What is a design specification? **[2 marks]**
2. What is critical evaluation and what does it allow you to do? **[2 marks]**
3. Why is it important to understand why you would need to modify a product? List four key reasons for modifying a product. **[4 marks]**
4. What is it essential to test in a product, and what does testing a product show? **[4 marks]**

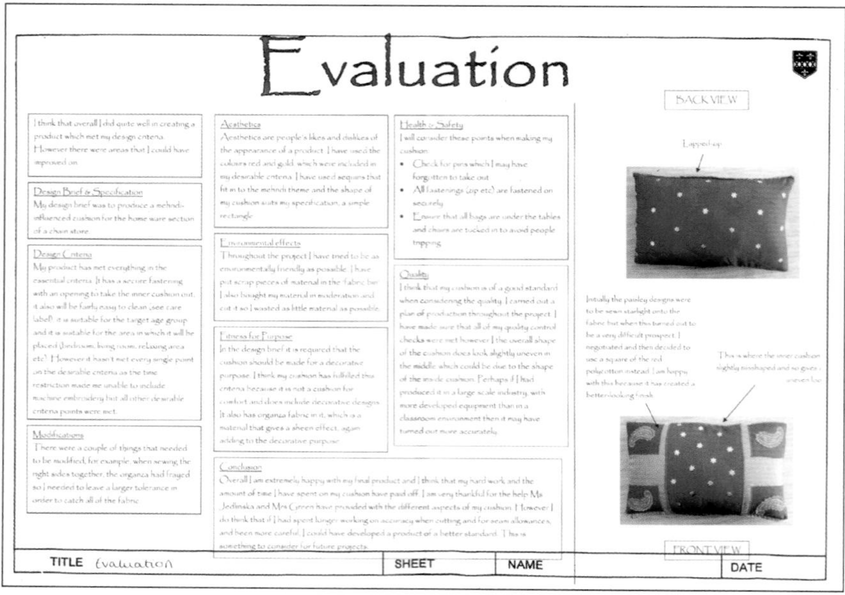

Evaluation

I think that overall I did quite well in creating a product which met my design criteria. However there were areas that I could have improved on.

Design Brief & Specification
My design brief was to produce a mehndi-influenced cushion for the home ware section of a chain store.

Design Criteria
My product has met everything in the essential criteria. It has a secure fastening with an opening to take the inner cushion out, it also will be fairly easy to clean (see care label). it is suitable for the target age group and it is suitable for the area in which it will be placed (bedroom, living room, relaxing area etc). However it hasn't met every single point on the desirable criteria as the time restriction made me unable to include machine embroidery but all other desirable criteria points were met.

Modifications
There were a couple of things that needed to be modified, for example, when sewing the right sides together, the organza had frayed so I needed to leave a larger tolerance in order to catch all of the fabric.

Aesthetics
Aesthetics are people's likes and dislikes of the appearance of a product. I have used the colours red and gold, which were included in my desirable criteria. I have used sequins that fit in to the mehndi theme and the shape of my cushion suits my specification, a simple rectangle.

Environmental effects
Throughout the project I have tried to be as environmentally friendly as possible. I have put scrap pieces of material in the fabric bin. I also bought my material in moderation and cut it so I wasted as little material as possible.

Fitness for Purpose
In the design brief it is required that the cushion should be made for a decorative purpose. I think my cushion has fulfilled this criteria because it is not a cushion for comfort and does include decorative designs. It also has organza fabric in it, which is a material that gives a sheen effect, again adding to the decorative purpose.

Health & Safety
I will consider these points when making my cushion:

- Check for pins which I may have forgotten to take out
- All fastenings (zip etc) are fastened on securely
- Ensure that all bags are under the tables and chairs are tucked in to avoid people tripping

Quality
I think that my cushion is of a good standard when considering the quality. I carried out a plan of production throughout the project. I have made sure that all of my quality control checks were met however I the overall shape of the cushion does look slightly uneven in the middle which could be due to the shape of the inside cushion. Perhaps if I had produced it in a large scale industry, with more developed equipment than in a classroom environment then it may have turned out more accurately.

Conclusion
Overall I am extremely happy with my final product and I think that my hard work and the amount of time I have spent on my cushion have paid off. I am very thankful for the help Ms Jedlinska and Mrs Green have provided with the different aspects of my cushion. However I do think that if I had spent longer working on accuracy when cutting and for seam allowances, and been more careful, I could have developed a product of a better standard. This is something to consider for future projects.

BACK VIEW

Lapped zip

Initially the paisley designs were to be sewn starlight onto the fabric but when this turned out to be a very difficult prospect. I negotiated and then decided to use a square of the red polycotton instead. I am happy with this because it has created a better-looking finish.

This is where the inner cushion slightly misshaped and so gives uneven loo

FRONT VIEW

TITLE Evaluation	SHEET	NAME	DATE

△ **Figure 7.13** Evaluations of end product and modifications for use

8.1 Social and cultural influences on the consumer market

Learning objectives

By the end of this section, you should have a key understanding of:

- the social and cultural influences on the consumer market
- the role and impact of the designer
- developments influencing consumer choice and product designs
- culture and its effect on textile products.

Key points

- Linking technology and design
- Values

Introduction

When designing a product, designers need to be aware not only of how the product will be made but also of the country that the product is going to. The growing global nature of the textiles and fashion industry means that designer should be aware of issues such as local traditions or what particular colours mean.

Culture

There are products made today that can be used by any culture and are called universal items, such as t-shirts, jeans and socks. They provide us with a standard type of uniform for everyday use.

The design of the product will be the same but the sizing might change, depending on the country/culture – due to the foods that we eat and our ethnic origins, different cultures have different body shapes and so the technical pattern used to create the product will be different.

One of the key things that can impact on design is culture. Culture can be subdivided into the following areas:

- language: old languages, new languages, street language
- media: music, art, pop
- class: working class (low culture), upper class (high culture), social class
- gender
- age
- traditions
- colour
- craft
- economics
- religion.

As part of their collection of evidence, designers will research various aspects of design in a series of trend boards and/or mood boards, which act as a starting point for further design development.

Key terms

Consumer choice – giving the consumer or buyer the opportunity to make choices from a range of products on sale.

Cultural issues – the issues affecting design in terms of background and other social issues.

Culture – a society, civilisation or people that have similar beliefs or a shared understanding or background.

Forecasting or thinking about future products is very important. Futurologists, such as Li Edelkoort from Holland, look at a series of events that happen around the world and in our everyday lives to develop ideas for colours, fabrics or new technologies.

Knowledge link

For more information on trends and forecasting, go to pages 159–60.

Content

There are textiles products that have impacted on our culture and the way we use materials. New materials that have been introduced to designers have allowed them to experiment with different features.

The introduction of nylon in 1938 allowed designers to use a modern fabric. The key features of nylon appealed to consumers and designers at that time:

- It was flexible.
- It was washable.
- It was quick-drying.
- New printing processes, such as transfer printing, could be used with it.
- The modern fabric fitted in with modern lifestyles because it was easy to care for.
- Consumers were no longer reliant on natural fibres, such as cotton, wool and silk as the key fabrics for clothing.
- The use of nylon allowed designers to experiment with a new fabric that could be used not only for clothing but also for a wide range of interior products.
- The use of nylon required the industry to develop machines that could be used to stitch or join the new high-tech fabrics.

Technological cultures

New fabrics and techniques have played a part in the historical development of textiles and textile products. One of the key characteristics of fabrics and textile products is that they have a range of uses for:

- clothing – indoor and outdoor
- interiors
- technical and medical applications
- architectural applications.

The Moon landing in 1969

Fabrics such as Neoprene, Mylar and Teflon®, as well as nylon and Lycra, had been in use in a wide variety of everyday products. These fabrics were combined in the 21-layer spacesuit that was used for the Moon landing.

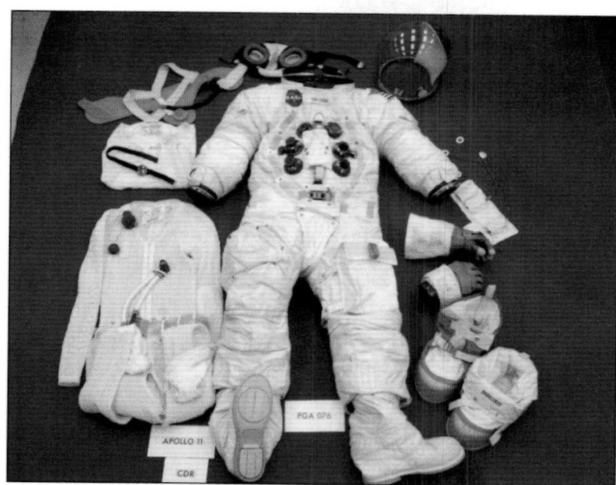

△ **Figure 8.1** Spacesuit from 1969

Habitat sells the first duvet cover in the United Kingdom

Lots of new products change the way we live, and one of the products to do just this is the duvet. The duvet was first introduced on the British high street in 1968 by Habitat, a leading interior store in London. Today, we use the duvet as an everyday product. It has replaced woollen blankets as the covering of choice on our beds. As fabric and fibre technology has advanced, this has been applied to products such as the duvet. Today, they are available in different weights for summer and winter, different fillings and a variety of sizes.

Designers get technological

Haute couture designers, such as Courrèges, Pierre Cardin and Paco Rabanne, started using the technical fabrics of the 1960s to create 'futuristic' and unusual shapes. Conventional machines had to be adapted to sew these new materials. New ways of joining fabrics were developed, and stitching and overlocking were replaced by welding or bonding fabrics.

△ **Figure 8.2** Fashion garments inspired by the Moon landing

Today, modern techniques and experimentation in fabrics are still carried out by leading textiles designers. Junichi Arai is a Japane designer and lead designer at a co the Nuno Corporation, based in To This textile company specialises in old and new craft and fabric manipulation techniques to create amazing textile products. One of the key things that the Nuno Corporation does is encourage experimentation, by taking fabrics used for one industrial area and bringing it into clothing, and by linking other surface construction techniques and surface pattern techniques.

Issey Miyake is another Japanese designer who engaged in using new fabrics for one of his main fashion lines in the 1990s. The range, called Pleats Please, used a lightweight, permanently pleated polyester, which he developed. It has the following properties:

- antistatic
- extra lightweight
- permanently pleated
- perspiration-absorbent
- fast-drying
- machine- or hand-washable
- can be dry-cleaned
- does not need ironing
- can be folded into a tiny square, ideal when travelling.

Miayke showed that adding finishes and understanding technologies can create products that fit in with modern lifestyles.

◁ **Figure** 8.3 Issey Miyake's Pleats Please range

△ **Figure 8.4** Student work showing cultural references

Summary

- The cultural impact of fashion and textiles can be local, national or global.
- Some products have a universal appeal and cross cultural boundaries.
- Many design companies, although global, will make products that 'fit' or work in particular markets, in particular countries.

Stretch yourself

Choose one of the following three designers of the 1960s: Mary Quant, Courrèges, Paco Rabanne.

Using historical information and two other sources, write a report about their use of new or modern materials. **[15 marks]**

Exam practice questions

1. Why is it important for designers to be aware of culture? **[2 marks]**

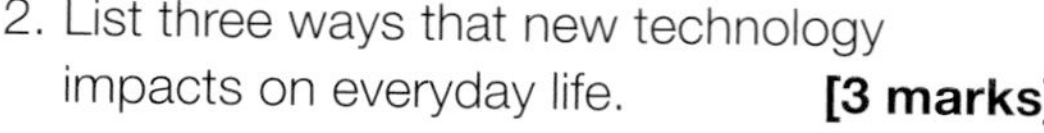

2. List three ways that new technology impacts on everyday life. **[3 marks]**
3. What is trend forecasting and what does it help designers to do? **[3 marks]**

8.2 Consumer choice and ethical issues

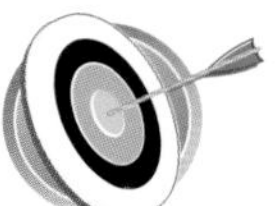

Learning objectives

By the end of this section, you should have a key understanding of:

- ethical trading and its impact on product development
- what sustainable design means for textiles and fashion
- what eco design is
- what fair trade is
- why we recycle textile products
- how environmental concerns are linked to textiles and fashion products.

Key points

- Innovative ideas
- Creative ideas
- Linking technology and design
- Values

Introduction

Designers of today have to understand how their designs and their products will be used, and the impact of their designs on wider society. The world is more interconnected through technology than ever before, enabling us to view and see countries and other people at the touch of a button. Having a good understanding of other people, cultures, genders and races allows for a better understanding of how design can impact on wider society and culture.

The impact of your design on society

When designing and manufacturing textile products, not only do you have to understand how the product is made, but you also need to understand the impact of your design on the wider society. Some of the things that need to be considered are shown in Table 8.1.

Values	Moral issues, such as the use of GM technologies in developing new types of fibres
Environmental issues	The impact of materials on the environment The use of compounds such as CFCs in products The use of chemical finishes on clothing and textile products Establishing your own carbon footprint or the carbon footprint of the product you purchase Offsetting your carbon emissions
Cultural issues	Such as celebrations Use of certain colours in designs Skills of craftsmen being either exploited or disappearing

△ **Table 8.1** Value issues in design

Cont.

Ethical issues in textiles	○ Having products made in poor conditions ○ Products created using cheap labour ○ Use of children ○ Lack of good working conditions for those making products
Globalisation	○ Related to manufacture and distribution of textile products ○ Worker exploitation ○ Textile products all looking the same ○ Need to recognise local crafts and skills of workers
Other issues	○ Such as gender and race ○ Responsibility and citizenship

△ **Table 8.1** Value issues in design *continued*

Consumers purchase products for a variety of reasons. These vary from replacing products that are old to satisfying the need for new products. However, this mode of replacing things and not thinking about the resources needed to make them or the resources needed to dispose of them has not always been at the forefront of consumer thinking.

Today's consumers are being encouraged to think more broadly about the products that they buy and also about disposal of their products. They are also encouraged to think about the working conditions of those employed to make their products, whether that is in England, Europe or other areas of the world.

The fashion and textiles industry is global and today many garments and other textile products and components are produced and manufactured in different parts of the world, but the final product will be put together in one place.

This process had led to new production systems, such as just-in-time (JIT).

Knowledge link

You can read more about production methods and systems in Chapter 9, pages 231–236.

Key terms

Disposal – to get rid of or throw away.

Environmental – understanding how to protect the natural world around you.

Sustainable design – also referred to as eco-design – the inclusion of any aspect of design that reduces the impact of processes or materials on other humans or the environment around them.

Life-cycle approach to design

Today's designers are encouraged to be responsible and develop ideas that incorporate sustainable and ecological viewpoints. This has to be integrated from the design phase through to manufacturing. This process is known as the life cycle.

By using a life-cycle approach to design, both the designer and the consumer can get a better understanding of what to do with textile products at each stage of their design and use.

If a product has a short lifespan or use, then the designer needs to think about how to reduce the energy consumption and review the use of alternative materials – for example, use recycled or recyclable materials or think about how to extend the life of the product.

If a product has a long lifespan, it is more likely to use lots of energy and resources, so the user can keep using it. In this case, the designer needs to think about how to reduce the amount of energy needed to keep the product useful, but this must also have a high environmental benefit.

Textile product	Use	Disposal	Production
Clothing and accessories	•••	•	•
Working wear/uniforms	•••	•	•
Household textiles (bedding/ pillows, etc.)	•••	•	•
Furnishings and furnishing fabrics	•	••	•••
Carpets	•	••	•••

△ **Table 8.2** Textile and fashion products that impact on the environment. Key: • = small/lowest possible impact, •• = medium possible impact, ••• = highest possible impact

Stage of design, production and manufacture	Key issues	Ideas, solutions or further developments
Design	Materials Manufacturing End user Aftercare Sourcing components Organic or non-organic Sustainable/ renewable resources Use of interlinings	○ Choose recycled materials. ○ Choose materials that are renewable or recyclable. ○ Choose suppliers of materials that are locally based. ○ Source from ethical suppliers. ○ Design products that can be easily taken apart or disassembled. ○ Restrict use of mixed or blended fibres unless of a similar fibre type (this type of fabric is hard to recycle). ○ Think about using digital technology (e.g. digital printing). ○ Create a database of companies that specialise in sustainable, ethical, fair-trade, organic and renewable fabrics. ○ Think about how the life of the product can be extended. ○ Reduce the need for complex designs. ○ Ensure product is of the highest quality to encourage the consumer to buy fewer items. ○ Give added value to products by adding embroidery or crafts skills. ○ Develop methods of utilising scrap or excess materials in the garment or accessories. ○ Think before using interlinings/interfacings, which are not always biodegradable.

△ **Table 8.3** How you can reduce use of energy and materials in the product life cycle for textiles and fashion products

Cont.

Stage of design, production and manufacture	Key issues	Ideas, solutions or further developments
Raw materials	Extraction Processing Energy use Pollution Transport	○ Use factories where they have closed-loop systems. ○ Use factories that have clear environmental development. ○ Use factories that are local to manufacturing plant. ○ Reduce use of chemicals. ○ Look at ways of reducing water use. ○ Look at ways of using natural energy sources. ○ Ethical issues around labour need to be considered. ○ Encourage companies to have a recycling programme for waste materials that might be reintroduced into the manufacturing system.
Manufacturing and production	Energy use Pollution Transport	○ Use a local factory for manufacture – should be in the country where the product will be sold. ○ Use a factory that looks at ways of reducing its carbon footprint. ○ Use a factory that uses a closed-looped system for manufacture. ○ Use a factory that might incorporate methods of reducing water usage. ○ Reduce the type of finishes that need to be added to fabrics. ○ Review ways of disposing of chemical/liquid waste.
Packaging	Waste Disposal Renewal resources	○ Review the different types of packaging used at different stages of production. ○ Use packaging that can be reused. ○ Ensure that packaging is made from one type of material; this makes it easier to dispose of. ○ Limit where the packaging is printed; this makes it easier to be reused and reduces the packaging's carbon footprint. ○ Engage end users in reusing or disposing of packaging responsibly. ○ Reduce the need for labels. ○ Make use of recycled plastics for packaging.
Transport	Carbon footprint Mode of transport	○ If factory is not local, then limit the use of air transport. ○ For designers or others in the company that might need to travel to meetings, consider the use of new technologies (e.g. video conferencing). ○ Make sure that the product is easy to transport.

△ **Table 8.3** How you can reduce use of energy and materials in the product life cycle for textiles and fashion products

Cont.

Stage of design, production and manufacture	Key issues	Ideas, solutions or further developments
End use	How long will the product last? How much energy does it use? How much cleaning does it need? What method of cleaning does it need?	○ The designer needs to think about how long the product will last. ○ How easy is it to repair the product? ○ What is the product maintenance like? ○ Use the new cool-wash washing products. ○ Do not recommend that the product be dry-cleaned. ○ Encourage the reduction of the use of the tumble dryer. ○ Use eco-friendly washing solutions. ○ Hand-wash where appropriate. ○ Change the type of washing product used (e.g. change from biological to non-biological or eco washing product).
Rubbish disposal	How is it disposed of? Is the product made of multiple components?	○ Ensure that the product can be recycled. ○ Make sure there are clear instructions for how to dispose of product. ○ Send to recycling plant. ○ Give to charity shop/donate to a charity. ○ Create a 'swishing party' to exchange clothes. ○ Create new clothes from old.

△ **Table 8.3** How you can reduce use of energy and materials in the product life cycle for textiles and fashion products *continued*

Know your signs

There is a range of symbols that can be added to products to prove that they are approved as being sustainable or ecological. Figure 8.5 shows the EU Ecolabel, which may be seen on a range of textile and fashion products.

△ **Figure 8.5** EU Ecolabel for ecological products

Values and ethical issues

In the textiles market today, there are growing concerns about how the products that are manufactured affect the lives and livelihood of the people who produce them. It has been highlighted that many of the leading brands of clothing and accessories are produced by young people and the labour is cheap. These are known as ethical issues.

All textiles companies now have to follow strict guidelines to lessen the impact of their production processes on the environment. These guidelines are issued by local government, national government and the European Union. There are also international guidelines that have to be followed. The guidelines include issues such as:

- reducing water usage
- reducing chemicals used in processing textiles
- changing from synthetic-based dyes to organic dyes
- reducing energy usage.

If companies follow certain guidelines, they can add special labels to their products, such as the Eco-Tex Standard 100 label or the European Eco label. Many countries have now adopted a variety of eco-labelling standards.

Key terms

Eco-labelling – special labelling to state that a product has been produced using eco guidelines.

Ethical – understanding moral rules and values in relation to other humans.

Ethical trading – ensuring that employees have basic rights with regard to labour and working conditions and that companies trade fairly with the developing world. Ethical companies are known as being sweatshop-free.

What is ethical trading?

Ethical trading aims to ensure that the conditions workers are employed in are fair. Companies, charities, voluntary organisations and trade unions all work together to ensure that workers are not exploited. By working together, they highlight ways that companies can make products that do not affect the workers in terms of number of hours worked, working conditions, pay, treatment, and health and safety. They can also help communities to grow economically.

This way of working applies not only to workers in factories, but also to those who work in small workshops or as part of a collective or cooperative.

One such initiative in the UK is the Ethical Trading Initiative (ETI), which has been in existence since 2000. The ETI extends across all areas of the supply chain in fashion and textiles, and involves retailers, suppliers and brands. By having all aspects of the fashion and textiles industry working together in the ETI, it means that key issues can be tackled as a group, rather than by just one company.

Through the ETI, companies can be shown the way forward in terms of best practice in all aspects of the supply chain. More information about the ETI and the work that they do can be found on their website: **www.ethicaltrade.org/about-eti**.

What is sustainable (eco) design?

Sustainable design (also referred to as eco design) is the inclusion of any aspect of design that does the following:

- Uses design to reduce or minimise the impact of products on the environment
- Reduces the dependency on renewable energy, such as oil and coal
- Uses energy efficiently
- Utilises materials that can be reused, recycled or even reintegrated into the environment
- Uses the spaces that we inhabit more efficiently
- Utilises more effectively how we use resources such as water

A sustainable approach to design allows companies to make decisions at each stage of the design-and-make process that reduce the impact of that process on the environment or other humans. In addition, it is an approach to design that integrates cooperation and compromise.

As the designer is involved in making key decisions related to the design and development of products, they need to take the lead in ensuring that the products they create and develop meet certain criteria with regard to environmental concerns, alongside human needs and well-being. Sustainable design includes exploring design practice (making) and design theories (history), along with economic, technical and human needs.

Table 8.4 lists some sustainable fibres and the environmental issues surrounding them. Other fibres that are considered sustainable and environmentally friendly are:

- nettle
- bamboo.

Other fibres being developed using renewable resources are:

- corn fibres (also referred to as biopolymers), which are protein-based fibres (e.g. Ingeo™)
- soya.

Textiles/ fibres	Environmental issues
Organic cotton	This is grown using fewer pesticides than other cotton products. However, it does not use less water.
Linen	Linen comes from the flax plant, a traditional fibre crop that needs few chemical fertilisers to grow and requires fewer pesticides than cotton.
Recycled polyester	Hi-tech fleece jackets can be made from recycled drinks bottles. Old fleece jackets can then be recycled and reused. Companies such as Patagonia lead the field in this development. The Patagonia fleece has been manufactured since 1993 and is made from 90 per cent recycled polyester. For the South African Football World Cup in 2010, Nike created football shirts for 13 of the football teams made from recycled plastic bottles (for more information, see Case study on page 196).
Hemp clothing	Agricultural hemp is specially grown for textile products. It is a versatile and productive fibre. The waste produced can be used for oil and plant food.
Organic wool	This is becoming more readily available. It is produced using sustainable farming practices and without toxic sheep dips.
Technical fabrics	Technical or hi-tech fabrics can potentially be recycled, but only if both the facilities and the systems exist. These include those fabrics that have water-based coatings (applied without harmful solvents) and membranes such as Sympatex®, which is 100 per cent polyester. But products that contain PVC, laminates and polyurethane are not suitable for recycling.

△ **Table 8.4** Issues to consider when looking for sustainable fibres

Lyocell

Lyocell (also known by it trade name Tencel®) is probably one of the best known of the cellulose-based fibres. It is derived from eucalyptus wood. Eucalyptus trees require no additional water irrigation to grow.

Lyocell is fully biodegradable and the process for making it works on a closed-loop system. This means that all the waste needed to manufacture the product is reused.

Modal (Lenzing Modal®) is similar to Tencel®, but is extracted from beechwood trees. These are sustainable, renewable resources and do not need additional water irrigation.

Key terms

Eco – used as pre-fix to describe issues related to ecology and the environment – for example, eco-design.

Fair trade – a trading partnership related to open dialogue and respect and transparent trading conditions on a global market.

What is fairtrade?

Fairtrade is what is known as a trading partnership. This trading partnership is based on the following:

- an open dialogue with traders and suppliers
- transparent trading conditions; everyone knows what things will cost
- respect
- equal opportunities in trade
- enablement and empowerment of marginalised workers, so they can compete equally on the open market, including the global market.

Fairtrade is all about the producer or maker and aims to put poorer workers at the centre of its trade cycle. Fairtrade thinking is also extended within companies through their corporate and social responsibility (CSR) documents.

Some of the key advantages of fairtrade to the small-scale farmer are as follows:

- access to both local and international export markets
- access to information about world market prices
- access to key information about the quality of goods
- support in accessing finance
- ability to respond quickly to market forces
- access to legal advice
- access to technical assistance for traders and producers.

In addition, the trading partnership works on a long-term basis, as the process of changing working conditions can take a long time.

Fairtrade certification

The FAIRTRADE Mark on products shows that international fairtrade standards have been met. In the UK the Fairtrade Foundation independently certifies products which meet these standards. This means that the producers in developing countries receive a stable price for their products and receive an additional Fairtrade premium which they decide how to invest in their communities.

Figure 8.6
The FAIRTRADE Mark (For more information visit www.info.fairtrade.net)

Recycling textiles

Recycling is the process of putting discarded textile products back into clothing or textile use. Recycling of textiles is not new, and many cultures recycle textiles and integrate them into new products.

Textile crafts such as patchwork have developed from reusing garments and discarded fabric. Textile techniques such as appliqué can also incorporate the use of recycled materials.

The key reasons for recycling are to:

- save energy
- save raw materials
- reduce the impact of production on the environment
- reduce energy use
- save resources.

Processes used for recycling textiles

1. **Primary recycling**: the textile product can be reused straightaway; no further processing is necessary. For example, second-hand clothing can be sold as 'vintage' fashion pieces.
2. **Secondary or physical recycling**: this process requires the textile product to be torn, shredded, melted or ground. This method of breaking down the fibre is often referred to as shoddy. Old woollen garments/products that are shredded can be reused as stuffing in bedding or as industrial felting.
3. **Chemical or tertiary recycling**: in this process, textile products can be broken down and reformulated. For example, PET plastic bottles can be recycled into fibres and then respun into polyester for use in fleeces and duvets.

Charity shops stock all types of textiles, including recycled products. You could also consider making your own clothes from old textiles – just take the textiles apart and make them into new products. To recycle old clothing, you can take your textiles to clothing banks. After sorting, the clothing can be resold in shops, sent overseas or used to make industrial rags.

Key terms

Built-in obsolescence – a product has been designed and manufactured with particular features to last a particular amount of time.

Recycling – to reuse textile products and fabrics.

6Rs – recycle, rethink, reduce, reuse, refuse, repair.

Vintage – a product that is the best of its type for a particular period in time.

The 6Rs

The 6Rs provide a simple way of remembering the rules related to reusing and recycling:

- Recycle
- Rethink
- Reduce
- Reuse
- Refuse
- Repair.

The 6Rs	Ways of applying thinking to textiles and fashion products
Recycle	Think about how your textile products can be recycled. What will stop you putting it into landfill?
Rethink	Review the textile product and its life cycle. What else can be done during the life cycle? How do textiles figure in your lifestyle? What would make a difference?
Reduce	Buy less; reduce your own usage. Change may be from 'fast' to 'slow' fashion. How do you reduce your own consumption? How can you reduce built-in obsolescence?
Reuse	How can the product be reused? Is there an alternative use? How do other cultures reuse materials?
Refuse	Reduce the impact on the environment. Think about ethical trading. Think about products that are made locally rather than in other areas of the world.
Repair	Do you need to learn new skills so you can repair your own textile objects? Could you combine objects? Could you be creative and make bespoke objects?

△ **Table 8.5** Applying the 6Rs to textiles and fashion products

Environmental issues and textile products

Producing fibre from cloth involves processes such as bleaching, dyeing and finishing, which use large amounts of energy and water, as well as producing a lot of water waste, adding to pollution levels.

Fibre/ process	Environmental issues
Nylon and polyester	These are made from petrochemicals. They are synthetics so are non-biodegradable. The processes to make both fibres also use a lot of energy.
Rayon (viscose)	Another artificial fibre, rayon is made from wood pulp, which seems more sustainable. There is now a new type of pulp-wood plantation that uses the eucalyptus tree, but this requires a large amount of water. To make rayon, the wood pulp is treated with hazardous chemicals, such as caustic soda and sulphuric acid.
Cotton	Cotton needs a large amount of pesticides to grow. These chemicals typically remain in the fabric after finishing and are released during the lifetime of the garment. Companies are now developing genetically modified cotton.
Wool	Both agricultural and craft workers in the UK suffer from exposure to chemicals from wool dips.
Dyeing	Dyeing alone can account for most of the water used in producing a garment; unfixed dye then often washes out of garments and can end up colouring rivers. Dye fixatives often contain heavy metals, which can also end up in sewers and then rivers.

△ **Table 8.6** Issues to consider in the use of fibres/processes

Cont.

Fibre/ process	Environmental issues
Cloth	Cloth is often bleached using dioxin-producing chlorine compounds. Virtually all polycottons (especially bed linen), plus all 'easy care', 'crease-resistant' and 'permanent press' cottons, are treated with toxic formaldehyde (also used for flameproofing nylon).
Leather	Leather is made using polluting tanning and dyeing processes.
Harmful solvents	These are used in textile production – for example, in glues and to stick plastic coatings to some waterproof fabrics.

△ **Table 8.6** Issues to consider in the use of fibres/processes *continued*

Summary

- The protection of the environment is important to us all.
- Textiles and fashion companies have made environmental issues part of their CSR.
- International, national and European legislation has been put in place to reduce the impact of waste on the environment.
- As a designer, you need to include information about environmental issues in your design specification and your research.

Activity

You have been asked to create a report about what teenagers think about ethical and fairtrade fashion. Using examples from a range of sources, and also from interviewing other teenagers, compile your report. Present your research as either a Microsoft® PowerPoint® or DTP publishing document or a blog. **[15 marks]**

Exam practice questions

1. It is really important to think about cultures when designing products. List four things that a designer has to consider about culture before they start designing. Give reasons for your choice **[8 marks]**
2. Interior products such as cushions are only used for short time. Name two ways in which they can be reused or recycled. **[4 marks]**
3. Name four reasons why nylon fabric appealed to designers and consumers when it was launched in 1938. **[4 marks]**
4. (a) What do the following terms mean:
   i) primary recycling
   ii secondary or physical recycling
   iii) chemical or tertiary recycling **[6 marks]**

   (b) Give an example of how a textile product might be recycled in each category. **[3 marks]**

5. What are the environmental issues to be considered when using the following fibres:
   (a) polyester
   (b) rayon
   (c) cotton
   (d) wool **[8 marks]**
6. What is the life cycle approach to design, and in what ways does it benefit the designer and the consumer? Give two reasons for your choice. **[4 marks]**

Resources

Organic fabrics: www.whaleys-bradford.ltd.uk

People Tree: www.peopletree.co.uk

[Re]design: www.redesigndesign.org

Environmentally friendly designers (supported by[Re]design): www.redesigndesign.org

Howies: www.howies.co.uk

Clothworks: www.clothworks.co.uk

Terra Plana: www.terraplana.com

Chris Carey's Collections: www.chriscareyscollections.co.uk

'FirstGroup urges passengers to put seats on feet': www.firstgroup.com/ukbus/latest_news/?id=000471

Urban Remade: www.urbanremade.com

Above+Below London: www.aboveandbelowlondon.com

8.3 Moral and environmental issues

Learning objectives

By the end of this section, you should have a key understanding of:

- environmental issues related to textile production in general
- key textile terms associated with environmental textiles
- environmental production methods
- recycling textiles.

Key points

- Communication skills
- Linking technology and design
- Values

Introduction

Environmental issues are concerned with the impact of the production and disposal of textile and fashion products. Environmental issues are now a very important factor in the development of textile and fashion products, and companies are governed by laws, at local, national, European and international levels. These laws and regulations outline how they can get rid of waste and also identify key ways in which they can reduce waste and reuse resources.

The textiles and fashion industry is renowned for its throwaway culture and, as such, has seen the need to review how it can reduce its carbon footprint. Many fashion and textile companies produce CSR reports that show how they are reducing waste.

Your controlled assessment

In your own work, you need to identify the green or environmental issues as part of the design-and-make process. To guide your thinking, you can use the 6Rs:

- **Recycle**: can this product be recycled at the end of its life?
- **Rethink**: how many textile products do you use or not use? What can be done with them once you have finished with them?

- **Reduce**: reducing energy use, reducing the impact on the environment by not buying a product with built-in obsolescence.
- **Reuse**: can the product be used again? Can it be re-purposed (given a new use)?
- **Refuse**: putting clothing or other products in the dustbin means they will end up in landfill. How will you decide to dispose of your clothes?
- **Repair**: can your item be repaired or customised so its life can be extended?

◁ **Figure 8.7** Textile recycling depot

The designer's responsibility

The designer now has a responsibility to develop products that:

- are not harmful to the environment
- can be reused or recycled
- are made using fewer resources
- are made using a range of renewable resources
- reduce the need for excess energy to make them
- use processes that reuse or clean water
- are not oil-based
- are acceptable to the client or the consumer in terms of look and price.

Environmental issues associated with the production of textiles and fashion products

Many textiles and fashion companies today are being encouraged to look at environmental issues when designing new products. Consumers often make decisions on whether

△ **Figure 8.8** Student work highlighting sustainable design solutions

to buy products based on their environmental credentials. However, many consumers still do not buy green products, as they may consider them to be unfashionable or not aesthetically pleasing. A growing number of designers are now trying to change this view.

Key term

Conservation – the process of preserving or conserving the Earth's resources.

Case study

Patagonia fleece

The Patagonia fleece has been manufactured since 1993. The average Patagonia fleece is made from 90 per cent recycled polyester or PET (polyethylene terephthalate). The fleece is both a fashion and a utility product and is popular among a wide variety of people. Patagonia encourages all its customers to 'help the environment by buying only what is needed, wearing it out and passing it on to charities for redistribution'. They also allow customers to take old fleeces to their retail units to be disposed of.

Tencel®, the modern, green fibre

Tencel is a modern fibre that reuses resources. As a lot of water has to be used in the manufacturing of the fabric, it has been developed so it can be manufactured within a closed-loop system. This means that waste created during the manufacturing process is recycled and reused during the production process and very little waste is produced. The Tencel® fabric is very soft and has a peach-like texture. It is used extensively in clothing, such as shirts, trousers and jeans. You can read more about the fibre on their website: www.tencel.com

Ingeo™, the modern, renewable resource

Ingeo™ has been developed as a replacement fibre for polyester. It is made from the renewable resource corn. Scientists are also working on developing further fibres based on potatoes, milk and other food sources.

Junky Styling

Annika Sanders and Kerry Seager are the duo behind Junky Styling, a modern fashion company based in the East End of London. They specialise in fashionwear made entirely of recycled clothes waste. They create a range of products for the menswear and womenswear markets, including garments and fashion accessories.

Nike 2010 World Cup football strip

Nike, the sportswear retailer, created a special football strip for the World Cup that took place in South Africa in July and August 2010. Half the teams present at the World Cup wore this special football kit, which was made entirely of recycled PET plastic. It was used to promote to men and boys that recycling is good for the environment, and that products, especially textile products, can still look good when made from recycled materials. Nike showed that these materials can meet the demands of a physical game such as football and be a great, technical sport fabric.

What does it mean to be green?

Being environmentally aware as a designer means that you need to consider how you can do the following:

- Make a product using fewer resources.
- Make a product using a range of renewable resources.
- Make a product where you reduce the need for large amounts of energy.
- Make a product that reuses and cleans the water.
- Make a product that does not rely on oil-based products.
- Make a product that is acceptable to the client or the consumer in terms of look and price.

Green or environmental issues now form part of the design process, with many modern designers, whether they be in fashion or textiles, reviewing how they work with materials.

Leading retail companies now have documents and guidelines relating to green issues as part of what is known as corporate and social responsibility (CSR). The CSR documents outline a range of things that a company will do to ensure that all its working practices are ethical. In addition, laws at local, national and international levels outline very strictly how companies may get rid of waste, and also identify the key ways in which companies can reduce waste, and reuse resources.

Key term

Green – issues related to political movements or thinking and their concerns for environmental issues.

Modern designers go green

Designers such as Stella McCartney now include green products in their design collections – for example, using alternatives to leather. The idea is that they show the consumer that green products can look good and be of the same quality as 'normal' products.

Designer Katharine Hamnett has been including green products in her designs since the 1970s, and she still makes green garments. Companies such as Conscious Earthwear make 'urban cool sportwear' that is both fashionable and wearable. The garments are made from fabrics that are either organic or renewable.

Terra Plana specialises in making textile products from leftover materials. The company has also worked with companies such a Virgin Airlines, using their discarded uniforms and making them into new bags and products.

Textiles designer Barley Massey focuses on how we can reuse everyday materials, from shirts and ties to seatbelt webbing, to make textile products that can be worn or that can be used in the home.

Design company Urban Remade has been working with train companies such as FirstGroup, reusing their discarded train seat covers. This is made possible through a partnership with TRiP (Transport Recycling in Partnership), which aims to reuse and recycle transport industry waste. The partnership shows the benefits of the reuse of materials such as passenger seating covers (called moquette) from FirstGroup, London Underground and other bus and rail companies. The seating covers are made into a unique range of recycled products, including footwear and bags. One of the first ranges to be produced was the Above+Below London footwear brand.

△ **Figure 8.9** Shoes made from bus seat covers

The first trainers to be produced from this partnership are regarded as one of the 'greenest' trainers on the market. They are made from 100 per cent UK waste: the uppers are made from reclaimed and restored rail and bus seat fabrics; the soles contain recycled tyre rubber; and the high-quality napa leather in the trim comes from chequebook wallets from a high street bank! This makes each pair of trainers a limited edition.

Key term	What does it mean?	How is it implemented?
Recycling textiles	To reuse textile products and fabrics.	By individuals and by others in society. Designers can also support this by creating products that last longer.
Waste reduction	The process where companies look at how they can reduce the waste produced across the design, manufacture and supply chain	By reviewing our own 'waste stream', or how we throw things away. In design, companies are looking at digital processes and other modern technologies as a way of reducing waste in the printing and cutting-out phases.
Organic cotton	Cotton that is grown using organic farming methods, for a minimum of three years; cotton that has been grown without the use of any synthetic or commercial additives, herbicides or fertiliser that is a threat to either the environment or human health	This only makes up a small percentage of the total cotton sold in the world, but is 1 per cent.
Fair-trade cotton	Cotton that has been fairly traded on the open market, offering the small growers and co-operatives in third world countries the opportunity to trade their goods fairly on the open world market, and obtain a fair wage to support families	This type of cotton is sold by a collective and the profits made go directly back into the community.

△ **Table 8.7** Key words that describe environmental textile practices *Cont.*

Key term	What does it mean?	How is it implemented?
Biofibres	Fibres that have an enzyme or other subrate added to the manufacturing process, before making up	How biodegradable are they? What else apart from the actual fibre do they actually contain? How do they degrade?
Biodegradable	The ability of a material to be broken down by bacteria so that it can be returned to the environment. These materials are important as they help to reduce pollution and the amount of waste associated with textile production.	By assessing the material to be broken down and ensuring the correct environmental conditions for the product to be broken down in. The possible impact on the eco-life of the area where the product is disposed of is also assessed.

△ **Table 8.7** Key words that describe environmental textile practices *continued*

Summary

- Understanding how fabrics are made and how they can be reused is an important part of the design-and-make process.
- Changes in production processes of fibres can impact on the products that are made.
- New technologies are being used to create more bio-friendly products.

Stretch yourself

1. Create a presentation about a fashion or textile designer who is developing designs that are environmentally friendly. **[10 marks]**

2. Choose two objects from your wardrobe that you have not worn in the last six months. How could you customise or reuse them to extend their life? Create a blog of your process. **[10 marks]**

Exam practice questions

1. What is the difference between organic cotton, fair-trade cotton and traditional cotton? **[3 marks]**
2. In what ways are companies making green products and encouraging consumers to purchase them? **[3 marks]**
3. What are the 6Rs and why are they important? **[6 marks]**

8.4 Environmental effects (health and safety issues)

Learning objectives

By the end of this section, you should have a key understanding of:

- function and safety of equipment, tools and components, and how to select appropriate materials
- health and safety, and safe working practices
- risk assessment
- consumer rights when purchasing goods.

Key points

- Analytical skills
- Communication skills
- Innovative ideas
- Linking technology and design
- Values

Introduction

The manufacture of all the products we use today need the use of some type of tool or equipment to design and make them. The tools and equipment that you choose should help you to make it easier to cut out and complete the making of the product.

At the design stage you may use tools such as pens and pencils to design ideas, then move on to a equipment such as a computer and use tools such as design software to develop ideas. At the modelling and manufacturing stage of your work you may use tools such as scissors, pins, tape measures, and equipment such as a sewing machine or overlocker. It is important to know how to use all of these tools and equipment safely.

Knowledge link

For detailed descriptions of the various tools, equipment and components used in textiles, see Chapter 9.

Health and safety, and safe working practices

Health and safety in the workplace

Working in clean and safe conditions is important in all workplaces. The HSE (Health and Safety Executive) and the HSC (Health and Safety Commission) are the bodies responsible in the UK for the rules and regulations that ensure that working environments are safe. They also work with the European Commission to ensure that the safe working practices that are being developed across Europe are also implemented in the UK.

Health and safety involves safe working practices in the work environment, and this can include the following:

- machinery and tools
- materials
- clothing
- tools
- surroundings you work in – for example, if you work outside
- noisy environments
- how to evacuate a building in the event of a fire.

In the textiles and clothing industry, safety is of the utmost importance, and companies go to great lengths to ensure that in all aspects of production, and throughout the supply chain, safety regulations are in force. This information might be found next to key equipment or online in company documents, such as the corporate and social responsibility (CSR) report.

Knowledge link

More information on CSR can be found on pages 73–74.

In most companies' CSR reports, there will be reference to ethical trading and production methods, which also includes reference to safe working practices.

Areas of concern related to health and safety are:

- long working hours
- working with chemicals
- operating machinery
- safe working clothing
- clear signs and signals
- working with fabrics/fibres
- operating computers.

Safety guidelines

All safety procedures are controlled by guidelines from the government, European safety laws or other key codes of practice, such as:

- the 1974 Health and Safety at Work Act, created to protect employees from hazards in the workplace
- the 1992 Workplace (Health, Safety and Welfare) Regulations, which reinforced the 1974 Act.

Companies will also work with quality systems to ensure that guidelines are followed. For example, the ISO 9000 is a system that is used by manufacturers to define the quality systems that are in place for the making of their product.

Health and safety – tools and equipment

Table 8.8 outlines the hazards and safety guidelines for the use of different types of tools and equipment.

Equipment/tools	Hazards, accidents or risks	Safety guidelines/information
Sewing equipment, including needles, and sewing machines	○ Injury to fingers and hands ○ Cleaning or repairing machines with power switched on ○ Eye injuries ○ Finger injury from needles ○ Injury from associated equipment	○ Machine must be switched off when cleaning. ○ Machine must be switched off for repairing. ○ Wear appropriate eye guards/ goggles. ○ Put away shears/scissors safely after use.
Spreading and cutting equipment (e.g. cutting shears)	○ Finger or hand injury when using spreading or cutting machines ○ Finger or hand injury from the use of pressing machines or mechanisms	○ Add visible safety guards. ○ Learn the correct way to handle the equipment. ○ Wear protective gloves.
Fusing equipment (e.g. heat press)	○ Finger and hand injury when using the press ○ Burns from the press	○ Check the safety guidelines. ○ Wear protective clothing. ○ Understand what to do in case of a burn.

△ **Table 8.8** Tools and equipment – risks and safety guidelines

Cont.

Equipment/tools	Hazards, accidents or risks	Safety guidelines/information
Pressing equipment, such as irons and steam presses	○ Scalding from steaming equipment or steam ○ Finger or hand injury from pressing equipment	○ Steam must be switched off before attempting to use the machine. ○ Operators must be well trained in the use of the machine before use. ○ Understand how to switch off the machine in case of emergency. ○ Follow all safety guidelines.
Stain removal (e.g. liquids)	○ Breathing in solvent vapours ○ Stains on clothing	○ Keep rooms well ventilated. ○ Follow all safety directions when using chemicals. ○ Understand the safety signs for using various chemicals. ○ Wear appropriate safety garments.
General working area (e.g. computers, tables)	○ Tripping or falling in the workplace ○ Internal injuries from accidental swallowing ○ Electrical injury ○ Incorrect handling of materials ○ Incorrect lifting of products	○ Work area to be kept clean and tidy. ○ Never use machines with damaged covers. ○ Do not carry too many things at one time. ○ Do not carry heavy objects.
Dyeing/printing equipment (e.g. heat press, batik pots)	○ Inhaling dye dust ○ Staining of dyes on skin ○ Getting dye dust in eyes	○ Wear appropriate mask or eye cover/goggles. ○ Ensure work area is well ventilated.

△ **Table 8.8** Tools and equipment – risks and safety guidelines *continued*

With all materials and tools, it is important to understand not only the risks in using them, but also the potential risks to the consumer when using the end product.

All companies take great care in ensuring that the products they make are safe to use by the consumer. Companies will put in place guidelines to recall products that have developed faults or where faults are not seen until the product reaches the end user. This process is called product recall. A company may display product recall information in a national newspaper, on their website or on specialist websites, such as Trading Standards (www.tradingstandards.gov.uk).

△ **Figure 8.10** Trading Standards website

> **Key terms**
>
> **Chemical** – a substance that is made up of atoms that can react together to create a new product.
>
> **Solvent** – a liquid that is capable of dissolving substances.

Health and safety legislation, rules and regulations

There are lots of rules and regulations (laws) that have to be used in the workplace to protect workers and they cover all aspects of the work and the equipment that is used (see Table 8.9). The latest health and safety guidelines can be found on websites such as **www.hse.gov.uk**.

Many companies are increasingly using automated processes and computer technology when manufacturing goods, as this is seen as a good way of reducing accidents and creating tighter controls over processes.

Act	Summary of Act
Health and Safety at Work Act 1974	The Health and Safety Act sets out the general duties that all employers have towards employees and members of the public, and that employees have to themselves and to each other.
Workplace (Health, Safety and Welfare) Regulations 1992	This regulation covers a wide range of basic health, safety and welfare issues related to the working environment (e.g. correct ventilation, heating, lighting, workstations, seating and welfare facilities).
The Management of Health and Safety at Work Regulations 1999 (the Management Regulations)	This act asks employers to carry out risk assessments in the work environment.
ISO 9000	This helps companies set up systems to manage different functions and activities in the workplace.
Signpost to the Health and Safety (Safety Signs and Signals) Regulations 1996	These regulations enforce the EC Safety Signs Directive (92/58/EEC). This is related to the use of safety signs at work. These regulations are being developed so that, wherever you are in Europe, the safety signs are the same visually and mean the same thing.

△ **Table 8.9** Key health and safety rules related to where we work

Cont.

Act	Summary of Act
Health and Safety (Display Screen Equipment) Regulations 1992	This sets the rules for working with visual display units (VDUs) and monitors, which may be on computers and other similar equipment.
Personal Protective Equipment at Work Regulations 1992	Employers have to provide the correct protective clothing and equipment for their employees. This also includes information on the use of gloves. Some gloves contain rubber or latex, to which some people are allergic, so warnings have to be placed on the gloves.
Provision and Use of Work Equipment Regulations 1998	This sets out the rules so that all equipment used at work, including machinery, is safe to use and has been tested as safe for use.
Manual Handling Operations Regulations 1992	This looks at the rules regarding moving objects, either by hand or by using bodily force, from one place to another around the workplace. It also looks at the safe way in which to lift and move objects.
Health and Safety (First Aid) Regulations 1981	This gives key information about what to do if you need first aid.
The Health and Safety Information for Employees Regulations 1989	A poster has to be displayed in a prominent place telling employees what they need to know about health and safety in the workplace.
Electricity at Work Regulations 1989	This outlines the regulations that ensure that electrical systems are safe to use and maintained in a safe condition.
Control of Substances Hazardous to Health Regulations 2002 (COSHH)	This is related to the safe use of hazardous substances in the workplace.

△ **Table 8.9** Key health and safety rules related to where we work *continued*

All the safety regulations are updated on a regular basis. Key safety information can normally be found on the packaging or the instruction manuals or guides that come with a product.

Health and safety in your controlled assessment project (design and make practice)

It is important that you are able to work safely and that others who work around you are safe as well. As part of the work that you do when making your products for your coursework or experimenting with new equipment, you need to make sure that you are in a safe environment.

To make sure that you can work safely, a risk assessment should be carried out (see pages 209–10). You will need to assess the risks posed by each piece of equipment you may need to use to complete your coursework.

Key terms

Risk assessment – identification and minimisation of the potential hazards in the workplace.

Safety – the implementation of safeguards to prevent hazards or accidents.

In your controlled assessment project (design and make practice), you will need to identify and include the key health and safety guidelines that are needed to enable you to:

- work safely when using equipment
- highlight all the risks associated with the making of your product
- highlight safe working practices in the classroom
- highlight the essential safety features of your product
- highlight to potential users any risks in use.

Working safely in the textiles room

When working in the textiles room, you will need to assess the risks and hazards linked with the following processes:

- manufacturing your textiles/fashion product
- adding colour by printing and dyeing your fabrics
- choosing and using the correct fabrics for the correct job
- choosing the correct tools and equipment
- safely using the correct tools and equipment
- matching the correct tools and equipment to the process.

At each step, you will need to make sure that any hazards in the working area are low and that it is safe to work.

Once you have looked at the equipment, tools and materials that you need to use, and listed the risks and hazards, you will need to list how these risks and hazards can be reduced or the work area made safe. This is very important, as the work area needs to be safe for everyone. In industry, these safety processes are controlled by the Health and Safety at Work Act.

Knowledge link

For more information on the Health and Safety at Work Act, see page 211.

Use of dyes (dust-based powders)	○ Check for hazard symbols. ○ Wear appropriate protective eyewear and clothing. ○ Check what to do in an emergency – for example, spillage. ○ Wear a dust mask where appropriate.
Cables	○ Ensure cables for all machines and equipment are stored or kept safely out of the way, and cannot be tripped over.
Irons or other heating equipment	○ Keep irons in upright position, and switch off when not in use. ○ Ensure that you understand how to use a heat press correctly.
Cutting equipment	○ Ensure all cutting equipment is kept in the downward position when being handed to another person.
Sewing machines	○ Ensure that all machines are correctly threaded. ○ Ensure that the needle is correctly inserted before use. ○ Ensure that the machine peddle is correctly attached.
Overlockers	○ Ensure that the safety guard is in place before being used. ○ Keep fingers away from cutting area on the overlocker.

△ **Table 8.10** How to reduce common risks and hazards

Working safely with tools and equipment

It is important to choose the correct tools and equipment while modelling and making products. Choosing incorrect tools and equipment can mean that the finished product is not suitable for the user. It is important that you check the equipment you are using, matching correct equipment and tools to product and manufacturing techniques.

Protection when working with equipment and tools

When working with equipment, you might be required to wear or use protective clothing or guards. These might include the following:

- Protective clothing, such as gloves, overalls or aprons: these protect your skin and your clothes.
- Protective machine guards, such as finger guards on sewing machines, overlockers and embellishers: these stop fingers getting too close to the needles and are only removed when doing maintenance or changing needles. The guards are always replaced when the machine is to be used again.
- Protective equipment, such as goggles, footwear and masks.

In addition, adequate ventilation is essential when working with dyes and other substances that may be dangerous if inhaled.

Safety when working with materials and components

As well as working with tools and equipment, you will be working with materials and components, so it is important to understand the materials that you will be working with, as well as the safety of the materials when they are worn or used. It is important to know the following about your materials:

- Is the material flammable?
- Is the fabric for children or adults?
- Are the components attached securely?

To ensure that the end product is safe to use and look after, it must also carry care instructions – these are called care labels.

Knowledge link

For more information on care labels and why you need to use them, see page 208.

Key terms

Care labels – a set of instructions that explains the aftercare of a fabric or product.

Safety signs – signage that is placed near either dangerous equipment or particular places in a workroom to warn the user that they are approaching dangerous equipment, or guides to fire exits.

Care and safety of disposal

All companies must follow guidelines on the safe disposal of materials, components and any liquid-based products. The rules for safe disposal are a legal requirement and follow strict environmental guidelines. You must always think before disposing of any materials or other products.

△ **Figure 8.11** Key safety signs

Product safety and labelling

All textiles products that are produced have to follow key health and safety regulations that ensure that the products are safe for the consumer to use. To make sure that the products are safe, certain standards and regulations are set for each stage of manufacture; this ensures that the products work as they are supposed to. Tests of textile products are created for the following reasons:

1. To make sure that the product has the correct properties for its end use.
2. To make sure that the fibres and/or fabrics used in the product are the correct ones.
3. To make sure that the finished product meets the requirements of the user.
4. To make sure that the product is safe to use by the user.
5. To make sure that the product meets both UK and European standards.

The testing of textile products takes place during the following phases of production:

- fibre processing and production
- fabric production
- garment and product production.

Products can be identified as being safe to use or as having been tested to certain standards if they have the following safety marks:

- the CE label
- the Kitemark
- the BEAB label
- a care label.

Key terms

CE mark (stands for European conformity) – a label that shows that the product meets the key European Union (EU) regulations and directives that relate to product safety and technical standards. It is applied to all products that are sold in the EU.

Kitemark – the symbol displayed on the labels of products to show that they meet the safety standards set by the British Standards Institute (BSI).

Testing – ensuring that standards are met.

The CE mark

The CE mark label shows that the product meets the key European Union (EU) regulations and directives that relate to product safety and technical standards. This label can be found on all products sold across Europe.

△ **Figure 8.12** The CE mark

The Kitemark

The Kitemark is also known as the BSI (British Standards Institution) Kitemark. When purchasing products with this mark, consumers know that the product has passed very strict tests and will be both safe to use and fit for its end use.

◁ **Figure 8.13** The Kitemark

The BEAB label

The BEAB (British Electrical Approvals Board) label is a key safety label applied to electrical products. It can be applied to products at point of sale and can be added to products each time they are tested for safety.

△ **Figure 8.14** The BEAB label

The care label

A care label will be added to a garment to tell the consumer the following:

- fibre content
- washing symbols
- country of origin
- dry-cleaning symbols
- special care instructions
- keep away from fire (on children's wear).

It is a legal requirement for all garments to carry this key information. This allows the consumer to make choices before purchasing the garment or product, or to understand how to care for the product once purchased.

△ **Figure 8.15** A care label

Knowledge link

More information on care labelling can be found on page 112.

Fire labels for furnishing fabrics

There are special labels for interior products, such as chair cushions and curtains, as these have to withstand certain conditions and can be found in both private and public spaces.

△ **Figure 8.16** The furniture fire label

Environmental labelling

In addition to the statutory labelling, many companies are now adding environmental labelling to their products. This added information enables companies and consumers to see where their products have come from and how they may be disposed of. Many companies will include information in their CSR documentation.

Knowledge link

You can find more information about environmental labelling on pages 110–115.

Hazard symbols

Hazard symbols are visual symbols that highlight possible dangers in the use of a particular product or machine. The symbols are displayed in bright colours and are easily recognised. The symbols used on products such as liquids are linked to COSHH (Control of Substances Hazardous to Health).

△ **Figure 8.17** Safety symbols: COSHH

Medical protection

The advent of more technological fabrics and textile research means that there are now more products available to protect those who have skin allergies. Labels might be applied to certain products to show that they have such protection. For example:

- bedding products such as sheets and pillows may be hypoallergenic
- socks may have antibacterial finishes

Irritant

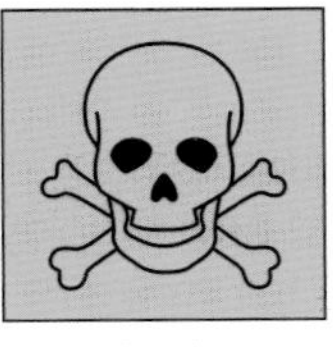

Toxic

Flammable

△ **Figure 8.18** Safety symbols: warning symbols

- clothing for extreme conditions may include mosquito repellent
- clothing such as t-shirts and swimwear may have UV protection.

Knowledge link

You can find more information about technical fabrics and finishes on pages 140–146 of Chapter 5.

Risk assessment

To identify which areas of design and production could be potential areas of danger (this includes both equipment and your normal working area), a risk assessment has to be carried out to highlight potential risks and show how they can be avoided or the risk lessened. A risk assessment is a very careful examination of what, in your work area, could cause harm to other people or to you personally. This work is usually carried out by the health and safety officer. The officer has to identify the risk and then identify how it can be made safe, or how the risk can be reduced or removed. This will be carried out for each process that a product goes through.

A risk assessment is carried out by:

- writing down all the risks at each stage of production
- creating a safety manual or safety guidelines
- creating a code of practice for all users of equipment
- identifying the relevant safety garments or other safety accessories needed

- ensuring that all the correct safety labels are on equipment and that key safety signs are posted next to equipment
- ensuring that all new employees and existing employees are fully trained on the equipment they will be using.

Risks can be classified into one of several categories:

- high risk
- medium risk
- low risk
- minimum risk.

All equipment, materials and components can be placed into these categories.

A risk assessment checklist

1. Look around your work area for potential hazards. What are they and how can they be avoided?
2. Identify equipment around you as having a high, medium, low or minimum risk, and check how you can use this equipment safely.
3. Decide who might be harmed by using the equipment, and how. Does this equipment or material carry a warning sign and do you recognise what this sign means?
4. List and evaluate each risk and then decide whether the existing instructions for use need improving.
5. Record your findings.
6. Every time tools or equipment are changed, you need to review your assessment and revise it if necessary.

Consumer rights when purchasing goods

Just as health and safety in the workplace is controlled by the health and safety officer, so goods that are purchased from various retail outlets, whether at a shop or online, are controlled by safety laws. The safety of products that you purchase is controlled by government legislation and is strictly controlled. The key laws that govern the safety of products that you purchase are:

- the Sale of Goods Act 1979
- the Consumer Protection Act 1987
- the General Product Safety Regulations (GPSR) 1994.

Key term

Consumer rights – the use of the law to protect consumers when they buy products.

Visual labels indicate that products have passed strict controls and guidelines, which means they are safe for use and can be sold directly to the public.

Key consumer Act	Key details of the Act
Consumer Credit Act 1974	○ Provides for control of consumer credit and hire and related services ○ Provides certain safeguards to consumers who purchase goods and services on credit
Consumer Protection Act 1987	○ Stops the supply of goods that do not meet with the general safety requirements or are unsafe ○ Provides for the safety and protection of consumers. ○ Provides approved safety standards ○ Provides key requirements for persons to publish notices warning of unsafe goods previously supplied ○ Provides liability for damage caused by faulty products ○ Stops misleading price information being displayed
Health and Safety at Work Act 1974	○ Controls the classification, packaging, labelling, carriage and storage of dangerous substances
Prices Act 1974 and 1975	○ Gives power to regulate the price display of certain goods ○ Provides protection and price information for consumers ○ Promotes fair trading
Trade Descriptions Act 1968	○ Stops mis-description on the supply of goods ○ Stops false claims being made for services, accommodation and facilities
Trade Marks Act 1994	○ Controls false or unapproved use or application of the use of a trademark
Sale of Goods Act 1979, Sale and Supply of Goods 1994, Sale of Goods (Amendment) Act 1995	○ Details and lists the rights of purchasers and the duties of sellers in the sale of goods
Supply of Goods and Services Act 1982	○ Details the rights of purchasers and the duties of suppliers of services

△ **Table 8.11** Consumer legislation

Regulations related to clothing or other textile products

Designers need to be aware of the issues related to products that they design. The regulations outlined in Table 8.12 need to be incorporated into their design specifications to ensure that the product created meets the demands of regulations and the end user.

Key Act/regulation	Which area of the textiles/fashion industry is it related to?
Children's Clothing (Hood Cords) Regulations 1976	Children's wear
Nightwear (Safety) Regulations 1985, Nightwear (Safety) (Amendment) Regulations 1987	Nightwear for adults or children
Furniture and Furnishings (Fire) (Safety) Regulations 1988, 1989, 1993	Any furniture or furnishings, including chairs and cushions
Toys (Safety) Regulations 1995	All toys
Textile Products (Indication of Fibre Content) Regulations 1986, 1988, 1998	All textile products, usually shown on the care label
Footwear (Indication of Composition) Labelling Regulations 1995	All footwear needs to clearly show the key details of fibre/fabric composition

△ **Table 8.12** Regulations related to the textiles and fashion industry

How are rules and regulations controlled?

Standards related to products in the UK are regulated by official organisations such as the British Standards. For Europe, this is done by the CEN (European Committee for Standardisation), which deals with all sectors of industry, except for the electro-technology and telecommunication sectors.

With the widening of trade across the world through electronic commerce (e-tailing, online trading, such as eBay, and internet shopping), there are now international issues related to these new areas that are discussed at international level, by organisations such as the WTO (World Trade Organization) and the OECD (Organisation for Economic Cooperation and Development).

E-commerce

E-commerce is the process of purchasing goods electronically from a virtual store or online retailer. This applies to buying goods over the internet or by mobile phone (e.g. text messaging).

When you buy goods using e-commerce, you have the same rights as when you buy in a shop and by distance sale (i.e. buying from a catalogue). This applies if you use e-commerce to buy goods in the UK or anywhere else in the European Union. There are other rules and regulations for buying goods from the US and other countries. The trader must give you additional information, as well as detailed instructions for completing your order. They must:

- tell you how to correct any mistakes you might make when placing your order
- supply any terms and conditions of the sale in a format that can be easily saved or printed out
- tell you whether they will keep a file of the sale for you to access
- tell you about any codes of conduct that apply to the sale and how you can look them up electronically
- send an acknowledgement that the order has been received.

For more information on consumer protection law, visit the Consumer Direct website: **www.consumerdirect.gov.uk**

Environmental Acts

Environmental issues are very prominent in all aspects of our lives. Here are the key Acts related to pollution and the environment:

- Control of Pollution Act 1974
- Environmental Protection Act 1990
- Clean Air Act 1993.

Copyright of designs

In textiles and fashion, designs are sometimes copied and there are laws that protect designs and designers. They are:

- Copyright, Designs and Patents Act 1988
- Trade Marks Act 1994
- Olympic Symbol etc. (Protection) Act 1995.

Advertising

Advertising of goods is controlled by the ASA (Advertising Standards Agency). The ASA dictates what can and cannot be stated in an advertisement and how adverts can be shown depending on the following:

- time of day
- the target audience the product is aimed at
- the media being used for the advert
- the language of the advert.

The ASA protects consumers from false claims and adverts that are not truthful or accurate. It has the right to remove adverts and also ensure that they are not displayed. You can find out about how adverts are controlled by visiting the Advertising Standard Agency's website: **www.asa.org.uk**

What is in a label?

Knowledge link

For more information on labelling, see Chapter 5, pages 140–146.

Testing textiles products

Tests are an essential part of consumer safety and, as such, are carried out on all products to ensure that they meet safety standards. Some of the key tests that are carried out on clothing are:

- flammability test
- abrasion test
- stain-resistance test
- showerproof (splashproof) and waterproof test
- stretch (elasticity) test
- insulation test
- absorbency test
- crease-resistance test.

Furnishings, soft furnishings, drapes and curtains also need to be tested following the BS 5867-1:2004 specification for fabrics for curtains and drapes. So, in addition to the above, they are tested for:

- their washing
- fading (also called colour-fastness)
- their ability to be dry-cleaned
- dimensional stability (if they change length or width during normal wear and tear or washing and cleaning)
- wear and tear.

Curtains and drapes also have additional labelling requirements to show that they conform to BS 5867. Labels must include:

- the standard number against which the product has been tested
- the manufacturer's name
- care label instructions, and aftercare information
- the correct care labels
- whether the fabric cannot be washed
- dry-cleaning labels
- fibre content (the highest content fibre is listed first).

It is illegal to mark textile fabrics or goods as being 'non-flammable' or 'flame-resistant'. The fabric has to meet a set standard of low flammability. The standard is one that has been worked out by the British Standards

Institution and is very strict. Since July 1983, all upholstered furniture has had to carry a fire label of some sort. It should either say 'resistant' if it is made from a flameproofed material, or it should carry a warning label about the dangers of fire from cigarettes. Nightwear for children must be made from low-flammability material.

Knowledge link

You can find other information related to the testing of textile products, including examples of tests carried out in controlled assessments, on pages 50–57 of Chapter 2.

Summary

- In your classroom, there will be safety guidelines that you need to follow when using materials, components and equipment. You will need to highlight in your project the key safe working practices for the following:
  - the correct and safe use of the equipment used to make your product
  - how your product can be used safely
  - the safe working practices to be followed when working
  - appropriate safety clothing when working with chemicals and dyes
  - the correct safety processes when working with electrical equipment.
- Health and safety is a very important aspect of the work environment and it is important that, at all times, you are able to work safely and use equipment safely. As well as the rules and regulations, you will need to use and recognise the key safety signs and signals.
- The use of standards for making sure that a product is ready for use by the consumer is an important part of the design process.
- When preparing your work, you must be able to choose the right tools and equipment. Care must also be taken with the fabrics, components and materials that you use, and you must follow the key rules regarding fabrics.

Activities

1. Referring to your coursework, create a list of equipment to be used. List the potential hazards or risks and how they can be reduced or avoided. **[10 marks]**
2. Using the information about the various rules and regulations regarding health and safety, create a poster that can be placed in a prominent place in your classroom that highlights the important facts about health and safety. **[5 marks]**
3. Identify and list the equipment needed for the following processes:
   (a) placing an embroidered logo on a baseball cap **[5 marks]**
   (b) inserting a zip into a pair of shorts **[5 marks]**
   (c) placing a sublimation print on a polyester t-shirt **[5 marks]**
   (d) decorating a cushion using the Batik technique.
   (e) You should highlight the key safety processes to be looked at in making each product and what key hazard symbols might be included on the equipment that you would use. **[5 marks]**

Exam practice questions

1. What do the following terms mean?
   (a) risk assessment
   (b) health and safety. **[4 marks]**
2. What key protective clothing is needed when using dyes or printing inks? **[4 marks]**
3. What is the difference between the Kitemark and the CE safety mark? **[2 marks]**
4. What information needs to be included on a care label? **[4 marks]**
5. What are the main points to be considered when purchasing curtains? **[2 marks]**

Stretch yourself

Look at the picture of the following product.

△ **Figure 8.19**

Design a care label for the product. **[6 marks]**

chapter 9 Processes and manufacture

9.1 Techniques and processes

Learning objectives

By the end of this section, you should have a key understanding of:

- manufacturing processes and techniques
- the use of CAD/CAM in manufacturing
- different tools and equipment for textiles
- using equipment safely.

Key points

- Communication skills
- Innovative ideas
- Creative ideas
- Linking technology and design
- Values

Introduction

When making any textile or fashion product, it is essential that you identify and know how to use safely the correct tools and equipment to make your product. You also need to ensure that you know how to use the correct manufacturing techniques and processes in constructing your product. Any product that is constructed needs to be:

- **fit for purpose**
- **safe to use**
- **aesthetically pleasing**
- **well constructed and made so that it can last a long time.**

Manufacturing techniques and processes

There are different types of techniques that can be used in the construction of textile and fashion products. These can be divided into the following:

- joining techniques
- manipulation techniques
- techniques for adding or forming shape
- decorating techniques
- finishing techniques.

Joining techniques

A seam is the term used to describe how you join two fabrics together. The seam should be 1.5 cm wide; this is to allow the seam to remain in place and not split.

You can join a seam together permanently using a straight stitch on a sewing machine. You can join a seam temporarily using a temporary stitch called a tacking stitch. You can also join seams temporarily using dressmaking pins, which are removed after a permanent method has been used.

Most seams are constructed with the right sides of the fabric facing each other. They are then temporarily held in place and stitched using a sewing machine.

Different types of seams are described and shown in Table 9.1.

Name of seam	How is it made?	What does the seam look like?
Plain seam	The fabrics to be joined together are placed with their right sides together, matching the raw edges of the fabric and any dots and notches. The layers are pinned together. The stitching line is 1.5cm from the edge of the fabric and can be marked using tailor's chalk or tailor's pencil. The seam is stitched along the stitching line using straight stitch, reversing at the start and finish of the stitching. Pins or tacks are removed and the seam is pressed.	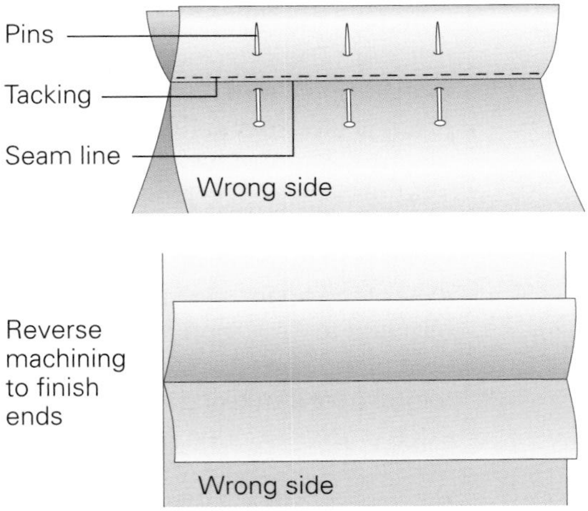 △ **Figure 9.1**
French seam	The fabrics to be joined are placed wrong sides together, matching the ends and notches. The material is pinned and tacked. The first row of stitching is done 1cm from the raw edges, reversing at the start and end of the row. The seam is pressed open and the seam allowance is trimmed to 3mm. The fabric is folded so the right sides are together, pinned and tacked and then machined using a straight stitch 5mm from the folded edge, reversing at the start and finish. The seam is then pressed.	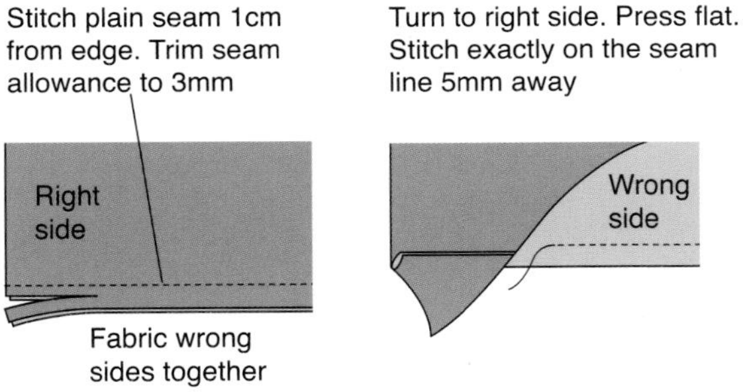 Stitch plain seam 1cm from edge. Trim seam allowance to 3mm Turn to right side. Press flat. Stitch exactly on the seam line 5mm away △ **Figure 9.2**

△ **Table 9.1** Types of seams

Cont.

Name of seam	How is it made?	What does the seam look like?
Double machine-stitched seam	The fabrics are placed to be joined wrong sides together, matching the edges and notches. The stitching line is pinned or tacked. A straight stitch is used along the stitching line, reversing at the start and finish. The pins or tacks are removed and the seam is pressed open. One side of the seam allowance is trimmed to 5mm and the other side of the seam allowance is folded over it, tucking the raw edge under. It is then pinned and tacked in place and machine-stitched close to the folded edge.	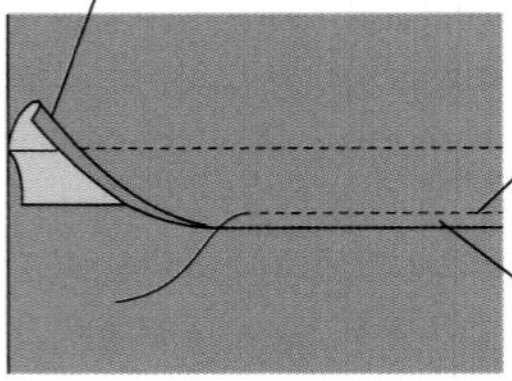 △ **Figure 9.3**
Curved seam	This seam is the same as making a plain seam, except that to ensure the fabric does not pull or pucker, you need to clip into the seam.	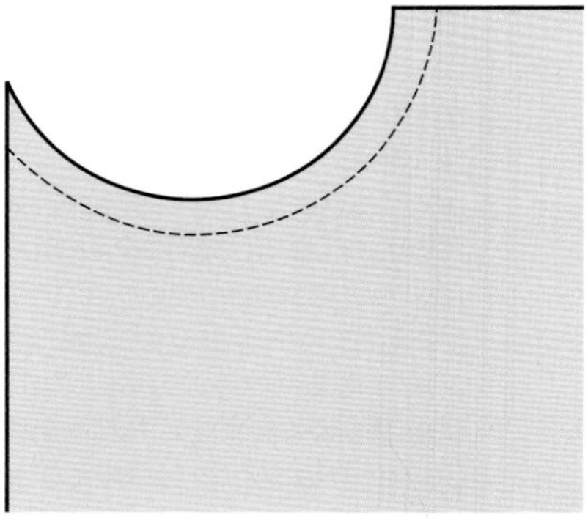 △ **Figure 9.4**

△ **Table 9.1** Types of seams

Cont.

Name of seam	How is it made?	What does the seam look like?
Angled seam	This seam is the same as making a plain seam, except to ensure that the fabric does not pull or pucker, you need to clip into the seam.	△ **Figure 9.5**
Overlocked seam	Using an overlocking machine. These machines do not have a lower bobbin, but use cones of thread on the top of the machine. Some overlockers stitch the seam, neaten it and trim off the excess fabric. An overlocked seam allows a certain amount of stretch.	△ **Figure 9.6**

△ **Table 9.1** Types of seams *continued*

Industrial applications

The types of seams that are applied to a textile product depend on what is being made. There are standard terms used for stitching that are set by British Standards. These are used by companies as a way of standardising the way products are constructed. This information is shown in both the product specification and the manufacturing specification.

Name of seam	British Standards name
Lockstitch	301
French seam	SSCE or ISO 1.06.03
Double machine-stitched seam	LSC or 2.04.06
Overlocked seam	504

△ **Table 9.2** British Standards terms for commonly used seams

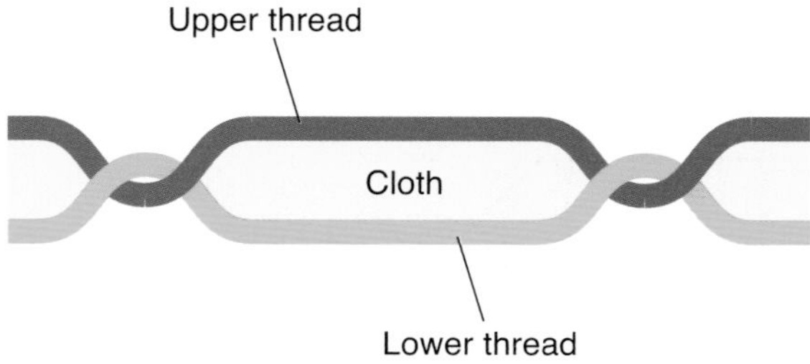

△ **Figure 9.7** Lockstitch

Manipulation techniques

Textiles can be manipulated using the following means:

- Using dry heat – for example, using a heat press. This technique is used to create pleats. This works effectively on synthetic fabrics.
- Using steam, as in Shibori (a traditional Japanese technique, which involves stitching and/or twisting fabrics, adding colour and then steaming the fabrics to create unusual pleated and colour effects).
- Using mechanical methods, such as gathering, tucking, smocking and pin tucks.

Where using a sewing machine or hand-stitching techniques, fabrics can be manipulated using any of these methods to remove fullness, to give fitted effects to garments or decorative effects to products such as cushions. These effects work on any type of fabric, but more pronounced effects can be achieved depending on the type of fabric used. For example, using a sheer nylon organza will give a stiffer and translucent effect, while using a lightweight silk will give the final product a softer effect.

Cut and slash techniques and layering of fabrics can produce effects that give a product a unique look. This technique requires the user to layer three or four fabrics of the same size one on top of the other; more can be added depending on the thickness of the fabric. Draw vertical lines 3cm on the top fabric, using a straight stitch follow the lines drawn and stitch the layers together. Once the stitching is completed, using small sharp scissors cut through only the first three layers. This process reveals the layers of the fabrics that have been stitched as well as the base layer. The more fabrics that are layered, the more pronounced the effects.

It must be noted that different manipulation techniques can be combined together, but this requires knowledge of the properties of fabrics to get the creative effect required.

Techniques for adding or forming shape

Shapes can be added to textile products through moulding or forming.

Moulding using steam or hot water

Moulding or forming textiles involves using steam or hot water and a mould of some description. For example, hat making uses moulds in the shape of a head; shoe making uses foot blocks known as lasts, which are used to shape and mould leather for shoes. Technical fabrics such as carbon and Kevlar® can be moulded with resin to make shapes for cars and protective garments.

Resins and starches

Fabrics can have resins or starches added to the surface to make them stiff or to hold their shape, as seen in products such as blinds and lampshades.

Interfacing

The addition of different types of interfacing can enhance the shape of a fabric when applied. Different weights of interfacing or interlining are used in the construction of Saville Row suits. Interfacings can be ironed or stitched into place and are used to add support and structure to a garment.

△ **Figure 9.8** Interfacing

Bonding

Bondaweb, a glue/paper product used in textiles can be used to bond two fabrics together, creating a stronger fabric and giving a two-sided fabric effect. It is also a useful material to use when doing techniques such as appliqué.

Soluble threads and fabrics

Soluble threads and fabrics are also known as stabilisers, and can be used in the creation of fabric designs. They are made from alginates and are applied to fabrics through stitching. Once the design is complete, the yarn or fabric can be dissolved using either hot or cold water, or a hot iron. These materials can be used to create unique textiles products, such as embroidered designs, and can be stitched onto soluble fabric. This can then be dissolved and the resulting embroidery draped over an upside-down bowl, then left to dry. Once dried, the resulting embroidery can be removed and then used as a decorative product.

Darts

Darts are added to garments or textile products to give added shape to the body. They can be used for functional effects or for decoration. There are different types of darts – for example, bust dart, contour or double-pointed darts. When used on garments they can give added form to the wearer. When used on textiles products they provide them with interesting shapes, surfaces and textures.

Other techniques

You can use a sewing machine to create more complex shapes and textures. Techniques will include pleats, tucks, godets, gathers, smocking, shirring and ruffles.

Decorating techniques

Decorating techniques are used to add texture and patterning effects to fabric. They can be divided into the following areas:

- hand embroidery decoration
- machine embroidery. This can be divided into two groups: freehand machining and computer-aided design, using specialised digitising software.

Sometimes machine and hand embroidery decorating techniques can be combined. New developments in embroidery software enable the designer to combine digital printing or transfer printing techniques with embroidery; this is known as print and stitch. It is important to note that when combining techniques you need to understand how this will affect the fabric that the technique is being applied to, and have an idea of what the effect will produce. In your own coursework, you will need to model ideas and showcase them.

△ **Figure 9.9** Computer-controlled embroidery

Finishing techniques

Finishing techniques are processes that can be used to enhance a product or add decoration. A range of finishing techniques are listed below.

Using an overlocker

This is for flatlocked seams, picot edges or lettuce edge. Rolled hems are decorative techniques that can be applied to jersey (knitted fabrics) and also woven fabrics.

Seams and hems

Using different seams and hems can give finishes to the outside of garments or textiles products. They are used as a design feature on garments and textiles products. There is a range of seams and hems that can be used:

- double-machine-stitched seams, taped seams, boned seams, exposed seams
- scalloped hems, rolled hems
- edges – for example, piped edges, biased-bound edges.

Trims

Using trims such as beading and lace can add features to garments and other textiles products. They are often used to enhance a product, giving it added value or decoration.

Buttons and buttonholes

Using covered buttons, making your own buttons and creating finished buttonholes, such as a bound button or corded buttonholes, are also used as finishing techniques.

CAD/CAM

The development of computer-aided design (CAD) software and computer-aided manufacture (CAM) enables today's designers to create effects and develop designs that might have taken several hours or a couple of days when using traditional hand techniques.

More and more designers are combining hand techniques with CAD/CAM techniques, which allows them to integrate materials and techniques to create unique fabrics, garments and other textile products.

CAD/CAM techniques will include the use of equipment such as lasers, embroidery, knitting and weaving, and digital printing. Designer Helen Amy Murray uses traditional hand cutting methods alongside using CAD to draw and develop her designs and create unique illustrations to digitally print on to fabric and create amazing 3D sculptural fabric.

Textile design companies such as Timourous Beasties explore combining traditional print techniques and motifs with digital printing. Design duo Basso and Brooke also combine traditional techniques with craft techniques through digital printing.

You can read more about these designers on their websites:

- Helen Amy Murray: www.helenamymurray.com
- Timourous Beasties: www.timorousbeasties.com
- Basso and Brooke: www.bassoandbrooke.com

△ **Figure 9.10** Helen Amy Murray's designs

Textile tools and equipment

As part of the design-and-make process, it is essential that you are able to identify the correct materials, equipment, tools and components that are needed to make your products. The equipment or tools you choose to work with in

Key term

CAD/CAM systems – computer-aided design and computer-aided manufacture. Computer-aided designs are designs created using a computer. Computer-aided manufacture is where computers are used in the manufacturing process.

textiles technology should be appropriate for the job they have to do. You will need to be aware of the health, safety and risk issues that are linked to the use of both simple and complex tools and equipment. All equipment used in textiles has specific features that allow you to do the job correctly and effectively.

In preparation for your exam and during the completion of your controlled assessment (design and make practice), you will be expected to:

- select the appropriate tools, equipment or components
- describe the tools, equipment and components you are using
- select the correct materials and fabrics to complete your work.

Equipment can be divided into the following areas:

- colour and design equipment
- sewing and joining equipment
- pressing and fusing equipment (e.g. irons, heat presses)
- fitting equipment (e.g. tailor's or dressmaker's mannequin).

Tools can be divided into the following:

- small tools (e.g. needles, pins, stitch unpick)
- large hand tools (e.g. large dressmaker's scissors)
- measuring and marking tools (e.g. tape measures, tailor's chalk).

Components, also known as haberdashery, are those items that are added to textile products that can become a permanent part or feature of the final design. These can be divided into the following areas:

- threads
- fastenings
- ribbons
- elastics
- shoulder pads
- interfacing.

Materials are the fabrics that you choose to complete the making up of your product. You may choose your materials based on the following factors:

- natural or synthetic fibres
- finishing process applied to fabrics
- strength or durability
- end use
- how the fabric can be manipulated
- application of colour
- application of surface pattern or decoration
- whether the fabric will be used indoors or outdoors
- the feel or appearance of the fabric
- the cost of the fabric
- whether the fabric has technical qualities
- how the fabric reacts to different temperatures.

Key terms

Components – parts such as buttons and interfacing that are an integral part of a textile product.

Equipment – larger machines that are necessary to make/manufacture a product.

Materials – the things needed for making something or the term used to describe a product made using synthetic, natural or regenerated fibres, from weaving, knitting or felting, or a non-woven production process.

Tools – pieces of equipment used to perform specific tasks; they are split into hand tools and machine tools.

Knowledge link

There are many factors that will determine your choice of fabrics. You can find more information on the properties of fabrics and fibre in Chapter 4.

Your choice of materials, components, equipment and tools for the design and construction of your textiles product needs to be discussed and analysed in your controlled assessment.

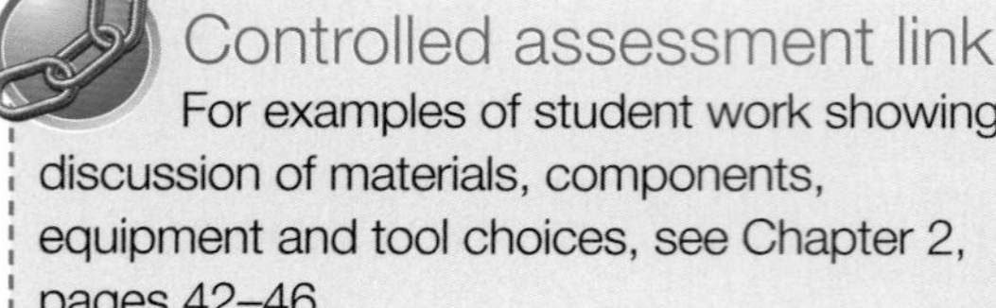

Controlled assessment link

For examples of student work showing discussion of materials, components, equipment and tool choices, see Chapter 2, pages 42–46.

Choosing equipment and tools

Colour and design equipment

The different types of colour and design equipment are outlined in Table 9.3.

△ **Figure 9.11** Batik pot

△ **Figure 9.12** Screen-printing equipment

Equipment	Description
Batik pot	Batik pots are specially developed pots that are used to melt the wax that is used for batik. Modern batik pots are heated using electricity. The wax is applied to fabric using either brushes or Tjanting tools.
Screen-printing equipment	Screen-printing is used as a method of applying surface pattern to fabrics. It consists of a wood or metal frame with a special mesh stretched over it. A squeegee is used to push the pigment through the mesh onto the fabric.
Digital printer	This type of printer allows the user to either print directly to fabric, called reactive printing, or print directly to paper and then transfer the design to fabric using a heat press, called sublimation printing.
Fabric crayons	Fabric crayons are a form of dye in solid form. There are different types of fabric crayons for use on different kinds of fabrics. Designs are heat-set onto the fabric by ironing on the reverse of the design. Once set, designs can be hand-washed safely at 40 degrees Celsius.
Fabric felt-tip pens	Different fabric felt-tip pens are used for different fabrics. They can be applied directly to the fabrics. The dyes are set into the fabric by ironing on the reverse. They can be washed in temperatures up to 40 degrees Celsius.

△ **Table 9.3** Colour and design equipment

Sewing and joining equipment – machine-based

There are different types of sewing machines dependent on the task that you want to do (see Table 9.4).

Sewing equipment	Description
Standard sewing machine	Can be used to join fabrics and create simple embroidery. They have limited features. They come with a variety of different accessories, such as 'feet' that allow different applications to be applied to fabrics.
Embroidery machine	This is similar to the standard sewing machine, except that it has lots of different decorative stitches and features. Can also include computer technology, which can make it easier to use and gives additional features in the use of a variety of stitches. They also come with a variety of different accessories, such as 'feet' that allow different applications to be applied to fabrics.
Computerised sewing machine	An advanced sewing machine with many features. The main difference is that it is controlled by a computer interface, which can also be connected to a computer, so designs can be digitised and developed, and then sent to the machine for sewing. There are different computerised machines, depending on how complex the designs are that you want to create. These machines work best with specialised embroidery threads. They also come with a variety of different accessories, such as 'feet' that allow different applications to be applied to fabrics.
Overlocker	This is a specialised sewing machine used for joining and finishing fabrics, giving them a professional finish. It can also be used for adding decorative edgings to fabrics. You can use a different number of threads – for example, three-thread, four-thread or even five-thread. Overlockers are also useful for stitching stretch-knit or jersey fabrics. The latest version of these comes with a variety of different accessories, such as 'feet' that allow different applications to be applied to fabrics.
Embellisher machine	Often referred to as a threadless sewing machine or mechanical felting machine, it is a machine that uses barb hooks to join fabrics together. It works in a similar way to a sewing machine, in that you need to put pressure on a sewing pedal to enable the hooks to go up and down.

△ **Table 9.4** Sewing equipment

△ **Figure 9.13** Standard sewing machine

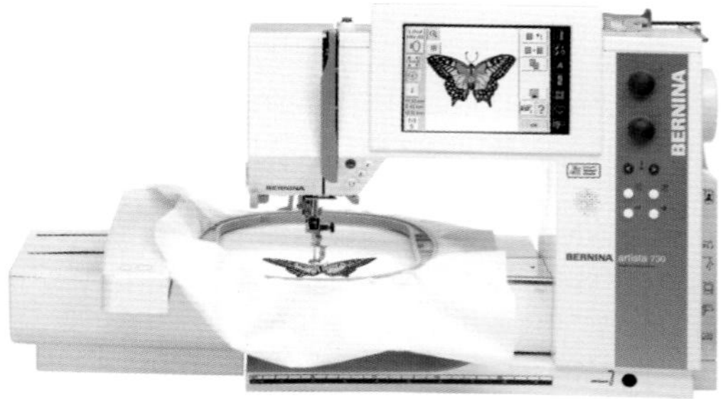

△ **Figure 9.14** Computerised sewing machine

Weaving looms

A weaving loom is used in the manufacture of knitted fabrics. There are different types of looms that are used to weave fabrics. They too can be linked to computers. Design software can be used to create new designs, which can then be downloaded to machines for manufacture.

Knitting machines

Knitting machines are used for the manufacture of plain, patterned or textured knitted fabrics. They are used to create garments, fabrics or textile products. Domestic and industrial machines can be linked to a computer. Designs can be created using software, which is then downloaded to the machines to be knitted.

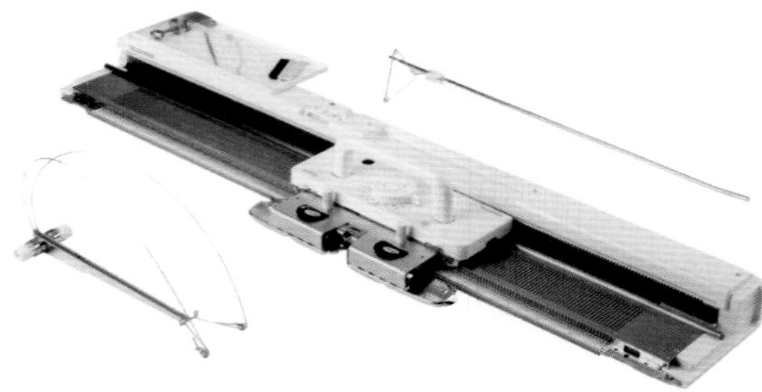

△ **Figure 9.15** Knitting machine

Knowledge link

You can find more information about how knitted fabrics are created on pages 99–102 of Chapter 4.

Knowledge link

You can find more information about how fabrics are woven on pages 94–99 of Chapter 4.

Washing machines and tumble dryers

These are essential pieces of equipment used for the aftercare of textile products that we make or buy. Used to clean our products, washing machines have now been developed that can wash our clothes at very low temperatures. These have been developed in response to the new types of washing products for clothes that use formulas that allow cleaning at lower temperatures, but also in response to the environmental issues related to cleaning our clothes.

With today's modern dyes, large products can be recoloured easily in the washing machine, so enabling the user to keep using the product.

Knowledge link

You can find more information on reusing materials and sustainable issues in design in Chapter 8.

Equipment	Description
Dressmaker's mannequin	These are used to fit garments. They can be adjusted to different sizes and there are mannequins for all different sizes and shapes.
Scissors/ pinking shears	There are many types of scissors used in textiles, each for different purposes. Pinking shears are a special type that can be used for either finishing off edges of fabric to prevent fraying or decorating edges of fabric.
Tape measure/ruler	Tape measures and rulers are used for measuring patterns or garments. Tape measures can be curved easily, making them ideal for textiles.
Embroidery frame	Embroidery frames are used to hold fabrics in place when sewing. They can be used for hand embroidery work or can be used to keep designs and fabrics in place when doing embroidery on sewing machines.
Tailor's chalk/ marker pens	Tailor's chalk is used to make marks on fabrics. It can easily be rubbed off and is available in different colours. There are also other types of fabric marker pens that can be used that disappear when the fabrics are washed.
Pins and needles	Pins are used to hold fabrics together when cutting out patterns. There are different needles used in sewing: some are for hand embroidery and others are for use on sewing machines. There are different sewing machine needles for different types of fabrics.
Unpicker	This is used to unpick both hand and machine stitches. It has a very sharp point.
Tracing wheel and carbon paper	This is used to transfer pattern markings to fabric or to a paper pattern.

△ **Table 9.5** Key equipment and tools

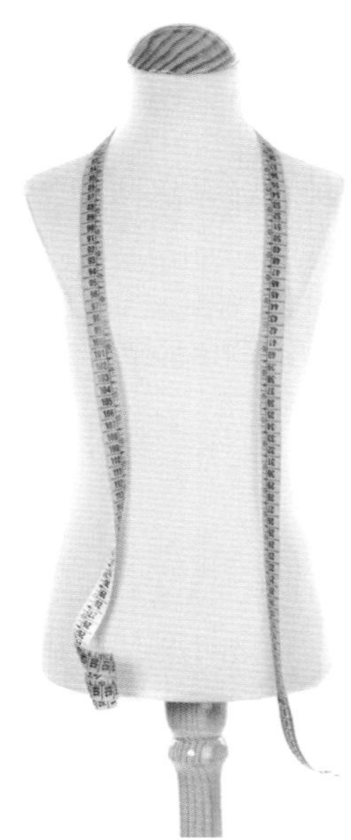

△ **Figure 9.16** Dressmaker's mannequin

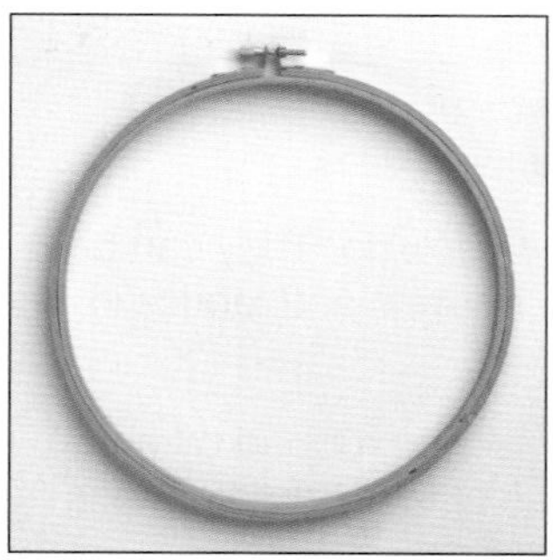

△ **Figure 9.17** Embroidery frame

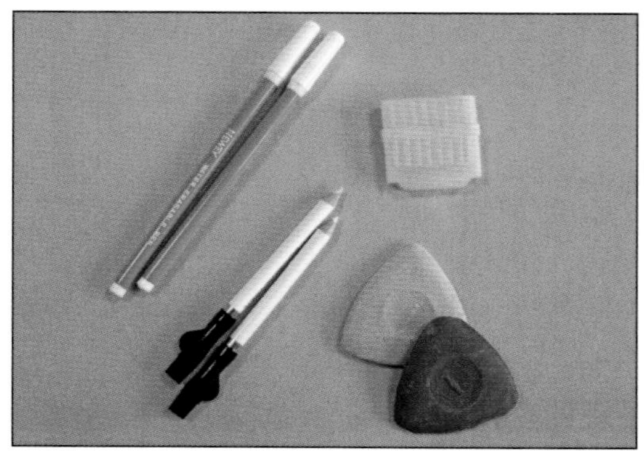

△ **Figure 9.18** Tailor's chalk/marker pens

△ **Figure 9.19** Tracing wheel and carbon paper

Digital tools

Other tools that might be used in the design and making of textile products are as follows:

- software design packages that are used for designing and modelling fabrics or designs
- software packages that can be used for creating or drafting patterns
- software design packages that can be used for creating embroidery designs
- specialised drawing or digital tools, such as graphics tablets, digi-memo pads or Livescribe digital pens, which allow you to transfer digital images quickly for development
- 'apps' as design tools in the classroom to capture images and for choosing colours.

Choosing components

Table 9.6 outlines the different components and what they look like.

Components	What are they?
Dyes	There is a range of dyes used in textiles. Some dyes can only be used on natural fabrics (such as reactive dyes and acid dyes); other dyes can only be used on synthetic fabrics (such as disperse dyes). You will need to know about the fabric you want to apply colour to and choose the correct dye.
Paints	There are different paints that can be used in textiles. Some paints create 3D textures on fabrics. There are also specialist paints that can be used on fabrics such as silk.
Inks	There is a range of inks used in textiles, depending on whether the fabric is natural or synthetic. They are normally used to draw onto the fabric.
Threads	There is a range of threads for use in textiles. Hand-embroidery threads are for decorative work. There is also a range of sewing machine threads. You can select threads depending on the fabrics and the end use of the product.
Fastenings/ Velcro	There is a range of fastenings that can be used in textiles and fashion. One of the most commonly used is Velcro (the technical name is hook-and-loop fastening). Other fastenings include zips, hooks and eyes, and buttons.
Knitting yarns	Knitting yarns are available for hand and machine knitting. They are available in different weights and thicknesses. They can be made of different fibres.
Elastic	Elastics are used in textiles for different purposes, such as to hold fabrics in place or create openings that are flexible. They can also be used for embroidery and special effects.
Bindings	Bindings, also known as narrow fabrics, are available in different colours. They can be used in a decorative or functional way.
Interfacings	Interfacings are used to reinforce or add stability to fabrics and garments. There are fusible (they have a low-melt glue and can be applied using an iron) and non-fusible types. They are also available in different weights and types, depending on the end use of the fabric or product.
Shoulder pads	Used to enhance the shape of garments for fitting. Used primarily in outerwear, such as jackets and coats.

△ **Table 9.6** Components

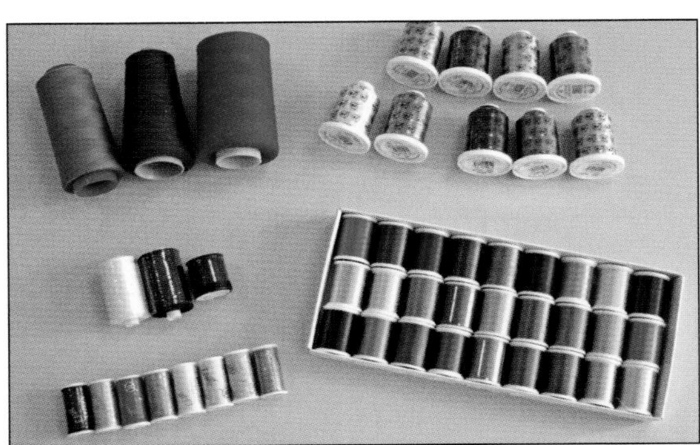

◁ **Figure 9.20** Threads

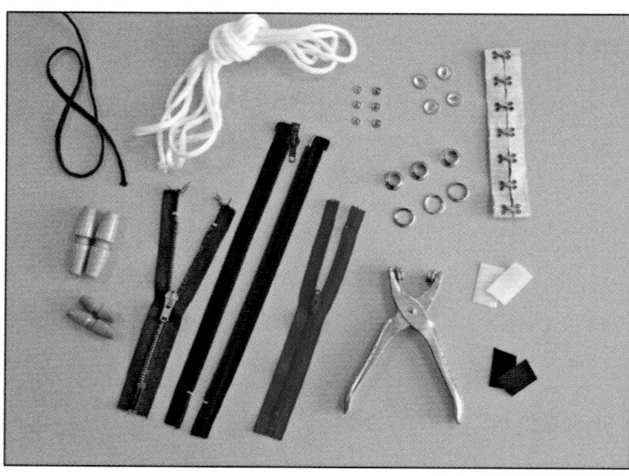

△ **Figure 9.21** Fastenings

Safety using equipment

It is a legal requirement that all equipment used in the workplace or in schools is correctly and safely maintained. All equipment should be inspected at least one a year, but some equipment will be tested more frequently, depending on how often it is used.

Faults can occur in equipment and it important that you always check equipment before using it to ensure that it is safe to use.

The British Standards Institution has a range of key safety checks that need to be carried out to ensure equipment is safe for use. The key points to be noted are:

- safety checks should include all equipment, tools and machines
- only trained personnel can adapt, repair or modify equipment
- all guards on equipment need to be robust, properly maintained and safe
- key and important health and safety information should be properly displayed near or on the equipment, in a prominent position.

All equipment is made to be used safely, and you must at all times adhere to safety rules when using tools and equipment. If in doubt about how to use equipment, you will need to either read the instructions before use or ask a teacher. In your coursework, you will include information about the equipment that you need to use to complete your project. This information will be included in your manufacturing specification in the health and safety section.

Summary

- It is important that you understand how and where to use the correct equipment and processes for each aspect of the work that you do.
- Choosing the correct equipment is important and you must know what each piece of equipment does and how to use it safely and correctly.
- Health and safety is an important aspect of work in school and in the workplace, so it is important to follow the rules for health and safety.
- You need to show clearly in your work that you understand how health and safety rules are applied to each part of your coursework.

Activities

1. Make a list of the equipment you would need to cut out and temporarily join textile products. Add two reasons for your choice of each piece of equipment. **[6 marks]**
2. You have been asked to write the safety instructions for using a sewing machine. Find a picture of a sewing machine, either from a book or the internet, and construct a safety guide for its use. **[6 marks]**

Exam practice questions

1. Where would you expect to find the following seams on a garment?
   (a) double-machine-stitched
   (b) French seam
   (c) plain seam
   (d) curved seam.

   Use sketches and diagrams to annotate your answers. **[10 marks]**

Stretch yourself

Looking at your own coursework, make a list of the equipment that you use in school to make your product. Using the internet and other sources of information, identify and/or and create a Microsoft® PowerPoint® presentation, outlining the type of industrial equipment that you could use to make each stage of your product. **[16 marks]**

9.2 Textile production and manufacture

Learning objectives

By the end of this section, you should have a key understanding of:

- industrial systems used for textile products
- types of production systems
- choosing the right techniques for making products.

Key points

- Analytical skills
- Communication skills
- Innovative ideas
- Creative ideas
- Linking technology and design
- Values

Introduction

The textiles and fashion industry is a global industry. Many fashion and textile companies now make products in different countries. This might be because of reduced labour costs, access to labour or particular specialist processes, such as decoration methods.

In order to ensure that products are made to a certain standard, companies standardise certain processes in the production chain. To do this, they will use different production systems that enable them to make the product in the quickest time and for the cheapest cost.

Production systems and methods

Production systems are needed to enable companies to produce the largest number of products effectively and efficiently for the lowest cost, but at the required quality.

The choice of production method or system depends on the following:

- the number of products that the client needs for each delivery
- the total number of products to be made
- the number of components that are needed to make the product
- the number of processes involved in making the textile or fashion product (e.g. a typical jacket might have up to 250 separate assembling methods, whereas a typical handbag might only have 30)

- the type of product that is being made
- labour costs.

Key term

Production system – the organisation of the workflow in a factory.

Other issues to think about that are related to production issues are:

- overall costs related to manufacture
- skill of the workforce (a more skilled machinist can work faster)
- ethical guidelines used in production
- transport costs
- materials/fabrics costs (creating an exact list and cost of all the materials needed to make the product)
- trimmings/haberdashery costs (again, an important area in the cost of a product)
- finishing costs
- labelling costs
- specialist manufacturing techniques (accessories such as hats, bags, belts or scarves might require special techniques).

The impact of ICT and CAD/CAM on the manufacture of clothing and accessories

Automation in production processes has increased with the use of CAD/CAM. More sewing processes are now automated, due to the increased capability of sewing machines to do these types of processes. CAD/CAM processes in production start with the production pattern and the cutting out of the product.

Knowledge link

You can see more information on the use of CAD/CAM in textiles and fashion on pages 265–272 of Chapter 11.

Name of production system	Process	Reasons for choosing the system/other information
Individual or batch production (also known as making through)	○ Complete products are made by a skilled individual or small team. ○ They use traditional methods of manufacture. ○ A fixed number of identical products are made. ○ Numbers of product made can be varied to suit demand.	○ It is relatively inexpensive method of production. ○ It is easy to repeat, quickly. ○ Stocks of fabrics and components need to be on site and stored, so adds to overall cost.

△ **Table 9.7** The different types of production systems and the reasons for choice *Cont.*

Name of production system	Process	Reasons for choosing the system/other information
One-off production (also known as individual or bespoke production)	○ This process uses traditional methods of manufacture. ○ It needs a very skilled workforce. ○ It is labour-intensive. ○ It uses a range of versatile machines. ○ It is a flexible method of production. ○ The end product is of a very high quality. ○ The end product is very expensive.	○ Haute couture and bespoke tailoring use this method of production. ○ It is flexible. ○ It is a very expensive method of production. ○ It uses a lot of hand and traditional craft methods of production.
Mass or volume production (1) – progressive bundle system	○ Large numbers of identical pieces of a product are made over a long period. ○ It is used for manufacturing items that are always in demand (e.g. t-shirts). ○ Bundles are passed from one operator to the next. ○ Automated machinery and computer-aided manufacture are used to keep manufacturing and labour costs low.	○ It is the cheapest system to use for manufacturing. ○ A low skill level needed to produce products.
Mass or volume production (2) – synchronised system	○ A worker does the same task over and over again. ○ They become very good at this job.	○ There is little flexibility using this method. ○ Jobs cannot be transferred easily.
Mass or volume production (3) – repetitive flow system	○ This system uses a semi-skilled labour force. ○ It is made of small sub-assembly lines that concentrate on one aspect of production. ○ Some processes are semi-automated.	○ The system can produce large quantities of goods quickly. ○ Low costs are related to the manufacturing.
Mass or volume production (4) – continual flow system	○ Products are made on this system 24 hours a day. ○ The system is used to make products using a limited number of components. ○ The product must be easy to construct.	○ It is one of the cheaper methods of production. ○ It keeps costs down. ○ It may use aspects of computer-aided manufacture.

△ **Table 9.7** The different types of production systems and the reasons for choice *Cont.*

Name of production system	Process	Reasons for choosing the system/other information
Cell or section systems	○ Workers are in small teams. ○ Workers need to be skilled or flexible. ○ This system can cope with production where the styles change frequently.	○ Jobs are rotated so that workers become skilled. ○ The system offers a degree of flexibility in the manufacture.

△ **Table 9.7** The different types of production systems and the reasons for choice *continued*

△ **Figure 9.22** Haute couture production

Key terms

Batch production – a production where small numbers of identical items are made.

Cell production – a process used in manufacturing a specialised product.

Just-in-time (JIT) – a form of stock control when goods are delivered just in time to use on the production line.

Line production – describing the process of production.

Mass or volume production – a system where large numbers of items are made on a continuous basis.

One-off (bespoke) production – the production of a unique product for a specific brief.

Sub-assembly – the components needed to make a particular part of a product.

Production terms

Off the peg

Off the peg refers to the process of making products that are transported directly to shops from the factory on pegs or hangers.

Just-in-time (JIT)

Just-in-time is a stock control management system. Companies using this system do not store fabrics or components on site at their factories. Instead, using a complex computer database, they are able to control exactly when fabrics and components arrive at the production factory so the product can be made and dispatched to the client.

The key issues with this system are:

- faults in the production can cause problems
- delays in transportation.

This system also requires that goods arrive already cut out and ready to be joined together. Many factories that use this system have very little storage on site.

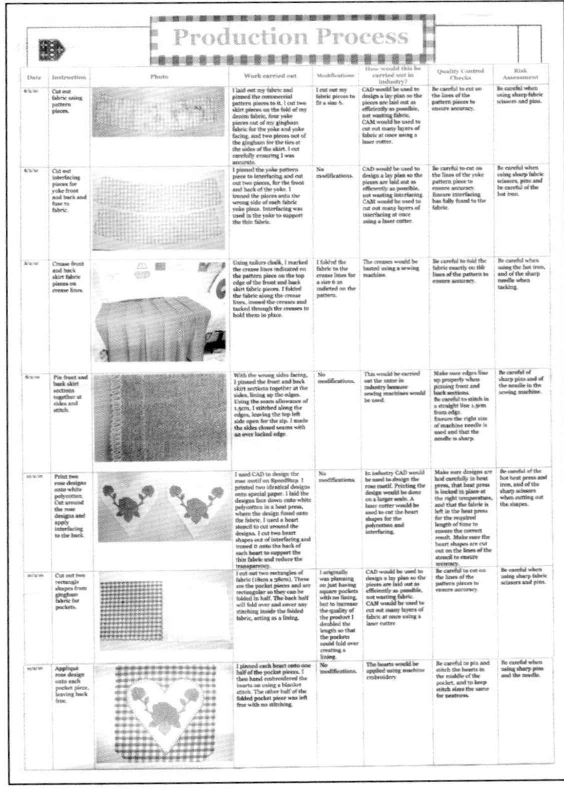

Production Process

Date	Instruction	Photo	Work carried out	Modifications	How would this be carried out in industry?	Quality Control Checks	Risk Assessment
[illegible]	Cut out fabric using pattern pieces.		I laid out my fabric and pinned the commercial pattern pieces to it. I cut two skirt pieces on the fold of my denim fabric, four yoke pieces out of my gingham fabric for the yoke and yoke facing, and two pieces out of the gingham for the ties at the sides of the skirt. I cut carefully ensuring I was accurate.	I cut out my fabric pieces to fit a size 6.	CAD would be used to design a lay plan so the pieces are laid out as efficiently as possible, not wasting fabric. CAM would be used to cut out many layers of fabric at once using a laser cutter.	Be careful to cut on the lines of the pattern pieces to ensure accuracy.	Be careful when using sharp fabric scissors and pins.
[illegible]	Cut out interfacing pieces for yoke front and back and fuse to fabric.		I pinned the yoke pattern piece to interfacing and cut out two pieces, for the front and back of the yoke. I ironed the pieces onto the wrong side of each fabric yoke piece. Interfacing was used in the yoke to support the thin fabric.	No modifications.	CAD would be used to design a lay plan so the pieces are laid out as efficiently as possible, not wasting interfacing. CAM would be used to cut out many layers of interfacing at once using a laser cutter.	Be careful to cut on the lines of the yoke pattern piece to ensure accuracy. Ensure interfacing has fully fused to the fabric.	Be careful when using sharp fabric scissors, pins and be careful of the hot iron.
[illegible]	Crease front and back skirt fabric pieces on crease lines.		Using tailors chalk, I marked the crease lines indicated on the pattern piece on the top edge of the front and back skirt fabric pieces. I folded the fabric along the crease lines, ironed the creases and tacked through the creases to hold them in place.	I folded the fabric to the crease lines for a size 6 as indicted on the pattern.	The creases would be basted using a sewing machine.	Be careful to fold the fabric exactly on the lines of the pattern to ensure accuracy.	Be careful when using the hot iron, and of the sharp needle when tacking.
[illegible]	Pin front and back skirt sections together at sides and stitch.		With the wrong sides facing, I pinned the front and back skirt sections together at the sides, lining up the edges. Using the seam allowance of 1.5cm, I stitched along the edges, leaving the top left side open for the zip. I made the sides closed seams with an over locked edge.	No modifications.	This would be carried out the same in industry because sewing machines would be used.	Make sure edges line up properly when pinning front and back sections. Be careful to stitch in a straight line 1.5cm from edge. Ensure the right size of machine needle is used and that the needle is sharp.	Be careful of sharp pins and of the needle in the sewing machine.
[illegible]	Print two rose designs onto white polycotton. Cut around the rose designs and apply interfacing to the back.		I used CAD to design the rose motif on SpeedStep. I printed two identical designs onto special paper. I laid the designs face down onto white polycotton in a heat press, where the design fused onto the fabric. I used a heart stencil to cut around the designs. I cut two heart shapes out of interfacing and ironed it onto the back of each heart to support the thin fabric and reduce the transparency.	No modifications.	In industry CAD would be used to design the rose motif. Printing the design would be done on a larger scale. A laser cutter would be used to cut the heart shapes for the polycotton and interfacing.	Make sure designs are laid carefully in heat press, that heat press is locked in place at the right temperature, and that the fabric is left in the heat press for the required length of time to ensure the correct result. Make sure the heart shapes are cut out on the lines of the stencil to ensure accuracy.	Be careful of the hot heat press and iron, and of the sharp scissors when cutting out the shapes.
[illegible]	Cut out two rectangle shapes from gingham fabric for pockets.		I cut out two rectangles of fabric (18cm x 38cm). These are the pocket pieces and are rectangular so they can be folded in half. The back half will fold over and cover any stitching inside the folded fabric, acting as a lining.	I originally was planning on just having square pockets with no lining, but to increase the quality of the product I doubled the length so that the pockets could fold over creating a lining.	CAD would be used to design a lay plan so the pieces are laid out as efficiently as possible, not wasting fabric. CAM would be used to cut out many layers of fabric at once using a laser cutter.	Be careful to cut on the lines of the pattern pieces to ensure accuracy.	Be careful when using sharp fabric scissors and pins.
[illegible]	Appliqué rose design onto each pocket piece, leaving back free.		I pinned each heart onto one half of the pocket pieces. I then hand embroidered the hearts on using a blanket stitch. The other half of the folded pocket piece was left free with no stitching.	No modifications.	The hearts would be applied using machine embroidery	Be careful to pin and stitch the hearts in the middle of the pocket, and to keep stitch sizes the same for neatness.	Be careful when using sharp pins and the needle.

△ **Figure 9.23** A student's production worksheet

In your own coursework (controlled assessment)

In your own controlled assessment (design and make practice), you will need to show how you might use different production systems depending on how complex your design or product is. Your project might include several elements and you would need to show how these would impact on the production. You might find that you have incorporated several hand techniques into your work, which would make your work more suitable for one-off production. You might consider modifications that would incorporate more automated options, which would enable your design to be made using mass or volume production methods.

Summary

- Companies choose production systems based on the type of product they need to make.
- Some production systems involve people working in teams, with each member of the team having particular skills.
- The higher the skills needed and the more complex the product, the higher the costs.
- Products that are not complex to make are cheaper to produce.
- The three main issues for manufacturing products are cost of the product, sourcing raw materials and choosing the correct manufacturing process.

Activities

1. Using the internet and other forms of research, create a report about the different types of sewing machines that are used for different types of processes in a factory. **[10 marks]**
2. Compare and contrast the features of an industrial sewing machine and a domestic sewing machine. Annotate your answers. **[10 marks]**

Exam practice questions

1. What are the main types of production systems, and what are the differences between them? **[6 marks]**
2. What are the advantages and disadvantages of the JIT production system? **[4 marks]**
3. What are the advantages to the manufacturer of incorporating CAD/CAM into the production system? **[3 marks]**

Stretch yourself

Style no:	Company name and logo						Date:
Design no:							Designer name:
Specification no:							
	Garment – Garment image and size details 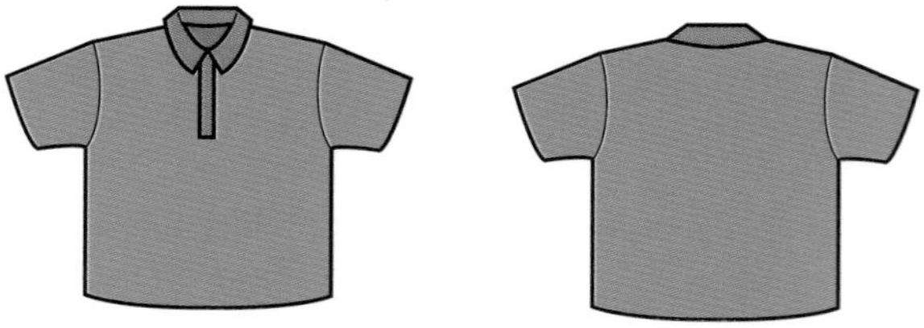						Checking Explanation
Measurements	Diagram reference/measure points	Tolerance 0.5cm	Size 1	Size 2	Size 3	Size 4	Comments
	A						
	B						
	C						
	D						
	E						
	F						
	G						

△ **Figure 9.24**

Study the picture of the t-shirt shown in Figure 9.24.

1. Create a flow chart for making the t-shirt. **[6 marks]**
2. Identify the types of stitches that would need to be used in the construction. **[3 marks]**
3. Identify the type of production system that should be used to make the t-shirt, giving reasons for your choice. **[4 marks]**
4. List the types of trimmings needed for the t-shirt. **[4 marks]**
5. Suggest three different fabrics that could be used to construct your t-shirt, giving at least three reasons for your choice. **[6 marks]**
6. Work out the cost of producing the following:
   - 10 t-shirts
   - 250 t-shirts
   - 2000 t-shirts

   Give three reasons why you think that the overall prices for producing the t-shirts are different. **[6 marks]**
7. Create the care label for the t-shirt. **[4 marks]**

chapter 10 Production planning

10.1 Planning the development and manufacture of a product

Learning objectives

By the end of this section, you should have a key understanding of:

- flow charts
- working drawings
- manufacturing specifications
- costing production
- time plans for producing products.

Key points

- Analytical skills
- Communication skills
- Innovative ideas
- Creative ideas
- Linking technology and design
- Values

Introduction

When creating new products, you will use a wide range of skills, such as designing and researching. An essential part of creating any product is also the planning, whether that be for a prototype, bespoke or mass-produced product.

Planning provides you with the key skills to highlight all the areas that you need to think about when making your product, from choosing the correct materials, components and tools, to costing the product you are making, as well as creating your manufacturing plan for making.

Once the product is made, reviewing the planning, making and costing helps to see where changes can be made, how effective the manufacturing plan was and whether the materials used were correct. The key elements to look at when designing, planning and making a product are:

- **designing costs**
- **costing – fabrics, trimmings, labour, transport**
- **materials required**
- **manufacturing process to be used**
- **finishing and labelling.**

Flow charts

In design and production planning, flow charts play an essential role. Flow charts are visual indicators that can be used to identify:

- the start and end of a project
- the key events that need to happen through the duration of a project
- the key people involved in a project, and their roles and deadlines
- when products need to arrive at the factory for production
- the successful parts of a project.

Flow charts can also be used as a tool for evaluating a project. They follow a set sequence, so the task or work can be completed in the correct sequence and on time.

Flow charts in the design process

Flow charts might be used in the following ways in design projects:

- Trend teams will use flow charts to map out design or colour trends over a period of time.
- Design teams will use flow charts to map out the process of putting a collection together, including, for example, the start and end dates for collections to be completed and details of all aspects of research sampling.

Flow charts in production

Flow charts might be used in the following ways in production:

- Production teams will use flow charts to help map out the various manufacturing processes of a product.
- The sample machinist might map out a flow chart showing the best method to construct a product.
- Manufacturing teams might use flow charts to map out the way that a product moves from one part of the factory to another as it is being made.
- Flow charts can be used to work out the various costing aspects of the manufacturing process.
- Flow charts can also be used to identify when products will arrive in a factory for a product to be made; this is called just-in-time (JIT).

In your coursework, you will create various flow charts or production charts. You might use the following:

1. A simple flow chart or Gantt chart, which is created using spreadsheet software, can be used to highlight an overall plan for the start and end of your project. You might also use this at the end of your project to evaluate your overall progress and key issues you have faced.
2. A manufacturing plan for the making of your product shows key points for feedback or checks. Your manufacturing plan will be created before you start making your product.

Key terms

Flow chart – a diagram that uses special symbols to show the sequence of a process.

Gantt chart – a chart that shows activities for a project, with the time, resources and people needed to complete the project.

Just-in-time – a form of stock control when goods are delivered just in time to use on the production line.

Time plan – setting up the guidelines for making a product over a period of time.

Working drawings

Working drawings are also known as specification drawings or technical specifications.

Key term

Working drawing – a detailed drawing showing all the information needed to make the design idea.

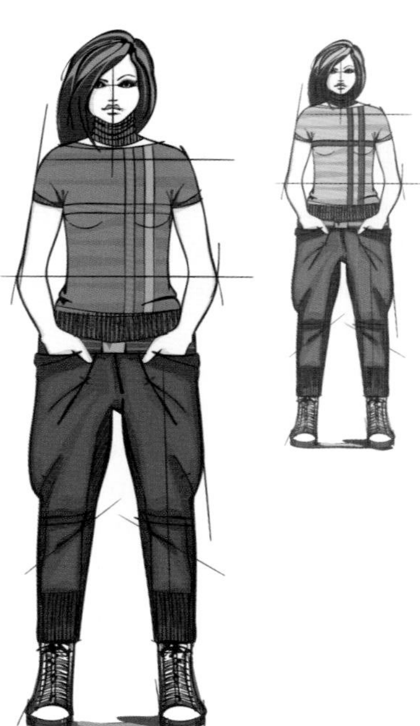

△ **Figure 10.2** Sketch of a textiles product

GANTT CHART

Week 1	Week 2	Week 3	Week 4	Week 5	Week 6	Week 7	Week 8	Week 9	Week 10	Week 11	Week 12	Week 13	Week 14
3rd September-7th September	10th September-14th September	17th September- 21st September	24th September- 28th September	1st October-5th October	8th October-12th October	15th October-19th October	22nd October- 26th October	29th October-2nd November	5th November- 9th November	12th November- 16th November	19th November- 23rd November	26th November - 30th November	3rd December - 7th December
	WORK EXPIRIENCE			Geography Coursework Deadline	School closed 11th October		H T A E L R F M				School closed 22nd Nov		
							DEVELOPING AND TESTING				DEVELOPING AND TESTING		
Development of design brief and collecting research to be carried out before the summer holiday			Designing and Developing										
Analysis of research and writing a design specification.					ICT Coursework Deadline						Exam Preparation		

Week 15	Week 16	Week 17	Week 18	Week 19	Week 20	Week 21	Week 22	Week 23	Week 24	Week 25	Week 26	Week 27	Week 28
10th December - 14th December	17th December - 21st December	24th December - 28th December	31st January - 4th January	7th January - 11th January	14th January - 18th January	21st January - 25th January	28th January - 1st February	4th February - 8th February	11th February - 15th February	18th February - 22nd February	25th February - 29th February	3rd March - 7th March	10th March - 14th March
MOCK EXAMS		C H R I S T M A S H O L I D A Y S								H T A E L R F M			
				Working Drawing			Plan of Manufacture, Health and Safety in Industrial Practice				DEADLINE!		Photos and Evaluations
				Product and Fabric Specification									

△ **Figure 10.1** An example of a student's Gantt chart

These are produced after the final design illustrations and range plans have been created. Working drawings turn your fashion or design illustrations into 2D technical sketches and highlight all the details that are needed to progress to the next stage in manufacturing the sample or the final product.

These technical drawings need to be accurate and highlight all the key information – for example, measurements and placement of decoration.

△ **Figure 10.3** A range plan

Manufacturing specifications

Manufacturing specifications are the details that are indicated on the specification sheet for all the components and materials needed to make the product.

Manufacturing plans are the step-by-step plans for cutting and sewing/making the product, including details of equipment needed in the construction. It is important that the manufacturing plan is accurate, and many manufacturing plans will include quality checks to ensure that the product is being made correctly. Your manufacturing plan will also include information on the equipment you will need to use to make your product, and the safety issues related to safe use.

Key terms

Manufacturing specification – the specific manufacturing details and instructions needed to make a product.

Specification – an outline that details all the requirements of a product.

In your own coursework (controlled assessment), you have to create a manufacturing specification to show how you would make your product step by step.

Plan of Production

Task Number	Materials and Equipment	Plan of Manufacture	Modifications Production problems identified	How would this stage be carried out in industry? When would CAD/CAM be used and why?	Quality Control Checks Tolerances	Feedback	Risk Assessment Health and Safety issues
1	Fabric, polycotton, organza Vilene and wadding, dot and cross paper pattern, small equipment (iron, pins)	Press fabric and pattern Place pattern on the fabric and pin		Lay plans (pattern pieces) (computerised)	Check for any marks or stains on fabric Fabric and pattern should be flat	If there any marks or stains are found on the fabric, do not use the piece of fabric or wash off. If fabric is not flat once pattern is pinned on, re-pin.	Take should be taken when using the iron as it can burn and when using the pins because they can be sharp and will scratch
2	Fabric, polycotton and organza, with pattern pinned on and fabric scissors	Cut both pieces of fabric along the edge of the pattern		Automatic cutting system	Edges should be smooth and no more than a 5mm allowance from the proper line	If edges are too off target so that the design will be disrupted (see quality control) fabric should be re-pined and re-cut as required	Take should be taken with the scissors and pins as both are sharp and could cut or scratch the skin
3	Fabric, organza and polycotton, pins, tacking thread, needle	Lay the two pieces of organza onto the polycotton, pin and tack along the edges		Semi-automatic machine	When pinning fabric should be flat The top and bottom edges should meet	If the stitching is off the line, unpick and re-stitch	Care should be taken with the needle and thread because both are sharp
4	Fabric, organza and polycotton (tacked together), sewing machine, deep red cotton machine thread	Sew along the edges of the organza on both sides, attaching it to the red polycotton using satin stitch and the machine guidelines to measure 2cm from the edge of the fabric		Semi-automatic machine	Stitching should be in a straight line The stitches should be very close together	If the stitches are off the line or not close enough together, unpick and re-stitch	Hair should be tied back when using the machine because it could get caught

TITLE Plan of Production	SHEET	NAME	DATE

△ **Figure 10.4** A student's manufacturing plan

Costing production

All products are costed to be sold at a certain price for a certain marketplace, so it is important for companies to keep costs at the correct levels.

Costing budgets are set at the start of the design process. Faulty goods cost companies money and lose them customers, so quality control and quality assurance play an important part in ensuring that products are well made. This then keeps costs low and customers happy.

Key term

Costing – the process of working out the cost of making a product.

Understanding the costs involved in the manufacturing of a product is very important. There are two types of costs that need to be considered: the direct costs and the indirect costs.

Direct costs are standard costs that the company has all the time; the company knows what these costs will be. Indirect costs are variable and they will change depending on different factors. Companies can control their indirect costs by:

- changing the quality of materials
- changing the types of components
- decreasing the number of products manufactured
- reducing labour costs
- reducing the complexity of the design
- reducing transport costs
- increasing efficiency in production and manufacturing
- reducing storage costs of materials.

The costing of products depends on the market place they are aimed at and the amount of work needed to complete them. Haute couture garments cost a lot of money because they take a long time to make, use high quality materials and need skilled specialists. The number manufactured is very low when compared to the mass market.

Key term

Haute couture – a French term for the highest quality in dressmaking.

Production and new technologies

New technologies have changed the way in which companies work in the fashion and textiles industry. Many companies used to concentrate on having high-street shops where you could shop and catalogues from which you could order products, but this adds extra cost to the final product.

The introduction of internet shopping has changed this. Many high-street companies, such as Next Ltd, have both high-street shops and catalogues. Others, such as Asos.com and Net-a-Porter.com, do not have high-street shops; all of their products can only be purchased in their online store. The set-up of the online store means customers can view garments in online catwalk stores or on virtual mannequins. Some online stores even allow you to create your own avatar that can be dressed in garments of your choice.

Some stores integrate social networking software into their online store, enabling friends to meet online and make comments about the suitability of the products being viewed. This means that both their direct and indirect costs can be kept low. Some companies also use virtual

Direct costs	Indirect costs
Materials	Research
Labour	Design
Components	Testing
Building	Equipment
	Utilities
	Storage
	Training
	Quality checks (including quality assurance and quality control)
	Packaging and delivery
	Advertising
	Profit 1: manufacturing – the profit that the manufacturer will make from manufacturing the garments Profit 2: retail – the 'mark-up' or profit that a manufacture will normally add to a product (usually between 100 and 200 per cent of the wholesale price); the price it is purchased for

△ **Table 10.1** Direct and indirect costs

websites, such as Second Life, to showcase virtual catwalks and garments, only making the garments when a customer selects a product.

Mass customisation

Mass customisation is the process whereby customers order from a pre-selected range of products and customise them for fit or style. This is very popular for products such as:

- denim jeans
- trainers
- t-shirts
- shirts
- football shirts.

This approach works well for these products as there are standard processes for making them.

How does it work?

The customer logs on to their chosen website, chooses their product, customises the product for colour, style, and so on, and then purchases the product from the online shop. The product is sent directly to the customer. The cost of the product is usually higher than purchasing a standard product.

△ **Figure 10.5** Mass customisation

Production and planning in your own work

In your own coursework, you will need to show how the costs for your final product have been calculated. The information for this will also need to be identified in your research.

Your own costs might include the following:

- the cost of materials
- the cost of components
- the cost of the pattern
- the cost of your time (use the current minimum wage for the UK)
- the cost of embroidery (e.g. the cost of the thread and the cost of the embroidery)
- the costs for making a single product, making ten, making 100, making 1,000.

Using ICT, you can use online web catalogues or online retailers' websites to work out the costs of different fabrics and components.

Ethical issues

It has been highlighted that some companies pay so little for labour that it has led to unethical practices, with workers being paid low wages to make products. Many companies now include information on ethical standards in their manufacturing plan. This will include information on minimum wage limits and clear guidelines on safe working practices.

Knowledge link

You can find more information on ethical practices in Chapters 3 and 8.

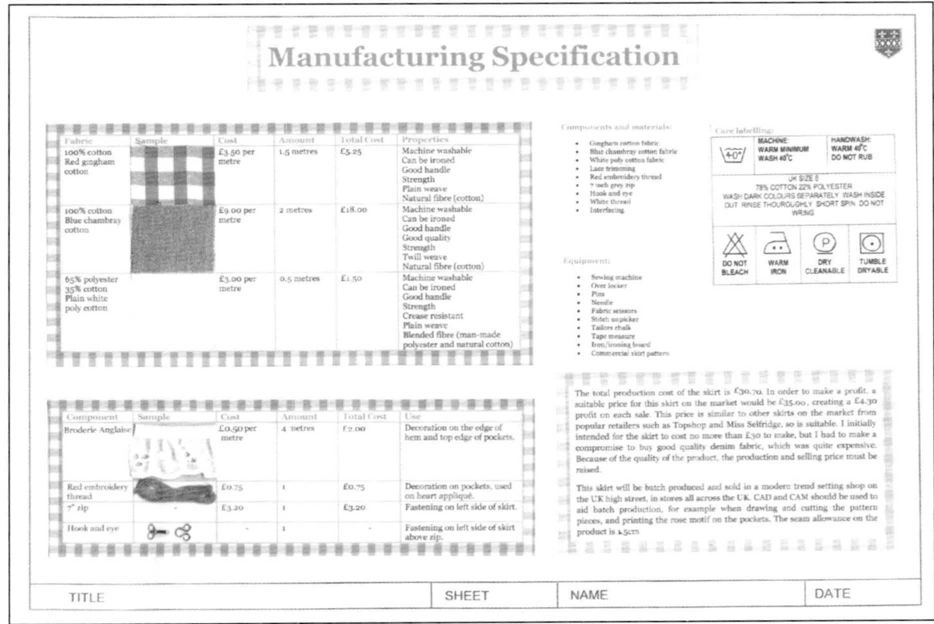

Manufacturing Specification

Fabric	Sample	Cost	Amount	Total Cost	Properties
100% cotton Red gingham cotton		£3.50 per metre	1.5 metres	£5.25	Machine washable Can be ironed Good handle Strength Plain weave Natural fibre (cotton)
100% cotton Blue chambray cotton		£9.00 per metre	2 metres	£18.00	Machine washable Can be ironed Good handle Good quality Strength Twill weave Natural fibre (cotton)
65% polyester 35% cotton Plain white poly cotton		£3.00 per metre	0.5 metres	£1.50	Machine washable Can be ironed Good handle Strength Crease resistant Plain weave Blended fibre (man-made polyester and natural cotton)

Components and materials:

- Gingham cotton fabric
- Blue chambray cotton fabric
- White poly cotton fabric
- Lace trimming
- Red embroidery thread
- 7 inch grey zip
- Hook and eye
- White thread
- Interfacing

Care labelling:

	MACHINE: WARM MINIMUM WASH 40°C	HANDWASH: WARM 40°C DO NOT RUB
40°		

UK SIZE 8
78% COTTON 22% POLYESTER
WASH DARK COLOURS SEPARATELY. WASH INSIDE OUT. RINSE THOUROUGHLY. SHORT SPIN. DO NOT WRING.

DO NOT BLEACH	WARM IRON	DRY CLEANABLE	TUMBLE DRYABLE

Equipment:

- Sewing machine
- Over locker
- Pins
- Needle
- Fabric scissors
- Stitch unpicker
- Tailors chalk
- Tape measure
- Iron/ironing board
- Commercial skirt pattern

Component	Sample	Cost	Amount	Total Cost	Use
Broderie Anglaise		£0.50 per metre	4 metres	£2.00	Decoration on the edge of hem and top edge of pockets.
Red embroidery thread		£0.75	1	£0.75	Decoration on pockets, used on heart appliqué.
7" zip	-	£3.20	1	£3.20	Fastening on left side of skirt.
Hook and eye		-	1	-	Fastening on left side of skirt above zip.

The total production cost of the skirt is £30.70. In order to make a profit, a suitable price for this skirt on the market would be £35.00, creating a £4.30 profit on each sale. This price is similar to other skirts on the market from popular retailers such as Topshop and Miss Selfridge, so is suitable. I initially intended for the skirt to cost no more than £30 to make, but I had to make a compromise to buy good quality denim fabric, which was quite expensive. Because of the quality of the product, the production and selling price must be raised.

This skirt will be batch produced and sold in a modern trend setting shop on the UK high street, in stores all across the UK. CAD and CAM should be used to aid batch production, for example when drawing and cutting the pattern pieces, and printing the rose motif on the pockets. The seam allowance on the product is 1.5cm

TITLE	SHEET	NAME	DATE

△ **Figure 10.6** A student's costing process

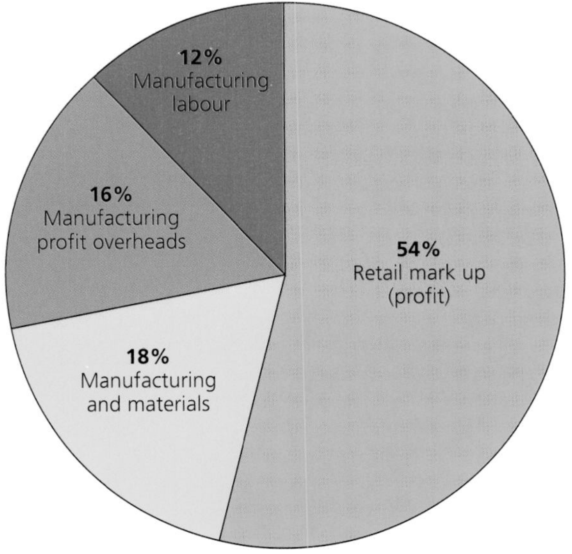

△ **Figure 10.7** A breakdown of the costs for making a pair of jeans

Summary

- Because of the large quantities of goods that need to be produced at any one time, companies will have in place time and production plans to ensure all products are made and delivered on time.
- Modern technologies make the process of planning production easier and quicker.
- Manufacturing specifications allow companies to match production with workforce skills and identify the key methods of production that can be used to make the product.
- Understanding the costs of producing goods is important. The longer a product takes to produce, the more it will cost.

Exam practice questions

1. Why do companies use flow charts to help plan production? **[3 marks]**
2. What is the difference between direct and indirect costs and how can companies reduce costs? **[3 marks]**
3. (a) How have modern technologies changed the way in which companies can plan production? **[3 marks]**

   (b) In what ways can modern technology help companies reduce selling costs? **[3 marks]**
4. Why are the costs of high-street goods so different from those for haute couture or Saville Row suits? **[4 marks]**

Activities

Choose an item of clothing that you no longer use and do the following:

1. Take a photograph of the product, including the front and back view, key stitch details, components and finishing details (for example, hems).
2. Use the care label to identify country of origin and other details about the product.
3. Using appropriate tools, take the product apart carefully, labelling and numbering all the components and parts. Record your details on a chart.
4. Create a manufacturing specification for the product.
5. Create a manufacturing plan for the product.
6. Create a costing sheet for the product.
7. How could you add more value to the product? For example, by adding decoration, making changes or reducing costs.
8. Design a garment or accessory that could be sold with the product, if it was to be made again. **[Total: 25 marks]**

10.2 Quality assurance

Learning objectives

By the end of this section, you should have a key understanding of:

- using specifications
- the processes for modifying products
- testing designs
- the role of quality assurance in production and planning
- the impact of globalisation on the fashion and textiles industry.

Key points

- Analytical skills
- Communication skills
- Linking technology and design
- Values

Key term

Quality assurance – a guarantee given to the customer from the company to assure the quality of the product.

Introduction

The modern fashion and textile industry operates on a global scale, with many companies having their design, sampling, manufacturing and production departments in different parts of the world.

Companies will use modern technologies to ensure that they can communicate across the company, but they also need to ensure that the products that are made are the same quality every time. This process is called quality assurance.

Quality assurance

For the client, quality assurance ensures that the product meets certain standards, that it will perform as stated and that it is fit for purpose.

The standards for tests are created by testing organisations such as British Standards, professional bodies such as The Society of Dyers and Colourists, or specialised laboratories.

Many products will carry additional labelling to show that the standards have been met. A common symbol that is applied to UK products is the CE symbol, or Kitemark.

Figure 10.8 The CE mark

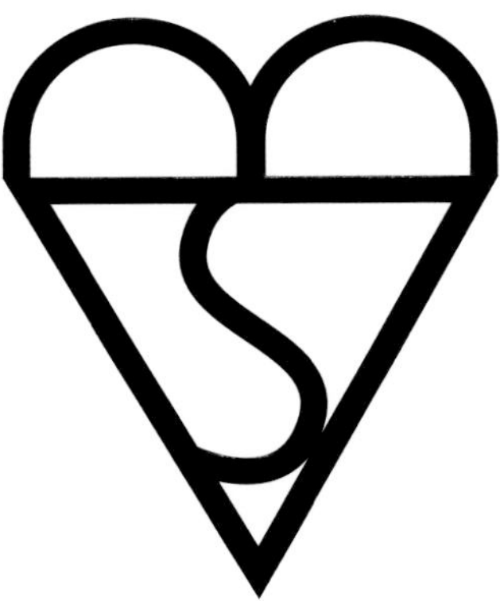

Figure 10.9 The Kitemark

Other marks of quality might be given to a product because it meets certain conditions or checks – for example, the Fairtrade mark or EU Flower for environmental standards. Companies can also use International Standards such as the ISO 9000, which helps companies to develop specific standards of quality referred to as total quality management, or TQM.

Care labels are a legal requirement on all garments and show the consumer the following:

- the fibres used in the product
- place of manufacture
- sizing details
- retailer details
- how to care for the product (e.g washing or cleaning instructions in symbol form)
- any hazards that you need to be aware of.

Care labels are also an integral part of the quality assurance process.

Knowledge link

For more information on care labels, see pages 112–113 and 208.

Once in production, products for a fashion range might be checked at the following stages:

- sampling stage
- fabric cutting and laying
- production – making the product
- packing and shipping
- retail.

For fabrics, testing looks at:

- fibre quality
- spinning yarn quality
- dyeing and colour quality
- fabric strength and quality.

For production processes, the quality assurance tests might check that:

- workers are using safe working practices
- the conditions of the workforce are safe and clean
- machines are working correctly
- correct processes are carried out for the making of the product.

For any stage in the production process, companies will use testing specifications, which give clear guidelines on what the quality of the product should be and the tests or checks that should be carried out.

Key terms

Testing – ensuring that standards are met.

Specification – an outline that details all the requirements of a product.

Companies will create a range of documents to show what is to be done if a product does not meet the required standards. This might be set out on a document such as flow chart. The flow chart might contain checkpoints and offer the opportunity for feedback.

Knowledge link

You can see examples of flow charts and feedback loops on pages 63–64.

Ethical values

Many companies will also ensure that the products are made in clean conditions and that workers are safe and treated in an ethical way.

Knowledge link

For more information on ethical values, see Chapters 3 and 8.

Many companies now produce a special report that shows how values and ethical processes are incorporated into their company, from manufacturing to retail. This document is called CSR (corporate and social responsibility).

Creating a specification

A specification is a document that states clearly how a product is to be made and the key information that is needed to ensure that the product meets the standards for design and production.

Design specifications

Design specifications ensure that all aspects of the final design are stated clearly and will include samples of fabrics, colour and decoration, key information for front and back views, and all the components needed to complete the product.

Information on the design specification has to be clear and concise, so that everyone involved in the production process can understand it.

Prototypes and sampling

Prototyping or sampling is an important part of the design-and-make process. Samples and prototypes provide the key information about how successful a design will be. Products will undergo several stages of testing before being put into production. Many companies will create samples of designs, and copies of samples will be kept at both the design office and the manufacturing plant for easy reference.

For example, a fashion product will go through a series of checks, starting with the sampling process. This is when the pattern maker will create the pattern from the designer's sketches and, using their own basic blocks, cut out the fabric and compile all the components for making the product. The sample machinist will then make the product. The newly created product can then be analysed and the following information will be added to the specification:

- the total amount of fabric and components needed to make the product
- the number of stages needed to make the product and the time taken to make the product
- at the fitting stage, how well the garment fits and what changes, if any, are needed.

The time taken to make each stage is recorded, along with a streamlined making guide. This will ensure that the product is made in the quickest number of steps and will keep a check on the possible labour costs.

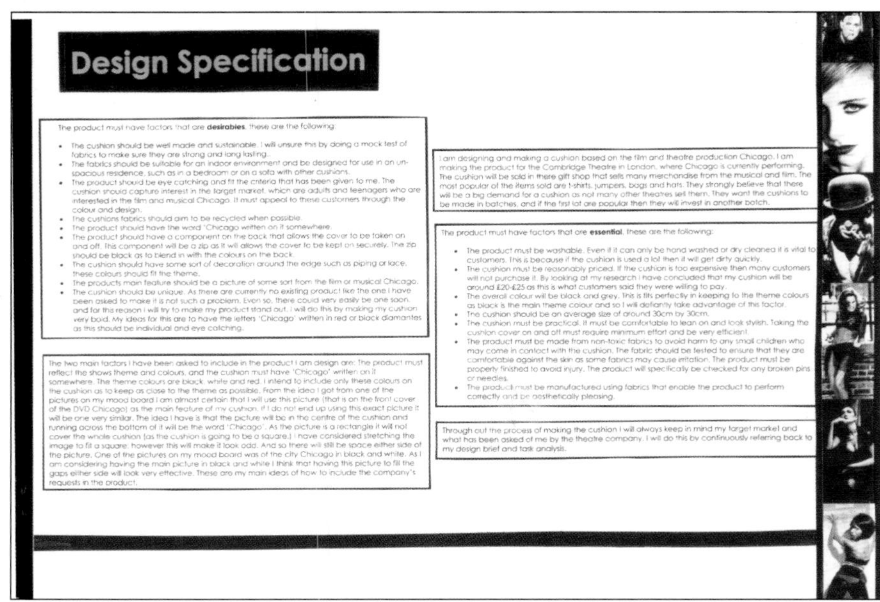

Design Specification

The product must have factors that are **desirables**, these are the following:

- The cushion should be well made and sustainable. I will unsure this by doing a mock test of fabrics to make sure they are strong and long lasting..
- The fabrics should be suitable for an indoor environment and be designed for use in an un-spacious residence, such as in a bedroom or on a sofa with other cushions.
- The product should be eye catching and fit the criteria that has been given to me. The cushion should capture interest in the target market, which are adults and teenagers who are interested in the film and musical Chicago. It must appeal to these customers through the colour and design.
- The cushions fabrics should aim to be recycled when possible.
- The product should have the word 'Chicago written on it somewhere.
- The product should have a component on the back that allows the cover to be taken on and off. This component will be a zip as it will allows the cover to be kept on securely. The zip should be black as to blend in with the colours on the back.
- The cushion should have some sort of decoration around the edge such as piping or lace, these colours should fit the theme.
- The products main feature should be a picture of some sort from the film or musical Chicago.
- The cushion should be unique. As there are currently no existing product like the one I have been asked to make it is not such a problem. Even so, there could very easily be one soon, and for this reason I will try to make my product stand out. I will do this by making my cushion very bold. My ideas for this are to have the letters 'Chicago' written in red or black diamantes as this should be individual and eye catching.

The two main factors I have been asked to include in the product I am design are: The product must reflect the shows theme and colours, and the cushion must have 'Chicago' written on it somewhere. The theme colours are black, white and red. I intend to include only these colours on the cushion as to keep as close to the theme as possible. From the idea I got from one of the pictures on my mood board I am almost certain that I will use this picture (that is on the front cover of the DVD Chicago) as the main feature of my cushion. If I do not end up using this exact picture it will be one very similar. The idea I have is that the picture will be in the centre of the cushion and running across the bottom of it will be the word 'Chicago'. As the picture is a rectangle it will not cover the whole cushion (as the cushion is going to be a square.) I have considered stretching the image to fit a square; however this will make it look odd. And so there will still be space either side of the picture. One of the pictures on my mood board was of the city Chicago in black and white. As I am considering having the main picture in black and white I think that having this picture to fill the gaps either side will look very effective. These are my main ideas of how to include the company's requests in the product.

I am designing and making a cushion based on the film and theatre production Chicago. I am making the product for the Cambridge Theatre in London, where Chicago is currently performing. The cushion will be sold in there gift shop that sells many merchandise from the musical and film. The most popular of the items sold are t-shirts, jumpers, bags and hats. They strongly believe that there will be a big demand for a cushion as not many other theatres sell them. They want the cushions to be made in batches, and if the first lot are popular then they will invest in another batch.

The product must have factors that are **essential**, these are the following:

- The product must be washable. Even if it can only be hand washed or dry cleaned it is vital to customers. This is because if the cushion is used a lot then it will get dirty quickly.
- The cushion must be reasonably priced. If the cushion is too expensive then many customers will not purchase it. By looking at my research I have concluded that my cushion will be around £20-£25 as this is what customers said they were willing to pay.
- The overall colour will be black and grey. This is fits perfectly in keeping to the theme colours as black is the main theme colour and so I will defiantly take advantage of this factor.
- The cushion should be an average size of around 30cm by 30cm.
- The cushion must be practical. It must be comfortable to lean on and look stylish. Taking the cushion cover on and off must require minimum effort and be very efficient.
- The product must be made from non-toxic fabrics to avoid harm to any small children who may come in contact with the cushion. The fabric should be tested to ensure that they are comfortable against the skin as some fabrics may cause irritation. The product must be properly finished to avoid injury. The product will specifically be checked for any broken pins or needles.
- The product must be manufactured using fabrics that enable the product to perform correctly and be aesthetically pleasing.

Through out the process of making the cushion I will always keep in mind my target market and what has been asked of me by the theatre company. I will do this by continuously referring back to my design brief and task analysis.

△ **Figure 10.10** A student's design specification

The next stage is called the sealing process. At this stage, the garment or product is passed through a series of tests and checks before being approved for manufacture:

- Bronze seal – first fitting or check, followed by modifications
- Silver seal – second fitting or check, followed by final modifications
- Gold seal – this is the final approved manufacturing sample and the product is now ready for manufacture. All future products made are matched against this final sample.

Key term

Product modifications – the process of changing or adapting a design or sample to meet new specifications or client requirements.

In developing models and prototypes of your own work, you will have created specifications for various stages of the design-and-make process. These specifications are working documents and can be changed depending on the following:

- client or market research feedback
- changes made at the modelling or prototyping stages
- changes to the manufacturing plan.

Prototyping and modern technology

With modern technologies, companies can use the following when developing prototypes:

- Digital cameras: these allow pictures to be taken of garments, which can then be annotated (commented on) and sent to the manufacturing plant.
- Webcams: connected to computers, these allow design and production staff to communicate in real time to discuss changes to products.
- Online video and media streaming: this allows pre-recorded materials to be sent.
- Virtual modelling software: this allows for patterns to be created on a computer. Using virtual fit pattern software, the design and production team can see how well a product

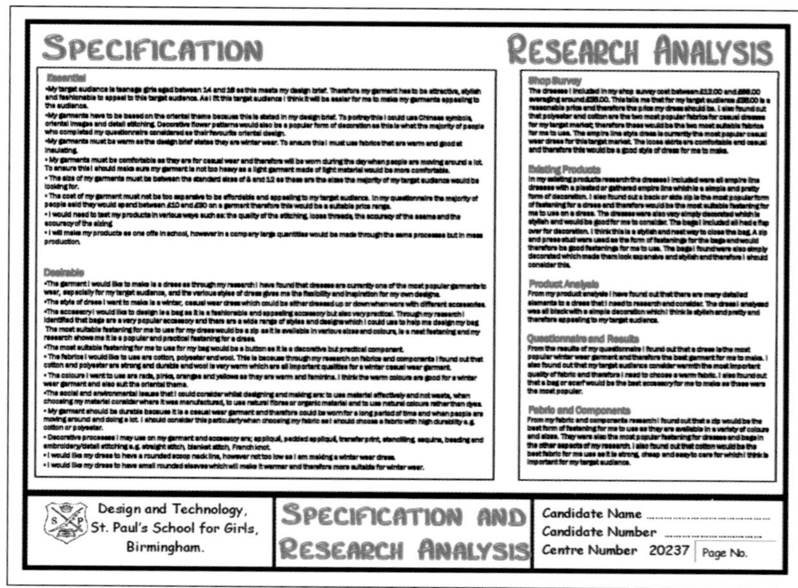

SPECIFICATION

RESEARCH ANALYSIS

Design and Technology, St. Paul's School for Girls, Birmingham.

SPECIFICATION AND RESEARCH ANALYSIS

Candidate Name ....
Candidate Number ....
Centre Number 20237 Page No.

△ **Figure 10.11** Student design specification

fits. The images are colour-coded – for example, red might show that the fit is too tight, blue that the fit is too loose, and green that the fit is fine.

Prototyping and sampling are an expensive part of the development process, so companies use modern technologies to reduce costs in sample making.

Product comparisons

As part of the prototyping process, companies will also conduct product comparisons. This might be done by comparing products created in the past or by comparing their work with that of a competitor. Comparing products allows changes to be made or new ideas to be developed.

What things might be compared?

The following are some of the things that might be compared when doing a product comparison:

- fibre that the product is made from
- size
- price
- fabric construction (e.g. knitted or woven)
- number and type of components
- instructions on the care label and aftercare issues
- special features (e.g. types of pockets, top stitching)
- design aesthetics (how it looks)
- colour or number of colours
- weight of the product
- fibre content (e.g. number of fibres – a mix or blend might mean that it will be difficult to dispose of)
- ethical issues (e.g. fair trade, organic fibres)
- place or country of manufacture (there might be issues with quality or with the carbon footprint)
- decoration (what is the type of decoration; is it surface patterned or manipulated? does this add to the cost?).

Testing designs

Testing a design is an essential part of the design-and-make process. Designs can be tested in several ways:

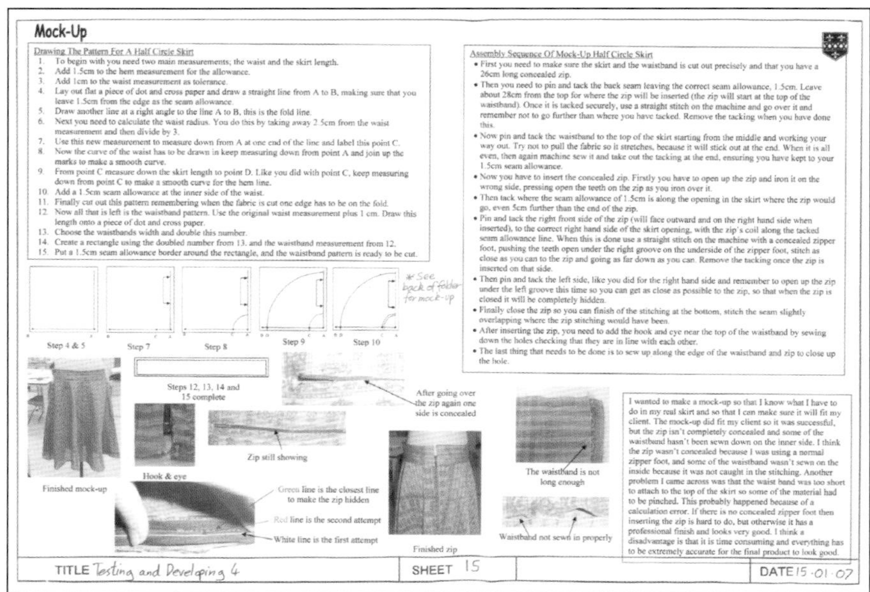

△ **Figure 10.12** A student's work showing prototyping

1. Prototypes can be tested by clients, using questionnaires or wearer testing.
2. Clients can feed back about how well the design meets the target market.
3. Clients can feed back on the fabrics or colours used.
4. The physical properties of the fabrics can be tested for suitability.

Testing all aspects of a design, at each stage of the design-and-make process, ensures that the design meets the key criteria shown in the specification.

Summary

- Specifications provide key information about a product.
- Companies need to have standard processes for testing and checking their products as they go through the production process.
- Standards are also created by outside agencies, such as British Standards, and the European Union, which all companies must follow in the production, manufacture and sale of products.
- The global nature of the textiles and fashion industry means that companies must have a system of checks at all stages of production to ensure that products are the same wherever they are made.
- Modern technologies are being used more and more as a key tool in the development of prototypes.

Activities

Look at the drawings of the T-shirt in Figure 10.13. The client has asked for the following changes to be made to the design:

1. Draw the design on and then create a specification sheet for this.
2. Change the length of the sleeve (from short to long).
3. Add a 10cm-square patch pocket on the right-hand side of the chest area.
4. Add a double-machine-stitched line around the hem.
5. Change the collar from a round neck to a V neck.
6. Complete the specification details.

[16 marks]

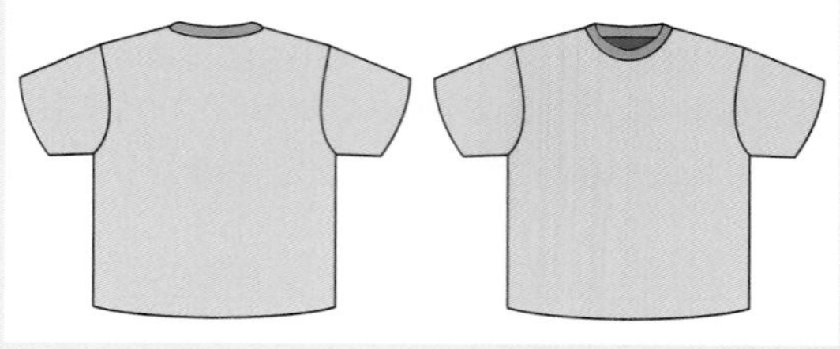

△ **Figure 10.13** T-shirt

Exam practice questions

1. (a) What does the term 'quality assurance' mean? **[1 mark]**
   (b) Why do companies need to use quality assurance? **[1 mark]**
   (c) Why is it important to include ethical checks in the quality assurance process? **[1 mark]**
2. What are the symbols that are used on products to show that they reach a certain standard? **[4 marks]**
3. Why is creating a prototype an important part of the quality and testing process? **[4 marks]**
4. What are the advantages of using modern technologies in the prototyping and sampling stages of garment production? **[4 marks]**

Stretch yourself

1. Choose a fashion or textile company and find out about their CSR and ethical issues. Write a report or create a presentation on your findings. **[6 marks]**
2. Using magazines, online shops or catalogues, compare three similar textile or fashion products.
   (a) Which product do you think is best value for money?
   (b) Using the results, create a new design based on your findings. **[6 marks]**

Case study

Faster Fit Sampling

Many design companies and retailers will spend vast amounts of money on creating samples, and while fitting on mannequins is okay for some of the sampling process, it is only when a garment is fitted on a human body that the key issues of fit become an issue. For some products this can mean between 10 and 20 fit sessions. This can mean a saving of between £20,000 and £40,000 a year. The problems are extended when companies have production plants overseas and the need to make decisions about product changes becomes important. Large retailers such as Tesco, Mothercare and Marks and Spencer, are using systems such as FastFit 360, a web-based system that can be used to upload pictures of a garment on a human body and then relay details to the design and production team via the web, where fit issues can be discussed. The images can be annotated and comments added. Because this can be done in real time, it means that sampling costs can be reduced and garment fits can be improved.

Resources

Fashion fit: www.fastfit360.com

Lectra: www.lectra.com

SpeedStep:www.speedstep.de

Browswear: http://browzwear.com

chapter 11 ICT

11.1 Computer technology and communication

Learning objectives

By the end of this section, you should have a key understanding of:

- research skills using ICT
- how to collect and sort a range of information
- how to present information
- how to use graphical techniques (including CAD/CAM) to design, develop, modify, enhance, model and communicate ideas.

Key points

- Analytical skills
- Communication skills
- Innovative ideas
- Creative ideas
- Linking technology and design
- Values

Key terms

ICT – information and communication technology, meaning all things digital and related to computers.

Primary research – original research that has not been done before and all sources, such as images and text, have been created by you. This is information that is not in the public domain.

Research – finding out information using a series of activities.

Secondary research – often referred to as desk research, this is research that has already been done by someone else or information that is already in the public domain.

Introduction

Information and communications technology, or ICT, has become very important for modern life and is seen as an essential tool for research and collecting information, as well as presenting information. Using modern technologies, the designer can collate a wide range of information to support the development of design ideas.

Using ICT as a research tool

What is research?

Research is the process of collecting information in both written and visual form to support your coursework. The information you collect will come from a range of sources, which can be primary or secondary.

Once you have collected information, you must analyse what you have found out and make decisions about how this research will impact on various stages of the design-and-make process.

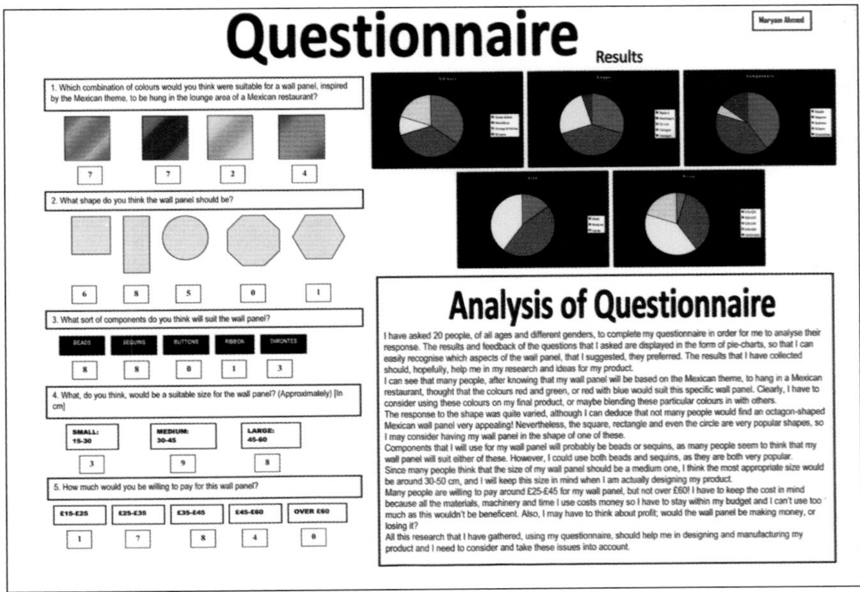

△ **Figure 11.1** Using ICT

ICT allows you to collect a range of information that can be stored on your computer. It is important that you are able to sort through the wide range of information available, and select and analyse the relevant information for your project. The research tools shown in Table 11.1 are all secondary sources of information.

Research tool	Type of information	Advantages	Disadvantages
Search engines (e.g. Google, Yahoo!)	Visual and written	A wide range of information can be collected and used.	Information and visuals are varied and it can be difficult to sift through the wide range of relevant information.
Databases	On and offline; contain a range of specialist information	These contain relevant information for your research.	May need to pay for access to specialised databases.
Wikipedia	Generic online research space; contributions from different sources	This is an online library created by people all over the world.	You need to use other sources of information to ensure that the information being used is accurate.

△ **Table 11.1** ICT research tools

Cont.

Research tool	Type of information	Advantages	Disadvantages
Flickr	Online picture database	This is a social network website with lots of pictures from all over world.	Issues regarding copyright – you need to get copyright clearance before you use the pictures in your work.
Tweets	Create a conversation in less than 140 characters	A way of sharing both written and visual information. Written information must be in fewer than 140 characters. Good for finding links to other emerging trends.	You will need to extend your research skills to get more information.
Facebook, MySpace, Bebo	Online social network websites for linking people	Online social networks allow you to share information about both social and professional life. Easy to ask questions to see if any other users can support research. Many fashion and textiles companies are on social networks, showcasing their new products.	Sometimes answers are more about personal likes and dislikes and less specific to the answer. Might be limited to close friends. Information might be out of date or not always accurate.
Survey Monkey	Online website for collecting survey information	Can create online surveys for distribution. Results can be collated and then imported into other spreadsheet software.	You have to email specific people to complete. You need a wide database of people to get back large results. You have to always be online to access information.
Blogs	A method of writing online information with text and visuals	Many specialist blogs exist on specific aspects of textiles and fashion. Many designers give updates on what they are doing, giving you the chance to explore their design thinking and processes.	Might not always be up to date.
Online library catalogues	Specialised library catalogues can be accessed for specialised information on fashion and textiles.	You can find books that are no longer printed or specialised information.	You may have to travel to a specialised library as the information is not always accessible online.

△ **Table 11.1** ICT research tools

Cont.

Research tool	Type of information	Advantages	Disadvantages
Podcasts	Online specialised series of programs you can subscribe to; usually audio, but can also contain video	You can find podcasts and videocasts on specific topics. You can choose to subscribe to podcasts, which keep you up to date with the stories and can be downloaded direct to a computer or smartphone.	You need to subscribe to podcasts to keep up to date. Information is usually specialised.
YouTube	Online video website, showcasing a range of videos on a vast number of subjects. Many companies use this to promote new collections.	Easy to collect a range of visual information in the form of videos	It can be difficult to sift through the wide range of videos now available.
E-books	Books that are published in an electronic format for specialised readers	Some books are free. Gives you the advantage of reading on the go without having to carry lots of books.	Currently limited in the range of books available. Some readers can only use text and others only black and white images. But as the technology gets better, this will move to colour images.

△ **Table 11.1** ICT research tools *continued*

Key term

Blog – (also known as a web log) a website or part of a website that is kept up to date on a regular basis, by an individual or group.

In industry, designers will use specialised websites or online journals to collect specialised information that is relevant to their market. They will also work with specialised consultants to get information.

Using ICT to collect information

With changing technologies, we now have a variety of methods of collecting both written and visual information.

Websites

Websites are specialised pages of information and are used by companies to provide a range of information about their products. Websites allow companies, both small and large, to showcase their products to a worldwide audience. This means that someone in China can see the work

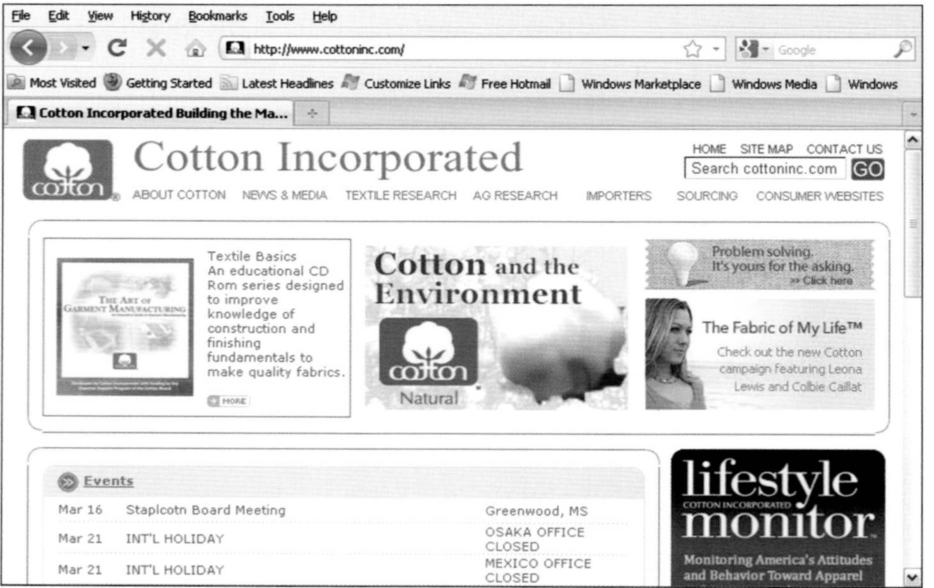

△ **Figure 11.2** Cotton Incorporated website

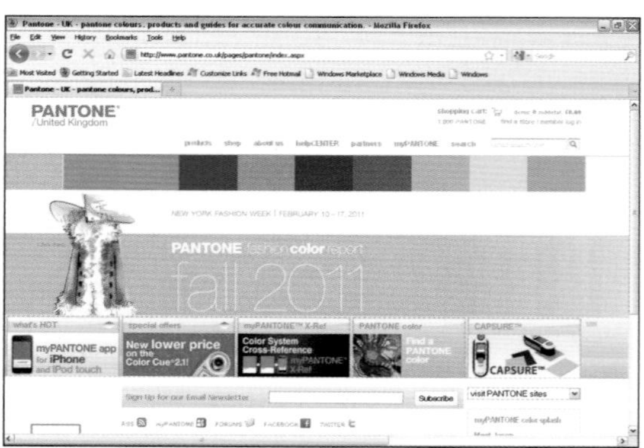

△ **Figure 11.3** Pantone website

of a British designer online. Before the internet, the only way to get that kind of information would have been to wait for a newspaper or magazine to be delivered, or to travel vast distances to visit the designer.

If you see a website or page that you like, you can either save the link to your Favourites folder, or 'take a picture' of the screen and save it to presentation or word-processing software. You can now search for websites using different tools and present your search results in either a text or a visual format.

You do not have to be at a computer to search for information. Many smartphones, netbooks and iPad tablets allow you to search for information on the go at a time to suit you. These can then be synchronized to a file on your computer or on an online webspace to be downloaded at a later date.

Questionnaires and surveys

Questionnaires and surveys allow you to collect and collate specific information to enable you to make key decisions in your research.

By using a questionnaire or survey, you are collecting primary information – this means first-hand information that is original and gathered directly from the client or target group that your product is aimed at. In the textiles and fashion industry, this is seen as an important part of the development process to ensure that the product being produced is suitable for the intended client.

Questionnaires and surveys can be created using standard word-processing software, printed, and then handed out to clients to fill in and return to you. When the questionnaires are returned,

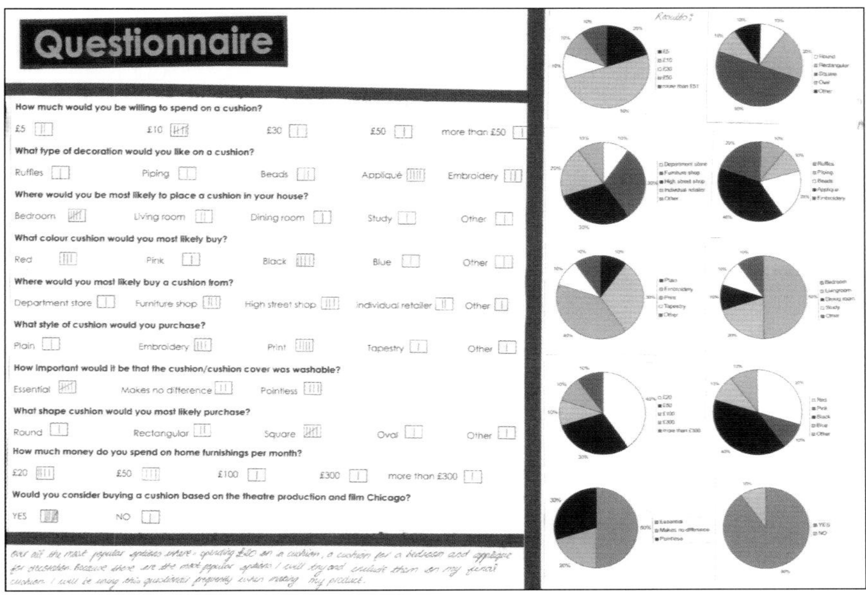

Questionnaire

How much would you be willing to spend on a cushion?
£5 | £10 | £30 | £50 | more than £50

What type of decoration would you like on a cushion?
Ruffles | Piping | Beads | Appliqué | Embroidery

Where would you be most likely to place a cushion in your house?
Bedroom | Living room | Dining room | Study | Other

What colour cushion would you most likely buy?
Red | Pink | Black | Blue | Other

Where would you most likely buy a cushion from?
Department store | Furniture shop | High street shop | Individual retailer | Other

What style of cushion would you purchase?
Plain | Embroidery | Print | Tapestry | Other

How important would it be that the cushion/cushion cover was washable?
Essential | Makes no difference | Pointless

What shape cushion would you most likely purchase?
Round | Rectangular | Square | Oval | Other

How much money do you spend on home furnishings per month?
£20 | £50 | £100 | £300 | more than £300

Would you consider buying a cushion based on the theatre production and film Chicago?
YES | NO

△ **Figure 11.4** A student's questionnaire

you can analyse the answers. Answers can be transferred to a spreadsheet-based software and displayed in a graphical format, such as a bar chart or graph. Using ICT allows you to collate and visualise answers to your questions quickly.

You can also use specialised online software to create surveys, such as Survey Monkey. This allows you to use email to send the survey to a wide variety of people. The respondents can then fill in the details online, click a submit button and the results are returned to your inbox, ready for you to analyse.

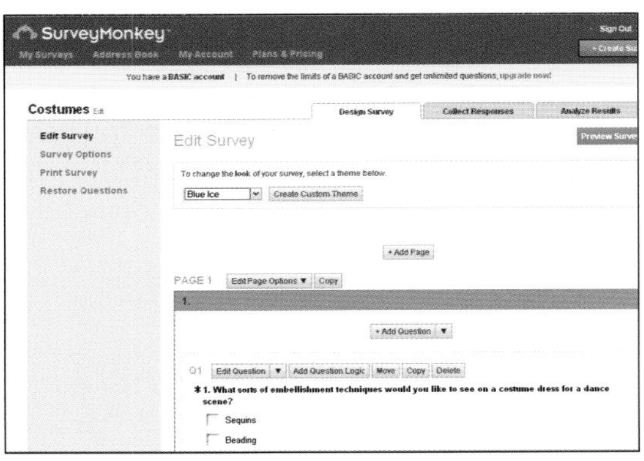

△ **Figure 11.5** Survey Monkey

With changing technologies, it is also possible to use text messaging and the features of a smartphone to respond to surveys. Some companies even use software such as augmented reality or QR codes whereby you aim your mobile phone camera at an 'augmented marker' or QR code marker, your phone reads the marker and, where an image or response is needed, an answer is automatically recorded.

△ **Figure 11.6** QR code

Digital media

Almost all the cameras and smartphones that we use today contain a camera. Some have digital still cameras and others incorporate video as well. Standard still and video cameras also allow you to upload your photos and videos, as soon as you take them, to specialist or social networking websites, such as YouTube, Flickr or Vimeo. You can then download them directly to your computer. The images can then be used in a variety of ways:

- as inspirational images for mood boards
- to help you analyse what people are wearing, known as 'cool hunting'
- to collect images that you have seen – for example, at a museum – as a starting point for inspiration.

You can also use digital cameras and videos to record the making process while you are doing your coursework.

Controlled assessment link

For more information on how you can use digital media in your Controlled Assessment see Chapter 2.

When using digital pictures, think about the following key points:

- Ensure that you have permission to use the images so you do not infringe copyright.
- Make sure that the pictures or video are the best quality they can be.
- Ensure that the pictures clearly illustrate the key points you want to showcase.

Colour information

For many designers, the use of colour is an essential tool in the development of design work. Traditional sources of colour information include fabric swatches, samples of paint swatches and pictures.

Today, designers can go directly to specialised websites to collect the latest colour information. They can also use software to collect images and then select the colours from the image to develop a colour range. New smartphone applications allow the designer to take photographs and then select the key colours from the image. The palette is then created and the designer can use this as a starting point to develop the colour stories needed for design collections.

Using ICT to plan work

Designers will use a range of ICT materials to plan work. It is an essential part of the design process to be able to identify how long it will take for work to be developed and finished.

Some design companies will use standard spreadsheet software to create a plan, using different colours to illustrate the task to be done and when it has to be completed. For your own coursework, it is important that you make an overall plan as soon as you decide on your design brief. This will allow you to do the following:

- check your progress through each stage of your project
- adapt your time plan to allow for any changes
- refer back to your plan when you write your evaluation.

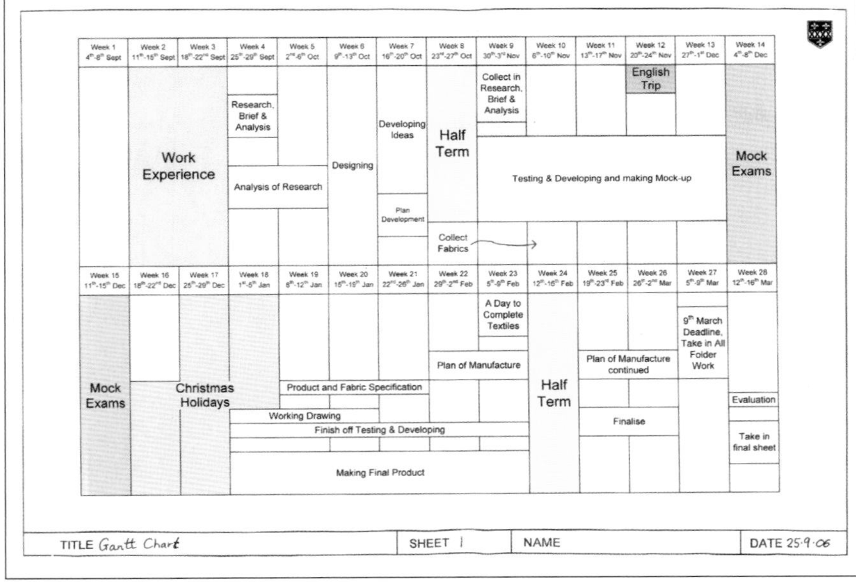

△ **Figure 11.7** A timeline created using spreadsheet software

Mind mapping

Other software, such as mind-mapping software, allows you to plan your project as well as plan your timeline. Mind-mapping software also allows you to incorporate visual images and export your finished mind map into either word-processing software or presentation software for further development.

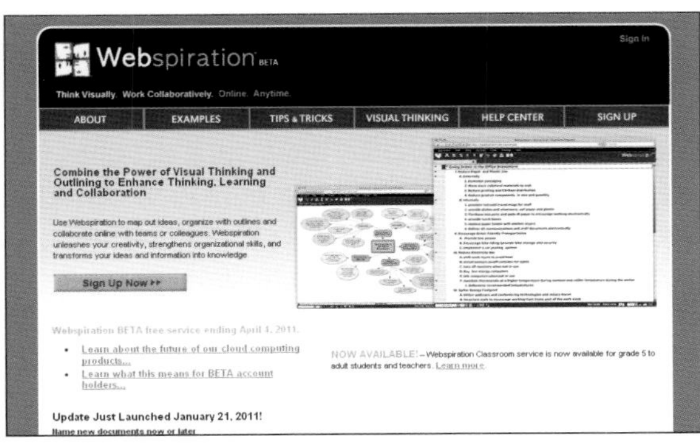

△ **Figure 11.8** Webspiration – mind-mapping software

Using ICT to present a range of information

You will be asked to present your coursework, showcasing all the key elements as needed, by the examination board. It is essential to concentrate on presenting information in a clear, concise manner, while showcasing your creativity and design thinking.

There is a whole range of presentation software that can be used to present your work.

- Using presentation software such as Microsoft® PowerPoint®, you could create a slideshow presentation.
- Using presentation software such as Microsoft® Producer for Microsoft® PowerPoint®, you could insert video and audio into your work.
- Using online software such as Prezi, you could create an interactive presentation.
- You could also use desktop publishing software, such as Microsoft® Publisher.
- You could create your own website.

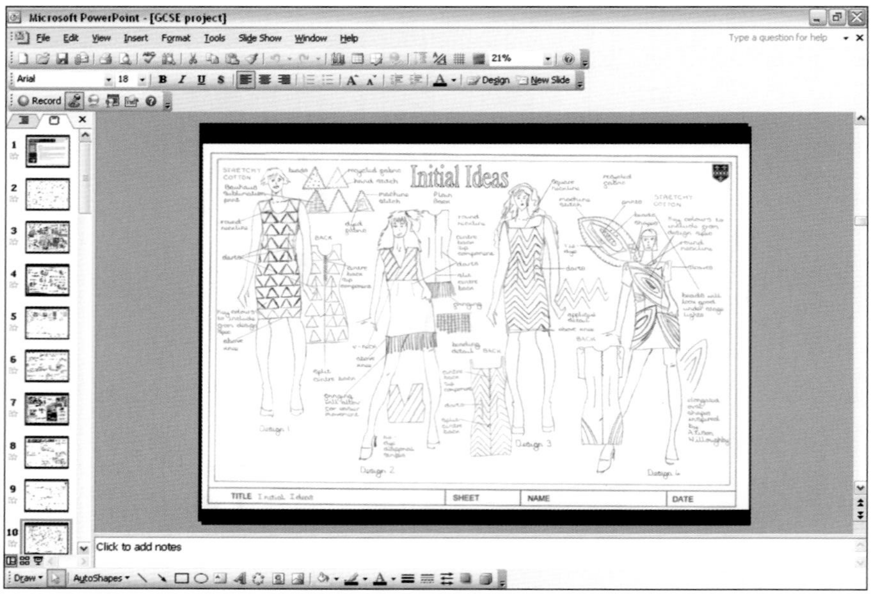

△ **Figure 11.9** Microsoft® PowerPoint® presentation

- You could create an interactive PDF portfolio.

The key things to consider when using any of this software is that you may also need to print out a hard copy to send to the examination board, but more and more boards are now allowing students to upload their completed portfolios online, which means that you can incorporate a range of media in your work.

When creating a presentation, you need to consider the following:

- Check that the images you use are of a good quality.
- If using images from the internet that are not your own, include a bibliography with details of your sources.
- Consider the information that is on each page.
- Ensure that any audio files can be clearly understood.
- Make sure that your work is easily accessible (easy to understand).
- Check that all hyperlinks and video files work.

Controlled assessment link

For more information on how to present your Controlled Assessment, see Chapters 1 and 2.

Graphical and modelling techniques

Your graphic and modelling techniques for showcasing your ideas are very important. You will need to communicate your design thinking using sketches. These can be done using a pencil, but if you are planning to scan your images for further development on the computer, then you will need to draw using a good drawing pen.

Key terms

Communicate – how well you can talk or write about your work or ideas.

Design – the process of creatively developing a concept or idea.

Develop – to expand a design or ideas, with the addition of sketches, fabrics, models, and so on.

Enhance – to add value to a product, making it more aesthetically pleasing.

Graphic techniques – the use of 2D tools such as pens and pencils to develop design sketches.

Modify – to change a product; to make it better.

Model – A 3D communication of your design, from a 2D sketch to a 3D model.

Input devices

There is a range of input devices that can be used to insert drawings or sketches so that they can be incorporated into your design work. Traditionally, most people will use a mouse to draw designs directly into the design software, but other devices are now available that allow you to develop electronic drawings (see Table 11.2).

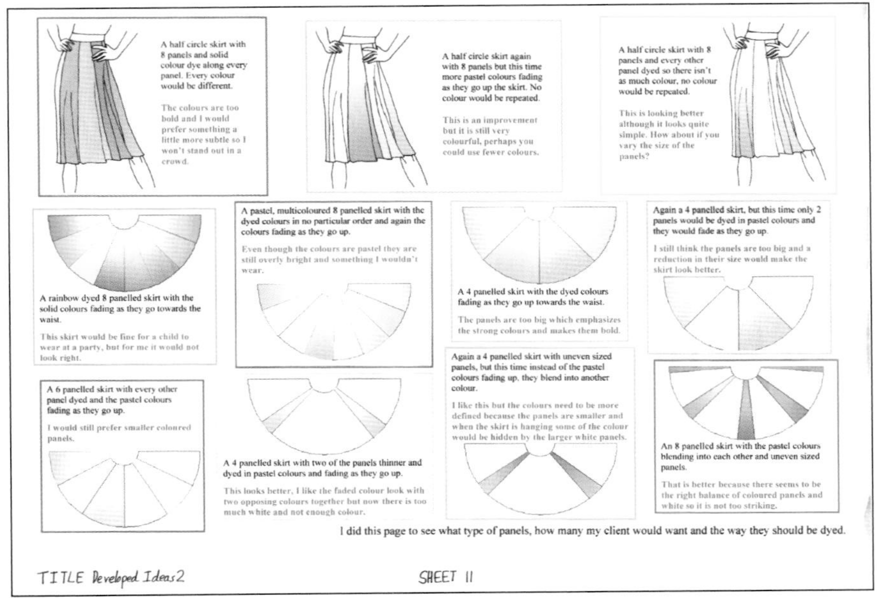

△ **Figure 11.10** A student's graphic techniques

Input device	What it does
Mouse	Allows you to move around the screen, but drawing can be difficult.
Graphics tablet	A flat pad with a drawing pen that allows you to draw directly onto the pad. Your image appears on your computer screen.
Digi memo pad	Allows you to draw with a pen on paper on a special electronic pad. Your work is uploaded to your computer and you can then import your image into the software for further manipulation.
Livescribe pen	This uses special electronic paper and a pen and allows you to add comments about your work. Once you have drawn your work, you can upload it to your computer for further development.
Touch screen computer/iPad or Galaxie pad	New electronic pads, such as the iPad, allow you to draw directly on screen with your finger, making the sketching process simple. You can work directly in the design software and add notes and other details at the same time.
Scanner	A flatbed device that allows you to place your design on a clear plate. Using your design software, you can then scan your image directly into your computer for further manipulation.

△ **Table 11.2** Input devices

△ **Figure 11.11** Graphics tablet

Virtual design: 2D to 3D

Once you have created your designs, you will need to visualise them. Modern software technology allows you to showcase your ideas using a wide range of software.

2D visualisation

Your work can be presented using 2D flat specifications, or fashion illustrations. In industry, many designers will use specialised drawing packages that contain libraries of garment or textile components. Using these libraries, designers can work quickly and efficiently to produce a range of design ideas. The best ideas are then selected for further development in style and colour.

Flat 2D sketches or specification drawings highlight all the key technical details of a textiles or fashion product. The information on the 2D sketch is then used to develop the final pattern, as well as helping to create the final making plan.

Your 2D flat sketch must be clear and illustrate all views related to the product. At this stage, this does not need to contain colour. It is to showcase your technical understanding about your design.

Once your specification flats are complete, most software will allow you to import your sketches or computer-based sketches directly into software that can manipulate colour.

It is important that you review your design images and ensure that they showcase the key design features of your work. You can link the research work that you showed on your mood boards, or in your sketchbooks, to the design work that you developed for your final designs.

Presenting your work in colour allows the viewer to see how your work might look when it is finished.

3D visualisation

As technology changes rapidly, there is software that now allows you to visualise your designs in 3D. The software allows you to apply your fabric design ideas to a 3D model and rotate the design, so you can see how the design would look when it is complete.

The finished images can be presented in portfolios or as a mini video in your online presentation.

Output devices

As well as designing products, you also need to be able to create your fabric or product. This can be done in a range of materials and on a variety of machines. An important part of your coursework is your ability to use CAD/CAM in the design and making aspects of your work.

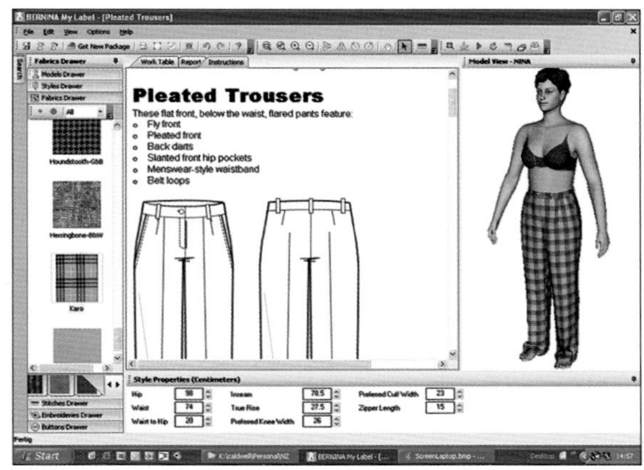

△ **Figure 11.12** 3D visualisation

Key terms

CAD – computer-aided design. Computer-aided designs are designs created using a computer.

CAM – computer-aided manufacture. Computer-aided manufacture is where computers are used in the manufacturing process.

Output device	What it does
Digital printer 1	Sublimation printers allow you to print special dyes called sublimation or disperse dyes onto paper, and then transfer the design on to 100 per cent synthetic fabrics or fabric blends with a minimum synthetic content of 50 per cent using a machine such as a heat press. You can then use the resulting fabric straight away, without further processing.
Digital printer 2	Reactive dye printers allow you to print directly onto pre-coated natural fabrics such as silk, wool and cotton. You will then need to steam the fabric, rinse and dry it before you can make your product.
Computerised (computer-controlled) embroidery machine	By creating designs using drawing software, or by drawing directly into the embroidery software, you can create motifs or embroidered fabrics that can then be developed into products.

△ **Table 11.3** Output devices

Cont.

Output device	What it does
Laser scanner	Sketches and images can be exported into the laser-cutting software. Lasers allow designers to create complex designs to make unusual products. The laser can burn the surface of fabrics to create engraved designs. You can also set the laser to cut intricate designs on different types of fabrics.
Router	A routing machine can allow you to create a print block to block-print your own fabric design.
Vinyl cutter	A vinyl cutter can be used to cut stencils that can then be used for screen printing. Alternatively, special textile vinyls can be used to create amazing designs that can be cut out and transferred to any textile product using a heat press.

△ **Table 11.3** Output devices *continued*

△ **Figure 11.13** Laser cutter

Controlled assessment link

You can see examples of CAD/CAM used in Controlled Assessment work, see Chapters 1 and 2.

Summary

- There is now a wide selection of tools available to the fashion and textile designer, but they must be competent and confident in using the technology and related equipment.
- Designers need to be able to collect and collate a wide range of visual and written information. This information needs to be clear and concise, and communicate ideas and design thinking in an easy format.
- Digital technologies allow designers to make bespoke fabrics and products that are also one-off or special products, as the designer can decide the elements that they want to keep in their work.

Activity

You have been asked by the student newspaper to report on the latest technologies used in textiles and fashion. Create a blog post about how you see the future use of new ICT technologies in fashion and textiles. Illustrate your answer with pictures, examples and web links. **[15 marks]**

Exam practice questions

1. Designers can use computers to design a printed fabric. Give three reasons why a designer would use a computer to design fabrics. **[3 marks]**
2. Companies are using a range of 2D and 3D modelling techniques to create virtual textile products. Give three reasons (excluding speed) why designers and manufacturers might use 2D/3D modelling techniques during design and prototype phase. **[6 marks]**
3. Designers can use a range of ICT research tools to look for information.
   a) Name four ICT-based research tools they may use. [4 marks]
   b) Give the advantages and disadvantages of each method. **[4 marks]**

Stretch yourself

1. A fashion company has asked you to do a shop report on a new range of t-shirts aimed at fashion-conscious teenage boys and girls in the 14–18 age group. The t-shirt needs to be priced between £8.00 and £15.00. Using appropriate ICT software, compile a report of your findings. **[10 marks]**
2. You have been asked by a leading fashion eco-design company to find out what 14- to 19-year-olds think about sustainable or eco fashion. Using Survey Monkey or other online software, create a survey and then analyse your results. **[10 marks]**

Case study

The PrintPattern blog has been identified as one of the top 50 creative 'IT' spaces, attracting a diverse range of readers and followers. The daily happenings in the studio are revealed by its blogger, detailing the key trends, ideas and developments in surface pattern design. The blog celebrates the world of pattern design. By showcasing designers from around the world, it shows how diverse the world of print is.

This blog provides a clear indication of the nature of the printed pattern and its application across fashion, interiors and accessories into the wider plain of other products, such as postcards, teacloths, wrapping-paper chair coverings, and so on. In addition you will also find inspiration if you are into embroidery or other areas, such as mixed media, as the designs represented open up a whole other arena for design development.

http://printpattern.blogspot.com

11.2 Use of CAD/CAM

Learning objectives

By the end of this section, you should have a key understanding of:

- how CAD/CAM is implemented in textiles and fashion production
- the benefits of CAD/CAM in textiles and fashion production
- CAD/CAM and globalisation
- how CAD/CAM can be used in planning
- how CAD/CAM can be used to reduce manufacturing costs
- how CAD/CAM can aid sustainable practices.

Key points

- Analytical skills
- Communication skills
- Innovative ideas
- Creative ideas
- Linking technology and design
- Values

Key terms

CAD – computer-aided design. Computer-aided designs are designs created using a computer.

CAM – computer-aided manufacture. Computer-aided manufacture is where computers are used in the manufacturing process.

Production – the conversion of products from raw materials to finished goods.

Manufacturing – the making of goods on a large scale using machinery.

Introduction

The fashion and textiles industry of today has been transformed by the advent of new technologies, especially in the area of information technology (IT), computer-aided design (CAD) and computer-aided manufacture (CAM).

Where CAD/CAM and other IT systems are used

The key areas where CAD and CAM are used are:

- design – all areas from presentation to creating specification sheets (CAD)
- manufacturing – all areas from sample making to final product (CAM).

IT is also used in other areas of the textiles and fashion industry. They are:

- production planning (e.g. order tracking, production schedules, quality assurance and control)
- administration (e.g. marketing and sales, orders, costings, stock control, retail sales).

In the production and administration areas of fashion and textiles, companies use generic word-processing and spreadsheet software to keep records and other information. This is known as computer-aided administration (CAA).

Companies also use specialist software that allows them to track all the elements and components needed to make a textile product as they go through the production and delivery system. This software is called product data management (PDM).

PDM software is made up of a database of the products being produced and all the components required. This is combined with other information needed to make the product and to deliver it to its destination.

The production and design teams are able to log onto a computer directly or via their smartphone and check where the product and all its components are in the production process. This process can now happen wherever the designers or other members of staff happen to be.

Many companies will use the PDM database to develop their just-in-time (JIT) production systems, ensuring that all materials and components that are needed for a product are delivered in time for production to start.

Other IT systems

In the retail sectors, textile and fashion products that are purchased either online or direct from stores are tracked using technology such as radio frequency identification tags (RFID) and are linked to ICT systems such as an electronic point of sale (EPOS).

These systems allow companies to track what is selling and where, and then decide whether to make more goods to meet demand. It is thought that, in the future, RFID tags will be applied to all products, making it easier for manufacturers to track what is selling and the consumer to know what they have purchased.

Computer-aided design

Computer-aided design (CAD) is a tool used in the process of designing products. In fashion and textile design, CAD has become an important part of the design process.

In textiles and fashion, designers have the option to use either off-the-shelf software, such as Adobe® Illustrator®, Adobe® Photoshop® and Corel Draw®, or industry-specific software, such as SpeedStep®, Lectra®, Stoll M1® or Colour Matters®.

Computers give the designer the ability to develop accurate designs and send them to the sample or manufacturing plant, which may be in another country. The design and manufacturing information is available instantly at the manufacturing plant. The key reasons for using CAD in the design process are as follows:

- It makes the design process quicker.
- Transfer of information from one country to another is faster and more efficient.
- It allows for the development of accurate styles with correct details.
- It reduces mistakes and allows corrections to be made almost immediately.
- It saves money and time.
- It has been linked to energy saving and developing a more sustainable approach to design.

Key term

Sustainable practices – the process of integrating both the theory and practice of sustainability into everyday design and design and manufacturing processes.

CAD in design presentation

All designers need to present their work at different stages of the design process, and the use of ICT makes this process quicker and easier to do.

Presenting images

Designers use mood boards and trend boards to present visual images to either their clients or other members of the design team. It is important, therefore, that these contain images that communicate clear, creative design ideas that can be developed later to form fashion or fabric designs. Designers are able to collate images and develop colourways and design ideas using design software. These can then be printed out or sent by email to the rest of the people involved in the project.

Designers will use a range of tools, such as digital cameras and scanners, as well as specific design software to present work.

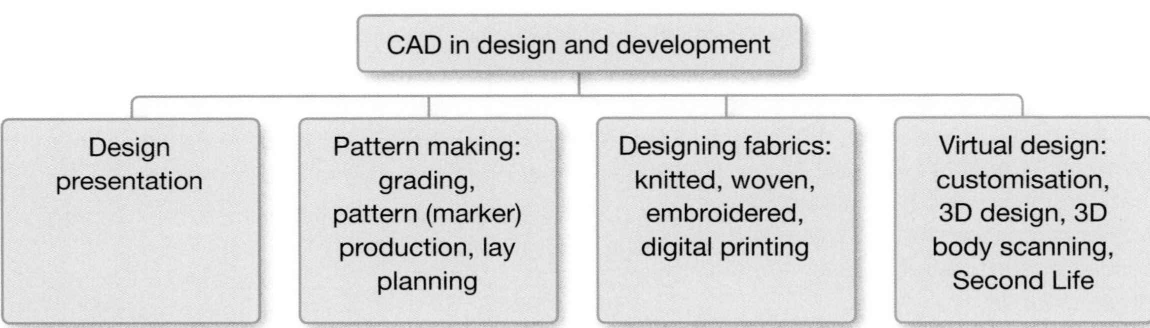

△ **Figure 11.14** Where CAD is used in the design process

Presenting ideas

Design illustrations and specifications can be developed using computer software or can be hand-drawn and then scanned directly into software to be further manipulated. Some pieces of specialist textile software contain databases of garment and fabric styles that can be edited. Designers are able to use these to help them present ideas, including the correct technical language and measurements.

CAD in pattern making

Pattern making is the process of converting the designer's sketches (2D images) and technical specifications into pattern pieces that will then make up the whole garment.

The pattern maker will use specialist pattern software that contains a database of pattern pieces and sizes. These patterns can be uploaded to the software and edited and adapted according to the designer's specification drawings.

The pattern maker can also convert paper patterns from a company's archive of patterns, using a machine called a 'digitiser'. The digitiser is used to plot points on a pattern, which are then converted to pattern pieces on the computer. Once the patterns are in the software, they can be amended or changed.

The patterns can then be printed and used to create the toile or sample garment, or sent by email to the sample manufacturing room, which might be in another city or country, to be made into a sample garment.

The pattern maker will also create the whole size range for the sample garments, known as grading, as well as create the master layout plans, which are needed for mass-produced garments or textiles products. They will ensure that the pattern pieces are laid out in the best way to ensure they reduce waste and get the best amount of pattern pieces from a given length of fabric.

CAD in designing fabrics

Knitting

Knitting is a method of constructing fabric. It can be done by hand or machine.

Knowledge link

For more information on knitting, see pages 99–102 of Chapter 4.

Using new technological software, designers can design knitted fabrics directly on a computer. They can do this in three ways:

1. By creating simulated fabrics using special software, which allows them to draw using stitches on screen.
2. By drawing using technical stitches, and then testing the virtual knitting on the knitting machine software. This type of software also allows the designer to view their work in a virtual environment and then simulate the knitting in a 3D film.
3. By creating a fashion drawing using specialised software. Once the fashion or textile image is created, a fabric simulation is applied.

Digital printing

Advances in printing technology have seen an increased use of digital printing, especially in the haute couture market. It is a process whereby generic graphics software or specific textile software can be used to create a fabric design. Unlike the screen-printing process, there are no limitations to the number of colours that can be used or the length that can be printed, giving designers the possibility to create unique images that can be applied to their products.

In digital printing in textiles, there are two main types of printing:

1. Transfer or sublimation printing: this is where a design is developed on screen and then the design is printed using transfer to disperse dyes directly to a special paper. The print can then be applied to synthetic fabrics or synthetic fabric blends only. This process is used on products such as swimwear and sportswear.
2. Natural fabrics such as cotton, wool and silk can also be digitally printed. For this process, the fabrics are coated with a special chemical wash, and then allowed to dry. The fabrics are then loaded into the printer and the design is printed directly onto the fabric. Once the fabric is printed, it is steamed and dried before it can be used. This process is used on dresses, scarves and interior products.

Digital printing is still fairly expensive when compared with other techniques, such as screen printing and rotary printing. But as the technology develops, this cost will be reduced.

The key benefits of digital printing to the designer are that:

- there are no minimum lengths
- designs can be printed with hundreds of colours
- it reduces the amount of water and chemicals needed to produce a print
- it reduces the waste water needed to produce prints
- it links to sustainable design practices
- colourways and designs can be printed immediately
- it can be used to test consumer response to a limited design range without the huge investment in screen printing
- it has reduced sampling times (e.g. from 6–8 weeks for screen printing to 1–2 days for digital printing).

△ **Figure 11.15** Digital printer

CAD in virtual design

Many design companies have design and production offices all over the world and, as such, they are developing ways in which designs can be changed or adapted without staff having to travel long distances. To do this, companies are using virtual media to enable clients and design and technical staff to view products and enable changes.

Using online conferencing

Using video and other software, such as Skype or WebEx, viewers can see a garment in real time and view it from all angles, to allow alterations to take place.

Using virtual design software

Companies can now use virtual design (cloud) software. This means that the software is not on a particular computer, but on a central computer elsewhere. Designs can be created and modelled, and then viewed in real time.

Using software such as Second Life also means that companies can create avatars and virtual worlds to display their products.

Using 3D body scanning

This process uses laser-scanning technology. The whole body or parts of the body can be scanned, giving the manufacturer a range of measurement data. The results of the scan can be imported to specialist software, where it can be used to create bespoke garments. The 3D body scanner is used in the military to create uniforms and by bespoke tailors to make suits. The shoe industry also uses 3D technology and scanning to make bespoke shoes and trainers.

Mass customisation

Many companies now have online stores. In many of these stores, you can now design your own trainers or sports top, for example. You will pay extra for this service, but you will also have a unique product.

Computer-aided manufacture

In computer-aided manufacture (CAM), computers play an integral part in the manufacturing of products.

Lay planning and cutting

The markers created by the pattern maker are sent to lay-planning software. This is then manipulated on a computer screen to give best fit on the fabric before being cut out. The fabric can be laid out on cutting tables several layers thick, enabling manufacturers to cut out several garments at a time, either using a laser cutter or a special fabric cutter.

Knitting

Manufacturers can now view designs in a virtual environment before sending the design to the knitting machines. With modern technology, companies can now knit all-in-one garments or even knit several parts of a garment at one time. Garments can be knitted on either flatbed machines or circular machines.

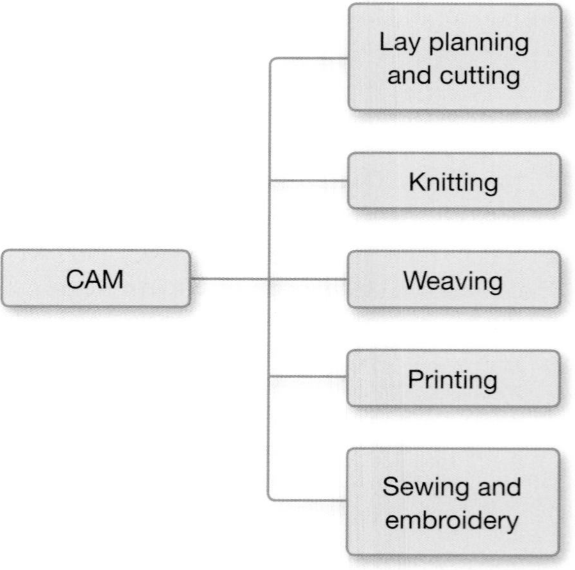

△ **Figure 11.16** Where CAM is used in the manufacturing process

Weaving

Advances in weaving technology mean that woven fabrics can be created in bespoke software. The designs can be woven on looms that can weave several layers. This is particularly true of fabrics being developed for the technical textiles industry.

Printing

Use of technology can speed up the process of making the screens or designs for screen or rotary printing, but the biggest advancement has been that of digital printing. New machines are being developed that can print directly to products such as t-shirts. Whole-garment printing machines are now being developed to make the printing process even quicker. The development of digital printing is leading to more bespoke designs and is becoming the process of choice because of its ecological credentials.

Sewing and embroidery

New machines allow for a range of automated processes to be done using specialised sewing machines. These specialised machines can carry out automated processes, such as sewing long seams or inserting zips.

New advances in embroidery machines mean that designs can be stitched in one go on several machines that are linked together through a central computer system.

△ **Figure 11.17** Industrial embroidery machines: an example of mass production and CAD/CAM

Key term

Globalisation – the process of how different regions, communities and economies have become interconnected around the world.

Benefits of using CAD/CAM

The benefits of using CAD/CAM in textile production are that:

- planning is made easier because of better communication
- designs can be checked more easily for accuracy
- efficiency of the manufacturing process is increased
- the aesthetic qualities of the made products are enhanced
- quality in textiles and fashion production is ensured
- manufacturing costs and waste are reduced
- companies are able to work within a globalised industry
- accuracy in the development of styles and designs is improved.

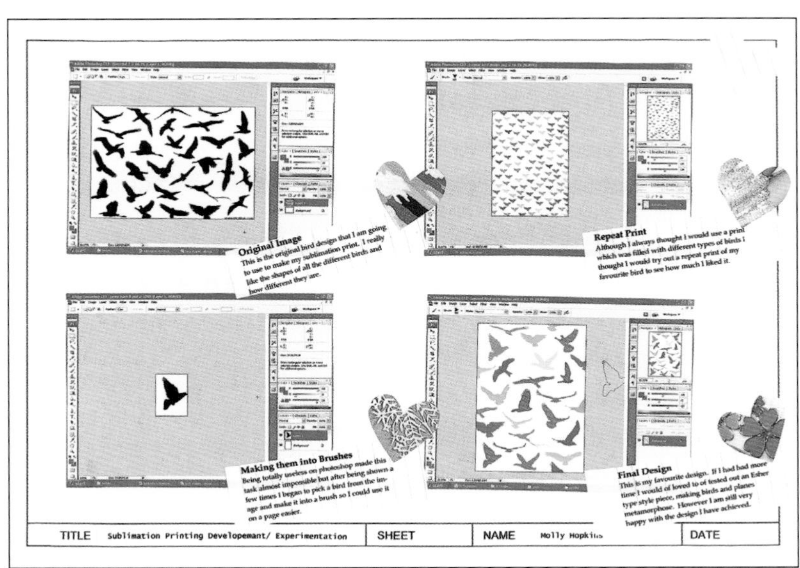

△ **Figure 11.18** Student examples of CAD/CAM

Summary

- The introduction of the internet has changed the way in which industries such as fashion and textiles communicate and work.
- Companies are connected through a range of technology and no longer rely on all aspects of their business being in the same location.
- Technology has changed not only the way in which production is done, but also the ways in which companies use IT as a design tool.
- To compete in today's market, companies now integrate IT in all aspects of their work in the textiles and fashion industry, from design, to production, to retail.
- The use of CAD/CAM has been integrated across the design and production processes of the fashion and textiles industry.
- The key benefits to companies integrating CAD/CAM are reduced costs, faster production turnaround, the ability to use a range of software for design and administration, and a reduced impact on the environment.

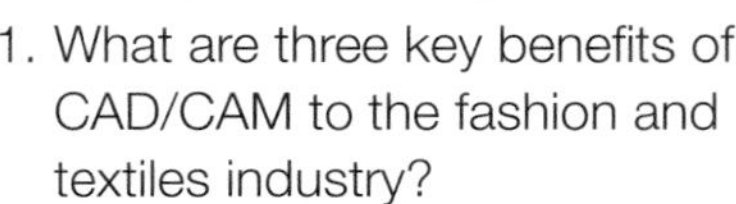

Exam practice questions

1. What are three key benefits of CAD/CAM to the fashion and textiles industry? **[3 marks]**
2. How has CAD/CAM helped designers in communicating their design ideas? **[4 marks]**
3. What do you think are the benefits of design companies using modern social networking technologies as one of the tools to communicate design ideas? **[6 marks]**

Stretch yourself

A textiles design company has asked that you create a range of graphics that can be used for a new bespoke online design service aimed at the 18–24 age group.

1. Using your primary and secondary research skills, collect together a range of visual imagery that can be manipulated using graphics software, either on a smartphone or on a computer.
2. Design a range of graphic images that can be downloaded using the internet and placed on the template of a product.
3. Present your design concept using images, in the form of a Microsoft® PowerPoint® presentation of no more than ten slides that explain your design ideas.

[Total: 20 marks]

Index

Note: page numbers in **bold** refer to key word terms.